The Legacy

The Legacy

A Centennial History of the
State Agricultural Experiment Stations
1887-1987

by
Norwood Allen Kerr

Missouri Agricultural Experiment Station
University of Missouri-Columbia
March 1987

Published by
Missouri Agricultural Experiment Station
University of Missouri-Columbia
in cooperation with
Cooperative State Research Service
U.S. Department of Agriculture
Washington, D.C.

Patricia Brazeel Lewis, editor
George Clark Laur, designer

Library of Congress Catalog Number: 87-60246
ISBN: 0-933842-05-8
Special Report 350
3/87/6M

Contents

FOREWORD

The first century of the state agricultural experiment station system has yielded nothing less than a scientific revolution. That revolution was brought about by a single system which generates new knowledge, communicates it to those who need it, and educates the next generation of scientists and agricultural producers. It was enhanced by a state-federal partnership that fostered the investments in research that produced hybrid crops and specially adapted animals, labor saving equipment, improved cultural practices, vaccines against diseases which threaten human and animal life, and chemicals which enhance growth and protect plants from pests. These developments have increased our standard of living and provided a wide variety of food and fiber at reasonable prices.

As remarkable as these achievements have been, they are merely the cornerstones for discoveries yet to be made. Among the fantastic tools now at our disposal is biotechnology. It gives us the ability to store animal germplasm indefinitely, and the ability to match agricultural products to the environment in which they are to be grown. The full potential of this tool is a long way from being reached, but it will provide a key in unlocking the answers to challenges facing both society and agricultural research today as well as tomorrow.

To meet growing consumer demands for variety, future research will give us new food products and we will better understand the relationship between diet, health, and disease with greater clarity. As an economic entity, agriculture will continue to be influenced as much by political policy as it is by science. The successful marriage of creativity with tools of application will depend even more on imaginative scientific research.

Research is the fuel for this dynamic industry we call agriculture. And today's dedicated researchers imbued with optimism based upon a legacy of success increasingly are pushing back the frontiers of science.

The partnerships, the organizational structures, and the legislative and funding trends that have promoted major research accomplishments and given us such an exciting future outlook are examined in *The Legacy*.

To all who contributed to the century of progress, thank you; to those who aggressively address the second century, good hunting.

John Patrick Jordan
Administrator
Cooperative State Research Service
March 2, 1987
Washington, D.C.

PREFACE

On March 2, 1887, President Grover Cleveland signed legislation promoting "scientific investigation and experiment respecting the principles and applications of agricultural science" through annual grants to each state and territory to establish agricultural experiment stations under the direction of the land-grant colleges. Envisioned as a way to advance agriculture in the rapidly industrializing United States, the Hatch Act created a structure for federated yet independent research institutions to address the location-specific problems of farmers and to build a core of basic scientific knowledge related to agriculture.

In the one hundred years that have passed since its signing, the state agricultural experiment stations in partnership with agricultural research agencies in the United States Department of Agriculture have seized upon the legacy of the Hatch Act to provide the knowledge that allowed the agriculture sector to meet the food and fiber needs of an expanding American population. How the administrative mechanisms evolved to successfully promote the discovery and development of scientific and technological innovations is the subject of this volume.

This study was initiated at the request of the Cooperative State Research Service, United States Department of Agriculture in association with the Centennial Committee of the Experiment Station Committee on Organization and Policy as part of the centennial observance of the passage of the Hatch Act of 1887. It was originally intended as an update of H.C. Knoblauch, E.M. Law, W.P. Meyer, B.F. Beacher, R.B. Nestler, and B.S. White, Jr., *State Agricultural Experiment Stations: A History of Research Policy and Procedure* which was, itself, published to commemorate the one-hundreth anniversary of the Morrill Land-Grant Colleges Act of 1862. While the current study does take the story of the state stations into the present, it also takes another look at the first seventy-five years of the system's operation in an attempt to incorporate scholarship produced since 1962 into a volume that will stand alone.

Like the earlier volume, this book concentrates on the evolution of research policy and procedure in a national framework, but gives greater attention to the development of research programs at the individual stations in light of changing social, economic, and political situations. Within a basic chronological approach, three main areas are focused upon. Administrative relations between the state and federal partners in the public agricultural research complex loom large in the story. The development of effective organizational structures by the state stations and the federal coordinating agency to pursue scientific investigations of benefit to the nation is a unifying theme. Legislative and funding trends which affected the system over its first century of operation are another major topic of concern. This book considers how legislation and appropriations reflected congressional and public attitudes and how research programs shaped and were shaped by legislative action. The changing demands of society upon agricultural research are another major part of the stations' history. Expectations of the lay public and the science community have shifted over the past century with enormous impact on the system and on the individual scientist within it. How the stations and their federal partner responded to these changing expectations is the third overarching theme in this study.

A number of individuals must be credited for their invaluable assistance in producing this book. Thomas S. Ronningen, Roland R. Robinson, and Wayne R. Rasmussen freely offered guidance based on their many years of experience as participants in and observers of the public agricultural research system. John Patrick Jordan, James E. Halpin, and Paul E. Waggoner were similarly helpful, reviewing the manuscript in whole or in part as it was written. Patricia B. Lewis provided expert editorial assistance and Grace I. Krumwiede compiled the index. Appreciation is also extended to the scientists and support staff of the Cooperative State Research Service and to my colleagues in the Agricultural and Rural History Branch of the Economic Research Service, USDA who helped identify and clarify issues of importance in the history of the stations. While this study owes much to the insights contributed by all of these individuals, the author alone remains responsible for any errors of fact or interpretation.

Author

CHAPTER I
The Farmers Legislation

The improvement of farming through science was advocated in America from the early years of the republic. Long scorned by tradition-bound farmers and often misunderstood by the rest, the idea of engaging in the systematic discovery and application of scientific knowledge to benefit agriculture was nurtured by a small group of scientists inspired by European examples and appreciative of American conditions. In the last quarter of the nineteenth century these proponents of public support for agricultural research succeeded in tying their proposals to more general efforts to improve farming and the farmer through education. In 1887, the movement culminated in national legislation which created a unique federal-state partnership of aid to agriculture.

Birth of Scientific Agriculture

An interest in applying science in farming came to America with British and European settlers in the colonial period. The new environment offered new challenges to agriculture and evoked the curiosity of those farmers with the leisure to test new ideas. With fewer books and less sophisticated apparatus than their European counterparts and confronted by a greater variety of crops and soil, the Americans with an interest in scientific agriculture were more likely to experiment in their fields than in the laboratory. The vast majority of farmers, of course, were too involved in scratching out a living in an often hostile new land to engage in any unproven farm practice.

Recognizing that most farmers could not invest the time that patient testing of new farm practices entailed and could not afford the economic consequences of an experiment's failure, the idea of setting up an experimental farm to do this work for an area's farmers was born at an early date. "Societies for the Promotion of Agriculture" in South Carolina, Pennsylvania, New York, Massachusetts, and Connecticut in the late eighteenth century offered prizes for individual investigation and called for experimental gardens. George Wash-

1

ington, in a 1796 presidential address, elevated the concept to the national stage by calling for a federally funded board of agriculture which, among other duties, would act as a center for encouraging experimentation. The proposal died in a Congress reluctant to extend federal power in any new area.[1]

Farm societies kept alive interest in agricultural improvement into the early nineteenth century through their meetings to exchange information. These were joined by a growing agricultural press which catered to the increasing number of literate farmers. The gatherings of influential farmers and the articles and correspondence printed in the farm periodicals discussed local trials of different cropping practices as well as available information on European laboratory investigations. In the 1840s, reports of European discoveries in soil analysis reinvigorated the movement to apply science to farming in the United States.

Liebig and Chemical Analysis

With the 1840 publication of *Organic Chemistry In Its Application to Agriculture and Physiology,* Justus von Liebig of Germany integrated many of the important discoveries gleaned from the scientific analysis of plants and soils, to offer a set of theories to explain plant growth. Liebig's theories prompted critical skepticism from discerning scientists in Europe but his reputation and his ideas were so attractive to American dabblers in the field that his influence, for good and bad, profoundly affected the development of agricultural science in this country. As distilled by the agricultural press for its audience of farmers, Liebig's studies promised that permanent soil fertility could be achieved simply by restoring the proper balance of nutrients necessary for plant growth. Liebig's adherents confidently predicted that science would soon perfect the techniques of soil analysis and thus soil treatments could be prescribed for individual farmers.

Popularizers of "scientific agriculture," including many agricultural journal editors, eagerly endorsed Liebig's theories and a legion of "soil analysts" sprang up to perform the service for interested farmers. The predicted benefits proved illusory as qualified chemists began to realize the true complexities of soil analysis and left the field to charlatans who exploited the farmers' eternal hope for guaranteed prosperity. Thus, the farmers' ingrained distrust of innovation and reliance on tradition were ultimately strengthened by the experience with the soil analysis craze. Agricultural science for many years became synonymous with agricultural chemistry and as such would engender continued suspicion from the nation's farmers.[2]

Old World Precedents

The renewed interest in soil chemistry may have been short-lived in the general farm population but it was of lasting importance to America's nascent scientific community. Liebig's fame led a succession of students to cross the Atlantic where they were exposed not only to Liebig's teaching laboratory in Giessen but to other centers of science on the continent and in Great Britain. There, they witnessed the beginnings of new institutional arrangements for agricultural investigation, ones which combined testing in the garden with analysis in the laboratory.

In Scotland, James F. W. Johnston was employed by an organization of progressive farmers in 1842 to undertake laboratory investigations and deliver instructional lectures in support of their own field work in building soil fertility. In the next year in neighboring England, Sir John B. Lawes persuaded Sir Henry Gilbert, a Liebig student, to direct experiments in farming on the former's Rothamsted estate. In the German state of Saxony, the concept of combining the laboratory with the farm plot was advanced by the government, which in 1852 established the first publicly funded *Landwirtschaftlich Versuchsstation* at Moeckern.

A number of other German states followed Saxony's lead so that by the mid-1870s there were over seventy experiment stations in the empire. The German system remained highly decentralized and, in the European scientific tradition, emphasized laboratory investigations detached from the nation's academic centers. After exposure to these developing institutional arrangements in Europe, a number of observers returned home invigorated with new ideas to aid the farmer through research and education. However, the system which evolved from the movement they initiated would be uniquely American.[3]

John Pitkin Norton

One of those impressed by European developments after first-hand experience was a young man from Connecticut named John

Pitkin Norton. At the urging of his Yale professor, Norton traveled abroad in 1844 to study under James F.W. Johnston, the Scottish agricultural chemist who two years earlier had established his famous laboratory-teaching facility. Norton came to Scotland with an abiding faith in practical farmer education and under Johnston learned the value of scientific investigation. Despite his mentor's own frustration over meeting the demands of education and research, Norton returned to the United States convinced of the necessity of combining the two in some institutional form. Upon his return to Yale in 1846, he established a teaching laboratory and further developed his ideas for effective agricultural education. Over the remaining four years of his short life, Norton unceasingly advocated, first in Connecticut and then in New York, a system of public agricultural education at the apex of which would stand an agricultural college with teachers for the classroom and chemists for the laboratory. Failing to overcome the farmers' distrust of "book farming," Norton never saw his proposals enacted.[4]

Johnson and Fertilizer Analysis

Norton's crusade for public support of agricultural science was taken up by one of his students, Samuel W. Johnson. Absorbing Norton's enthusiasm for agricultural experimentation, Johnson traveled to Germany to study under Liebig. While awaiting admission to the master's program, Johnson visited the two-year-old experiment station at Moeckern, seeing for the first time a government-supported laboratory with attached experimental garden plots. The facility's dedication to research unencumbered by the demands of teaching must have impressed the American traveler who had witnessed his Yale tutor's frustrating failure to gain acceptance for an agricultural college with a research component.

Johnson embarked on a campaign for an American system of agricultural experiment stations even before his return to Yale as an assistant in the chemistry laboratory. In letters to leading farm journals, he countered the farmers' backlash arising from the dashed hopes of agricultural chemistry by insisting that more science was necessary for agricultural improvement, not less. If soil analysis had failed to deliver precise prescriptions for guaranteed abundance, he maintained, then more information on plant physiology and soil composition must be discovered through careful scientific investigation.

Back in Connecticut in 1855, Johnson succeeded in overcoming

Samuel W. Johnson was the first director of the Connecticut Station at New Haven, serving from 1877 to 1899, and a long-standing leader of the agricultural experiment station movement in America. (*National Archives and Records Administration photo*)

some of the farmers' distrust of chemistry by successfully allying his cause with an effort to protect consumers against unscrupulous retailers of artificial fertilizers. The sale of prepared mixtures of chemical soil enrichers, first introduced at the end of the 1840s, had grown into a scandal in a short time. Dealers preyed upon Connecticut farmers desperate to hold on to markets threatened by competition from more fertile western lands, promising miracle fertility restorative properties for their often worthless mixtures. Responding to the outrage of their victimized members in 1857, the Connecticut State Agricultural Society appointed Johnson as its chemist to protect purchasers from fraud by analyzing the nutritive content of fertilizers offered for sale. Johnson hoped to expand his inspection duties into a full-scale experiment station on the German model, but his position was discontinued in 1861 as the country convulsed in civil war.[5] His campaign for science in the service of agriculture would be revised following the conflict, ultimately intersecting with other movements designed to enlighten the farmer.

USDA and Colleges for the Common Man

While the Civil War interrupted Johnson's crusade, it brought success to other agricultural reform drives. With southern obstructionists away from Congress, the newly ascendant Republican Party repaid its political debt to the farmers of the Midwest by enacting a series of bills which came to be known as the "Farmers' Legislation." Among these acts signed into law by Abraham Lincoln in 1862 were a Homestead Act and a Transcontinental Railroad Act. One held out the promise of free land to farm families willing to open the West while the other encouraged railroads to provide these new settlers with access to markets. Although neither bill actually operated in the interest of the individual farmer, each was important as a symbol of the changing attitude toward the government's role in encouraging agriculture. Of equal importance were the other two pieces of farmers' legislation which created a national department of agriculture and provided an endowment for a national system of agricultural colleges.[6]

The creation of an agency at the national level to look after the interests of farmers was a persistent idea in the United States. Following Congress' failure to act favorably on President Washington's proposal to create a national board of agriculture, what meager government efforts there were to encourage agriculture came through the Patent Office. A division of the State Department, the Patent Office began its agricultural program in the 1820s as the distributor of foreign seeds sent by American consuls to their Washington headquarters. In the next decade the Patent Office expanded its duties with a $1,000 appropriation from Congress to distribute seeds and compile statistics on the nation's farming sector. This work continued after the office was transferred to the Department of Interior in 1846. Ten years later a bill was introduced in Congress to establish an agricultural department as an independent agency.[7]

Not until 1862 did the bill become law and then only in a rather abbreviated form. Even with the Southern strict constitutional constructionists out of Congress, opposition remained to establishing an agency devoted to a particular economic sector. As a result of these misgivings, the new Department of Agriculture was not accorded cabinet status and its chief was entitled a "commissioner" rather than a "secretary." Nor was the new Department given as broad a mandate as some of its proponents had hoped.

The House version of the organic act had included a strong call for departmental botanists, entomologists, and chemists to pursue scientific investigations into the principles underlying agriculture. Concerned about calling into existence a large new government agency while the nation was involved in a treasury-draining war, the Senate limited the act's wording to a suggestion that the Department collect "useful information on subjects connected with agriculture" by whatever means available, including "practical and scientific experiments." Congress also directed the Department to disseminate the knowledge it collected; it was this charge to educate rather than investigate that the agency's early commissioners would most energetically pursue. Begun under the Patent Office in 1858, a large garden for propagating imported seeds and plants was continued but initiatives to establish an agricultural research system reverted to the states.[8]

Unlike support for scientific investigations into farming, the political backing for practical education for the farmer had become overwhelming by 1862. From the early years of the nineteenth century, a period of intellectual awakening was taking place in the United States as Americans developed an increasingly high regard for advanced education. An ingrained distrust of elitism and a devotion to the "practical" aspects of education caused them to spurn the offerings of existing universities, most of which were exclusive and based on English models of classical curricula.

Justin Smith Morrill, Vermont congressman, authored the Land-Grant College Act of 1862 as well as the act of 1890 that led to the creation of black land-grant institutions in the southern states. (*USDA photo*)

The demand grew for government sponsorship of vocational higher education that would serve the common man in an agrarian, but industrializing, America. By mid-century a chorus of educators, most notably Jonathan Baldwin Turner of Illinois, was advocating a plan to create a system of state colleges with proceeds from federal land grants. A congressional representative from Vermont consolidated this idea into legislation which was introduced in December, 1857. Representative Justin Smith Morrill's original proposal was for each state to be given 2,000 acres of land for each of its members in Congress. From the money realized from the sale of this land grant, each state would have a fund for the perpetual endowment of a college to instruct its citizens in "such branches of learning as are related to agriculture and the mechanic arts. . . ." The House Committee on Public Lands, to which the bill was originally sent, quickly killed the measure.

Morrill Acts

Two years later, Morrill reintroduced his bill and saw it passed by the House and Senate only to die under the veto of President James Buchanan who avoided antagonizing the Southerners who prized states' rights and feared any expansion of Federal sovereignty. With the South in rebellion, President Lincoln had no such qualms when an amended version of the Morrill Bill was brought before him in 1862.[9]

The Morrill Land-Grant College Act promised each state public land in the amount of 30,000 acres for each of its Senate and House members. Since most of the states did not have that much unsold public land within their borders, they were given scrip to the public domain in those states and territories with sufficient excess acres. Each state was to use its money as a trust fund to endow a college where practical education in agriculture and engineering would be emphasized. Ten percent of the principal could be expended to purchase lands either "for sites or experimental farms" if the state legislature so desired but none of the funds could be used to buy, build, or refurbish buildings.

Grand in design, the land-grant college act of 1862 proved less so in its initial execution. High administrative costs in combination with a soft market for land sales caused by the Civil War and the Homestead Act prompted most states to sell their entire entitlement to dealers at prices of between fifty cents and one dollar an acre. Heeding political demands for new institutions more than fiscal realities, most states legislated into existence new "agricultural and mechanical colleges" rather than endowing existing state universities. Suddenly, many states found themselves supporting two colleges. For one of them they had to furnish most of the land and all of the buildings. As a consequence, agitation for further federal aid to the states began within a decade, led again by Justin Morrill who was by then a senator.[10]

First introduced in 1872, the Second Morrill Act was finally passed in 1890 to give direct annual appropriations to each state to support its land-grant college. Congress gave to each state and territory $15,000 the first year, then increased the appropriation in annual $1,000 increments until the sum reached $25,000 yearly. The Second Morrill Act contained one other new feature: it forbade racial discrimination in admission to colleges receiving the funds. A state was allowed to escape this provision, however, if separate institutions were maintained and the newly available funds were divided in "a just and equitable," but not necessarily equal, manner. The Southern states hastened to comply by a number of institutional means. Maryland assigned its monies to a private black college which subsequently became a state institution while Alabama, Arkansas, Florida, Texas, Kentucky, Louisiana, Virginia, Mississippi, and Missouri gave portions to existing publicly funded black schools. Delaware, Georgia, North Carolina, Oklahoma, South Carolina, Tennessee, and West Virginia created new land-grant schools for their Negro residents. These "1890 Colleges," as they came to be called, generally were founded on a tenuous financial base and suffered from continuing neglect, if not hostility, until the 1960s when the civil rights movement reminded the public of their existence.[11]

Research Tied to Teaching

The state institutions endowed by the Morrill Land-Grant College Act of 1862 did not have racial antipathy to battle, but they did have a number of other obstacles to overcome in their early development. To meet the high expectations of the public for which they were created, the colleges simultaneously had to attract qualified students and develop "practical" coursework. The task proved difficult in the extreme.

Proponents of the land-grant colleges had secured support for their idea by citing the hunger of the common man for higher education. Yet once their movement triumphed, it was the land-grant colleges that almost starved — from lack of qualified students. The older, more populous states generally had colleges, either public or private, with academic reputations that made them the first choice of the best educated youth. In the states where a newly created land-grant school was the only college, there was seldom an adequate secondary educational system to prepare students for university study. Desperate for pupils, some colleges lowered admission standards to a point where they became little more than high schools, attempting to create a demand for their eventual service as true colleges. Many of the colleges retained preparatory departments for decades even as they moved slowly toward a system of encouraging, then accrediting secondary schools which could furnish capable young scholars. Already established institutions had little more success in attracting students to their new agricultural curricula which, more often than not, meant a course in agricultural chemistry added to the traditional classical studies.

To farmers already suspicious of the value of "book farming," this development looked like betrayal. They had been enlisted to support the college movement with promises of ennoblement of the farmer through education, but saw public money going to elitist education instead. In Mississippi, Rhode Island, North Carolina, New Hampshire, and Connecticut, farmer dissatisfaction with the half-hearted efforts of the existing colleges to implement agricultural curricula forced legislatures to shift the Morrill endowment to new state schools. The land-grant institutions of Wisconsin, Ohio, Illinois, Michigan, Missouri, Minnesota, and California weathered similar battles as they tried to

The Morrow Plots, established in 1876 on the Urbana-Champaign campus of the University of Illinois, are the oldest research plots in the United States. *(University of Illinois photo)*

develop courses acceptable to their eminently practical patrons.[12]

With farmers demanding visible evidence of the colleges' commitment to their well-being and agricultural professors searching for practical ways of instruction, demonstration and model farms were early additions to the facilities of many land-grant schools. From their beginnings as orderly garden plots to impress visiting farmers and to keep students employed, the college farms evolved into rudimentary research facilities. As farmers became increasingly sophisticated in their requests for answers to their immediate problems and agricultural professors began to exhaust their meager supply of science-based knowledge, experiments began. Often these consisted of little more than test plots for combinations of crops and fertilizers with supporting chemical analyses performed in the college laboratory. This arrangement was common to a number of the land-grant colleges by 1875 when the nation's first facility to be designated as an agricultural experiment station was born.

Connecticut Agricultural Experiment Station

In the process of developing a public research institution which combined the farm with the chemical laboratory to investigate agricultural problems, Connecticut emerged from the Civil War with a head start. Samuel Johnson had served the state agricultural society as its chemist until the post was discontinued in 1861 as war-induced prosperity mitigated some of the concern over fraudulent fertilizer claims. Post-war recession and revived fear about Western competition prompted the designation of Johnson as state chemist in 1869 under a State Board of Agriculture. From his official post as analyzer of commercial fertilizers, Johnson resumed his campaign to broaden his laboratory to a full-scale research institution along the lines of those he had encountered in Germany. The Board of Agriculture in 1875, impressed by Johnson's service in upgrading the quality of fertilizers sold in the state, introduced a bill to finance such a laboratory at public expense under its control. The legislature resisted until a trustee of Wesleyan University in Middletown offered his personal funds and the university's laboratories in return for a two-year appropriation of $5,600 from the state. Within the year, the Connecticut Agricultural Experiment Station was installed in Judd Hall at Wesleyan. The debt to the German model was acknowledged in the literal translation of *Landwirtschaftlich Versuchsstation* as the title of this first American agricultural research institution.

The college's new professor of chemistry, Wilbur O. Atwater, became the station's director by the terms of the agreement arranged by the Wesleyan trustees. A student of Samuel Johnson at the Yale Sheffield Scientific School, Atwater shared his former teacher's concept of the independent station and worked assiduously to keep separate the duties of teacher and researcher. Unhappy with the Wesleyan arrangement but apparently pleased with the station concept after its two-year trial period, the legislature moved the station to New Haven, appropriated $5,000 yearly for its support, and placed it under the direction of Samuel Johnson. For a time, the Sheffield Scientific School loaned office and laboratory space to the station but in 1882, buildings and land were purchased at a separate site. In both Middletown and New Haven, the Connecticut station retained its laboratory orientation and its detachment from academics insisted upon by its first two directors. Committed to the German model for independent scientific research at public expense, Atwater and Johnson became leading spokesmen in the experiment station movement even as the station they founded was emulated less.[13]

Other States Follow Suit

In the decade before the Hatch Act provided federal encouragement to the movement, thirteen states followed Connecticut in providing public funds directly to agricultural experiment stations. The variety of institutional arrangements developed at the stations in these formative years ranged from independence as a state agency to subordination as a college department, the final form usually dependent upon how their founders balanced the demands of farmer groups with the desires of educators/scientists. Connecticut's station represented one extreme while the nation's second agricultural research station represented the other.

The University of California began experiments on its college farm at Berkeley in 1874 in an attempt to win support for the land-grant institution from the state's farmers. Success gradually followed after the arrival of Eugene W. Hilgard as director in the next year. He combined new laboratory investigations with plot work and reoriented the entire program after traveling the state by railway handcar to acquaint himself with the needs of California's varied agriculture. Impressed with the director's efforts to merge the potentials of science with agricultural realities, the state legislature in 1877 designated the facility an agricultural experiment station under the control of the university Board of Regents.[14]

In the same year, North Carolina's general assembly located an agricultural experiment station on the grounds of its land-grant college at Chapel Hill. Designated as an "Agricultural Experiment and Fertilizer Control Station," it used the University of North Carolina laboratories but was administered as a part of the State Board of Agriculture which had been created by the same piece of legislation. Much like the Connecticut station in its early years, the North Carolina station concentrated on chemical analyses rather than field work.[15]

Eugene W. Hilgard brought the California Agricultural Experiment Station to life when he arrived in 1875 to become its director and subsequently emerged as a leading spokesman for a national system of state stations. (*National Archives and Records Administration photo*)

In Massachusetts, the Agricultural College at Amherst founded an experiment station in 1878 with money donated by its professor of agriculture from royalties he had earned by developing commercial fertilizers. By 1881, the endowment proved insufficient for the station's operation and it closed. The legislature resurrected it in the next year, leaving it on the Massachusetts Agricultural College campus but placing it under a board of control comprised of college trustees, state agriculture board members, and a representative from the state's leading agricultural society.[16]

On the Ithaca, New York campus of Cornell University, an agricultural experiment station was established in 1879 by the College of Agriculture faculty in combination with a variety of state and local farmer organizations. An administrative arrangement which included representatives from each of these groups proved so cumbersome by the early 1880s that the Cornell station was subsumed as a university department. In the meantime general agitation for state aid to farm research prompted the New York State assembly to authorize funds for another agricultural experiment station in 1880. Located at Geneva two years later, this New York State Station operated under a controlling board appointed by the governor.[17]

The scientific school of Rutgers College was designated as New Jersey's land-grant beneficiary in 1864. A model farm was attached to the institution's agricultural division within the next year. When the legislature directed money for a state experiment station in 1880, it was located at Rutgers and the director's position was filled by the professor of agriculture. The same law created a governing board separate from Rutgers trustees but limited to the governor and top university administrators.[18]

The Ohio Agricultural Experiment Station was established in 1882 along similarly peculiar administrative lines. Ohio's land-grant college at Columbus had been the object of attack by farmers unhappy with its traditional curriculum since the school opened in 1873. When the Agricultural and Mechanical College changed its name to Ohio State University five years later, the state's agricultural interests were further enraged. Thus, when an agricultural experiment station was funded by the legislature in 1882, Ohio's powerful farm groups insisted that it be placed under the control of a board independent of Ohio State University. Still, only the college had the facilities and expertise necessary to perform the work of a station, so it was located on the Ohio State campus. It subsequently employed many of the personnel of the agricultural college. The result was a confusing mix of research, teaching, and regulatory work carried out by state and college staff governed by separate boards of directors.[19]

Created in the same year as the Ohio station, the Tennessee Agricultural Experiment Station had no apparent opposition to its being placed under the state land-grant college. Already in operation for three years, the University of Tennessee college farm became the official station in 1882. It was put under the general supervision of a committee of the university trustees and the specific direction of the school's professor of agriculture. In 1883, the legislature added fertilizer analysis to the station duties.[20]

The Alabama Agricultural Experiment Station's genesis and development was much like that of Tennessee's. Rudimentary variety trials had been carried out on a farm connected with the land-grant college at Auburn since the mid-1870s. In 1883, the institution's faculty, with the support of the state agriculture society, convinced the Alabama assembly to support an agricultural research station out of monies it would earn from certifying commercial fertilizer for sale. The station that resulted was operated by the Auburn trustees and directed by its agriculture professor. A branch station for the state's Black Belt region was funded by the legislature beginning in 1885. A separate board of control was named for it but the professor of agriculture at Auburn was named director.[21]

State funds for Wisconsin's experiment station also developed out of the college farm work at the land-grant university. There, farm demands for practical educational programs led to an 1870s revival of the University of Wisconsin's moribund agricultural program. In 1883, an agricultural experiment station was created under the direction of the school's professor of agriculture.[22]

In Louisiana, the legislature authorized a state agricultural experiment station as part of Louisiana State University at Baton Rouge in 1884 but did not actually put the facility in operation until two years later. In the interval a group of sugar planters established their own private Sugar Experiment Station in 1885 on a plantation near the community of Kenner. The chemist employed as the Sugar Station director also became the director of the State Station when a fertilizer control law was enacted in 1886.[23]

Fertilizer control legislation also created an experiment station for Maine in 1885. Maine's State College at Orono had maintained a small farm even before its first students arrived in the late 1860s. When farmer outrage over fraudulent fertilizers compelled the state to intervene, the college farm, as the natural site for an inspection facility, was designated the "Maine Fertilizer Control and Agricultural Experiment Station."[24]

Kentucky's college farm shared a similar destiny. It was designated as an agricultural experiment station by the Kentucky Agricultural and Mechanical College trustees in 1885. In the next year, state acknowledgment and support was gained when fertilizer inspection duties were assigned to it.[25]

Created by an act of the state legislature in November 1886, the Vermont Agricultural Experiment Station followed years of agitation for a fertilizer control facility. The State Grange introduced legislation to create an experiment station with fertilizer inspection authority in 1884. Vermont's land-grant university, at odds with the state's farmers over the addition of agricultural faculty, declined to support the bill and assured its defeat. Two years later, the university proved more receptive as an experiment station was located on its Burlington campus, sustained largely by fertilizer analysis fees.[26]

By 1887 then, fourteen states scattered over the nation had established agricultural experiment stations. In perhaps an equal number of other states, the land-grant colleges were engaged in the same types of activities on a less formal basis. Practicality characterized the research at every site. Chemical analyses of soils and fertilizers, comparisons of different soil treatments on plant growth, and identification of plant varieties and insect species absorbed the attention of the investigators, when they could spare time from their teaching duties. Because of the importance of agriculture in the land-grant colleges, the professor of agriculture often was one of the university's chief administrators as well. Lacking the time, the facilities, and the knowledge to fulfill all the demands placed upon them as researchers, educators, and administrators, these pioneers early sought to develop communication lines with others in the land-grant community who confronted the same obstacles. Although their work was almost entirely practical, the station leaders aspired to more. As the nation's first agricultural experiment station director, Wilbur O. Atwater, stated in the Connecticut station's first annual report, "It has been felt from the first that more abstract scientific investigations would afford not only the proper, but also the most widely and permanently useful work of an Agricultural Experiment Station."

Advances Through Association

The movement to associate to share experiences and work for common goals among the land-grant schools was begun less than a decade after the Morrill Act was passed. In the summer of 1871, representatives from a dozen state colleges met in Chicago at the call of faculty officers of the Illinois Industrial University. The "Friends of Agricultural Education," as their convention title suggests, spent most of their two-day meeting discussing academic programs at the new institutions. Yet the conferees found time to consider and adopt a proposal prepared by Willard C. Flagg to encourage the founding of agricultural experiment stations as adjuncts to the state land-grant universities. One result of the deliberations was the appointment of an interim committee to encourage the state legislatures and the national Congress to establish research facilities.

Early in the next year, the United States Department of Agriculture assumed responsibility for a follow-up meeting of agricultural educators. Delegates from thirty-two states and three territories convened in Washington to consider uniting behind the new land-grant college support bill introduced in that year by Senator Morrill. As at the previous convention, a committee was created to propose means of establishing agricultural experiment stations in the states. Dominated by Connecticut scientists Johnson and Atwater and including the members of the earlier interim committee created at Chicago, the group wrestled with the question of how to plan administrative and funding mechanisms to pursue effective agricultural investigations. In 1872, there were no precedents for either operation or government subsidization of an agricultural experiment station and the committee recommended only its own continuance until the next annual convention.

Experiment Stations Bill Introduced

That next convention did not meet for ten years. Economic depression and Department of Agriculture disinterest stalled the national movement for the remainder of the 1870s, leaving the states to their own resources. By the early 1880s, enough states were struggling with the problems of institutionalizing experimentation to revive sentiment for a concerted national approach. A new federal Commissioner of Agriculture, anxious to garner the backing of the land-grant colleges for the Department, gave the experiment station advocates an opportunity when he called a convention of agricultural college and farmer organization delegates to meet in Washington in 1882. As in the previous two national meetings agricultural education was the planned focus of convention discussions but agricultural experimentation was also a concern, especially among the representatives from the five colleges which had formally established experiment stations on their campuses.

After declaring that scientific investigation was a necessary complement to agricultural teaching, the 1882 convention stopped short of urging the founding of college-attached experiment stations. Instead, the delegates endorsed a proposal by the Commissioner of Agriculture to have his office serve as coordinator of joint research efforts among volunteering stations and colleges and entrusted to him the task of convincing Congress to subsidize this new mission.[27]

When another round of meetings was called in Washington for 1883, its delegates were given the chance to act more decisively; they were asked to endorse a pending congressional bill to create a national system of agricultural experiment stations. Seaman A. Knapp, professor of agriculture at Iowa State College, authored the proposal to fund experiment stations connected with the state agricultural colleges out of the national treasury. Frustrated after failing to convince the Iowa legislature to fund an experiment station and unable to interest the federal department in addressing local farm problems, Knapp devised a solution which combined state and federal support. By the terms of the Knapp proposal, introduced into Congress by Iowa Representative Cyrus C. Carpenter in May of 1882, each state agricultural college would receive $15,000 annually from the national treasury to operate an experiment station which would pursue research into a number of broad areas. Since the federal grants could be used only to pay the salaries of scientists and support staff and to defray the expenses of investigation, the college would furnish buildings, land, and other facilities. The college trustees would maintain "general control" and furnish a professor of agriculture to supervise the station. Presumably this director and the station staff would decide on the specific experiments to be performed; the "general character" of the work was to be determined by the station superintendent, the college president, and the federal Commissioner of Agriculture. By retaining ultimate authority over funds, the Commissioner could shape station programs to national concerns. The Carpenter Bill justified federal financial support for state stations in a preamble noting the charge of the Department of Agriculture "to acquire and diffuse among the people of the United States useful information on subjects connected with agriculture . . .," and thus required these "national experiment stations" to send status reports to the Commissioner.[28]

After endorsing the proposed legislation, the Washington Convention of 1883 selected a five-man committee to lobby the bill in Congress, to which it was resubmitted in December of 1883 by Iowa Congressman Adoniram Judson Holmes, who had unseated the original sponsor of the proposal. Referred to the House Committee on Agriculture, the bill emerged in July, 1884 with substantial revisions insisted upon by college interests fearful of the imposition of federal authority.

The redrawn proposal, now referred to as the Cullen Bill in honor of Agriculture Committee Chairman William Cullen of Illinois, more closely connected the proposed stations to the colleges. The station was made a distinct department under the college and was placed under the control of the college trustees acting through a director and scientific staff appointed by them. The Department of Agriculture chief's role was limited to furnishing forms for data tabulation, setting standards for fertilizer valuation, and suggesting lines of inquiry if so requested by a station. His office would no longer directly receive reports from the station; they first were channeled through the state governor. The Cullen Bill also more clearly specified the college's responsibility in station operation. In addition to selecting the station personnel the college was to maintain an experimental farm of at least twenty-five acres and distribute bulletins every three months to keep the public abreast of the station work. The federal grant remained at $15,000 per annum to each station under the Cullen proposal but allowed 20 percent of the first year grant to be expended on buildings and up to 5 percent of the funds in subsequent years. Despite the weakening of the control functions of the Department of Agriculture in the new version of the proposal, the Cullen Bill still was promoted as a means of fulfilling the mandate of Department's organic act of 1862.[29]

After it was reported favorably out of committee in 1884, the Cullen Bill languished in Congress. But 1885 witnessed a resurgence of interest sparked by a meeting of agricultural educators called in Washington by the Commissioner of Agriculture. The convention endorsed the principles of the experiment station bill and appointed another committee to work for the measure's passage. Made up of college presidents, the committee developed a new rationale for support of legislation based on the duties of the state land-grant

William H. Hatch, Missouri congressman, championed the first successful state station-founding bill in Congress in 1887. *(USDA photo)*

institutions, not on the duties of the federal agricultural agency. The presidents' committee contended that the national government had exercised its obligation to provide for the welfare of farmers by creating a land-grant college system to educate them and improve their practices. In fulfilling this responsibility, the colleges had embarked on a search for new knowledge to assist farmers straining their meager resources to the limit. New assistance from the federal government specifically directed to agricultural experimentation was necessary to continue the good work at the colleges.

The land-grant committee's support of the Cullen Bill struck a responsive chord in the House Agriculture Committee, which had at least seven other station bills under consideration by 1886. Its chairman, now William H. Hatch of Missouri, recommended to the full House in March a bill incorporating the college committee's justification as its preamble. An identical bill sponsored by James Z. George of Mississippi was brought to the floor of the Senate for debate in January of 1887. There, those in favor of federal subsidies but fearful of an extension of federal power demanded even greater restrictions on the Department of Agriculture's role in the proposed system. One camp went so far as to eliminate mention of the Department altogether and would have divided the money between the state legislatures to disburse in whatever way they thought most appropriate for the purposes of the act. Other legislators, prodded by the National Grange, wanted to limit station connections with the land-grant colleges. Such sentiments did not carry the day but they resulted in a much amended station-founding act.[30]

Hatch Act of 1887

The Hatch Act signed into law by President Grover Cleveland on March 2, 1887, was identical to the original version of the bill written by Knapp in 1882 in only two particulars. Each experiment station still was "to conduct original researches or verify experiments . . . [on subjects] bearing directly upon the agricultural industry of the United States . . ." and was given $15,000 annually to do so. The Morrill Land-Grant College Act was cited in the preamble as the authority from whence the station act arose, thus the stations were to be "established under the direction" of those institutions founded under the provisions of that earlier legislation. However, in deference to the existing structure of the Connecticut station, a state could chose to apply its grant to stations unconnected with its agricultural colleges. Due to a combination of sensitivity to states' rights issues and recognition of the site-specific nature of production agriculture, the Hatch Act left to the stations the task of determining programs of investigation "having due regard to the varying conditions and needs of the respective States or Territories." The Commissioner of Agriculture in Washington was limited to indicating subjects of potential interest, and to supplying forms and offering advice to encourage "uniformity of methods and results in the work of said stations."[31]

By providing funds, a suggestion for organizational structure, and discretionary authority in designing research programs around local needs, the Hatch Act presented an opportunity to benefit agriculture through the application of discoveries of scientific investigation. Over the next century agricultural scientists, land-grant college administrators, and United States Department of Agriculture officials labored within this framework to evolve an agricultural experiment station system which would realize the promise of the 1887 legislation.

Notes

[1] Alfred C. True, *A History of Agricultural Experimentation and Research in the United States: 1607 - 1925* (Washington: U.S.D.A. Miscellaneous Publication 251, 1937), pp. 6-21.

[2] Margaret W. Rossiter, "Organization of Agricultural Improvement in the United States, 1785 -1865," in *The Pursuit of Knowledge in the Early American Republic*, eds. Alexandra Oleson and Sanborn C. Brown (Baltimore: Johns Hopkins, 1976), pp. 280-281.

[3] H.C. Knoblauch et al., *State Agricultural Experiment Stations: A History of Research Policy and Procedure* (Washington: U.S.D.A. Miscellaneous Publication 904, May 1962), pp. 7-9, 14-17; Vernon W. Ruttan, *Agricultural Research Policy* (Minneapolis. University of Minnesota Press, 1982), pp. 68, 72-74.

[4] Knoblauch et al., *State Agricultural Experiment Stations*, pp. 9-14.

[5] Rossiter, *The Emergence of Agricultural Science: Justus Liebig and the Americans* (New Haven: Yale University Press, 1975), pp. 129-135, 152-156; Knoblauch et al., *State Agricultural Experiment Stations*, pp. 19-21.

[6] Wayne D. Rasmussen, "Lincoln and the Liberation of the Man on the Land," in *That We May Eat* (Washington: U.S.D.A. 1975 Yearbook of Agriculture, 1975), pp. 23-24.

[7] A.C. True, "The United States Department of Agriculture: 1862 - 1912," in *Proceedings of the Twenty-Sixth Annual Convention of the Association of American Colleges and Experiment Stations* (September 13-15, 1912), p. 3; W.D. Rasmussen and Gladys L. Baker, *The Department of Agriculture* (New York: Praeger, 1972), p. 5.

[8] Knoblauch et al., *State Agricultural Experiment Stations*, pp. 25-27; Rasmussen and Baker, *The Department of Agriculture*, p. 7; Milton Conover, *The Office of Experiment Stations: Its History, Activities, and Organization* (Baltimore: Johns Hopkins, 1924), p. 31.

[9] Edward D. Eddy, *Colleges for Our Land and Time: The Land-Grant Idea in American Education* (New York: Harpers Brothers, 1957), pp. 5-7, 23-25; Allan Nevins, *State Universities and Democracy* (Urbana: University of Illinois Press, 1962), p. 14; Fred A. Shannon, *The Farmers Last Frontier: Agriculture, 1860 - 1897* (New York: Harper and Row, 1945), pp. 272-274.

[10] Thomas LeDuc, "State Disposal of the Agricultural College Land Scrip," *Agricultural History* 28 (July 1954): 100-104; Shannon, *Farmers Last Frontier*, p. 274.

[11] Eddy, *Colleges for Our Land and Time*, pp. 101-102; Henry S.Brunner, *Land-Grant Colleges and Universities: 1862-1962* (Washington: U.S. Department of Health, Education, and Welfare, 1962), pp. 7-42 passim.

[12] Nevins, *State Universities and Democracy*, pp. 43-46, 52-59; Roy V. Scott, *Reluctant Farmer: The Rise of Agricultural Extension to 1914* (Urbana: University of Illinois Press, 1970), pp. 52-53.

[13] Rossiter, *Emergence of Agricultural Science*, pp. 158-160, 167-169; Knoblauch et al., *State Agricultural Experiment Stations*, pp. 21-24.

[14] True, *Agricultural Experimentation*, pp. 70-71, 87.

[15] From 1867 to 1887, the land-grant endowment was forwarded to the University of North Carolina; in the latter year, North Carolina State College became the state land-grant institution. True, *Agricultural Experimentation*, pp. 89-91; North Carolina Agricultural Experiment Station, *A Century of Service* (Raleigh: A.E.S Bulletin 459, North Carolina State University at Raleigh, February 1979) pp. 5-7.

[16] True, *Agricultural Experimentation*, pp. 92-93.

[17] True, *Agricultural Experimentation*, pp. 94-97; Ulysses P. Hedrick, *A History of Agriculture in the State of New York* (New York: Hill and Wang reprint ed., 1966; original ed., 1933), pp. 414, 422-424.

[18] Carl R. Woodward and Ingrid N. Waller, *New Jersey's Agricultural Experiment Station: 1880-1930* (New Brunswick: New Jersey A.E.S., 1932), pp. 24-26, 34-35.

[19] Alexis Cope, *History of Ohio State University: Volume I, 1870-1910* (Columbus: Ohio State University Press, 1920), pp. 454-457, 479, 495.

[20] True, *Agricultural Experimentation*, p. 100.

[21] Norwood Allen Kerr, *A History of the Alabama Agricultural Experiment Station: 1883-1983* (Auburn University: Alabama A.E.S., 1985), pp. 8-10, 20-21.

[22] Vernon Cartenson, "The Genesis of an Agricultural Experiment Station," *Agricultural History* 34 (January 1960): 14-18.

[23] True, *Agricultural Experimentation*, pp. 104-105.

[24] David C. Smith, *The Maine Agricultural Experiment Station: A Bountiful Alliance of Science and Husbandry* (Orono: Life Sciences and Agricultural Experiment Station, University of Maine at Orono, 1980), pp. 2, 7.

[25] True, *Agricultural Experimentation*, pp. 105-106.

[26] J.L. Hills, *Five and Fifty Years: 1888 - 1942* (Burlington: Vermont A.E.S. Bulletin 515, September 1944), pp. 3, 8-9.

[27] Wilbur O. Atwater, *First Annual Report of the Connecticut Agricultural Experiment Station: 1876* (Middletown: Wesleyan University, 1877), p. 353; True, *Agricultural Experimentation*, pp. 118-120; Knoblauch et al., *State Agricultural Experiment Stations*, pp. 30-41; Alan I. Marcus, *Agricultural Science and the Quest for Legitimacy* (Ames: Iowa State University Press, 1985), pp. 169-170.

[28] The text of Knapp's proposals is reprinted in True, *Agricultural Experimentation*, pp. 121-122.

[29] True, *Agricultural Experimentation*, p. 123; Knoblauch et al., *State Agricultural Experiment Stations*, pp. 47-48.

[30] True, *History of Agricultural Experimentation*, pp. 124-129; Knoblauch et al., *State Agricultural Experiment Stations*, pp. 49-52; Marcus, *Agricultural Science*, pp. 197-211.

[31] Hatch Act, 24 Stat. 440 (1887).

CHAPTER II
Fulfilling the Original Mission: 1887-1940

In implementing the provisions of the Hatch Act, no proven precedents were available to the experiment stations with their associated state colleges or to their federal partner. The legislation itself offered little guidance, failing even to specify why the government should undertake "to aid in acquiring and diffusing among the people of the United States useful and practical information on subjects connected with agriculture, and to promote scientific investigation and experiment respecting the principles and applications of agricultural science." As the experiment station system evolved over the next half-century, an implicit answer to the question emerged as research concentrated on increasing farm production efficiency and bettering the economic status of commodity producers.[1]

Implementing the Hatch Act

The Hatch Act was no more explicit in resolving other central issues with which early station organizers had struggled. Still to be determined were effective working relations between the federal Department of Agriculture and the state stations, between the stations and their allied land-grant colleges, and between the demands of farmers and the changing capabilities of science. As the states turned to take advantage of the legislation, they were confronted with these issues expressed in ways specific to their local situations.[2]

Although the Hatch Act specified that quarterly payments were to begin on October 1, 1887, the first installment was delayed to those states whose legislatures had accepted the provisions when the Comptroller of the Treasury ruled that the legislation actually failed to appropriate any monies. In the confusion of amending the bill and pushing it successfully through Congress before the close of the session, the measure's sponsors misworded that section dealing with funding. The oversight was corrected when the lawmakers rushed through a special appropriations bill effective on its February 1, 1888, date of approval. By the end of that year experiment stations were organized (or in some cases, reorganized) in all thirty-eight existing states and in the territories of Utah and Dakota. Each state interpreted the Hatch Act according to local political conditions, producing an array of institutional arrangements which conformed to no standard pattern.

The Northern States

The Connecticut experiment station at New Haven increasingly was an anomaly by 1888 when almost every other experiment station operated in connection with a college. Recognizing the value and tradition of this pioneering American station but equally mindful of the advantages of providing a station close to the farmers, the Connecticut legislature split its Hatch endowment in half. The Connecticut Agricultural Experiment Station at New Haven retained its board of control and added $7,500 of federal monies annually to its state appropriations and its fees for fertilizer, feed, and food analyses. The Storrs Agricultural Experiment Station, under the board of trustees of the Connecticut Agricultural College in Mansfield, was established and financed with the remaining $7,500. Competition between the two stations for support from state farmers was keen. In the 1880s and 1890s the state station at New Haven was the target of abuse for its neglect of "practical" farmer needs while the newer station at Storrs encouraged farmers to help shape investigations. In the first decade of the twentieth century it was the Storrs station's turn to weather similar complaints. In 1912, a single director was named for the two stations yet their board of directors and programs maintained separate identities.[3]

Like Connecticut, Massachusetts used the promise of its federal endowment to create an entirely new facility in 1887. This new "Hatch Experiment Station" was located on the Amherst campus of the Massachusetts Agricultural College where the State Agricultural Experiment Station continued to operate entirely with state appropriations. While the State Station increasingly confined its duties to laboratory analyses of fertilizers, the Hatch Station undertook broader investigations utilizing field plots. Both stations were directed by the college president who, in 1895, convinced the legislature to fuse them in name as well as function.[4]

New York already had two separate stations when Hatch money became available. Initially, the federal funds went entirely to the Cornell Station, allowing the university to revive its dying agricultural program by doubling its staff. After 1894, the New York State Experiment Station at Geneva was given a 10 percent share of the Hatch monies. The stations maintained independent controlling boards until 1923 when the Geneva station was placed under the supervision of the Cornell College of Agriculture. Still, it retained its identity and separate program of work.[5]

New Jersey's legislature responded to the Hatch Act in much the same way as had Massachusetts, creating a new station to receive the federal appropriations and attaching it to the college where the state agricultural experiment station already operated. The two stations on the Rutgers campus shared facilities, faculty, and a director but maintained separate managing boards and accounts for many years.[6]

Maine avoided the bother of keeping separate accounts by rescinding the state funding legislation that had supported a college-connected station since 1885. When the Hatch Act passed, the Maine lawmakers discontinued their $5,000 annual appropriation to the station. When the initial Hatch payment was delayed they hurriedly granted emergency funds which carried the Maine station through 1887. Even after regular state appropriations ended, fees from the analysis of fertilizers provided some local support. Similarly, Vermont's assembly, which had financed its year-old station only through fertilizer fees from the outset, designated the Burlington facility as the Hatch beneficiary.[7]

Pennsylvania State College had been engaged in rudimentary plant variety and fertilizer tests for some thirty years when the Hatch Bill passed. Thus, in 1887, the legislature simply accepted the act's provisions by organizing the work at the college under the professor of agriculture who became director. The Delaware, Maryland, and West Virginia assemblies followed the same course in the next year by naming their state colleges as the sites for agricultural experiment stations.[8]

New Hampshire's lawmakers chose Dartmouth as the recipient of the state's portion of the Hatch money. The college had maintained a small research farm on its Hanover campus since the mid-1870s. In 1891, the state was given a large estate near Durham on the condition that an agricultural college would be established on the land. Dartmouth surrendered both its agricultural school and its experiment station when the New Hampshire legislature accepted the bequest.[9]

In Rhode Island, passage of the Hatch Act more directly led to the creation of a new agricultural college. For a quarter-century the state's farmers had resented the use of the Morrill Act endowment by Brown University to fund scholarships for study in its classical curriculum.

When federal support for agricultural research became available in 1888, this dissatisfaction crystallized into demands that the legislature create a new agricultural school under which an experiment station could operate in the interests of the farmers. With the help of the town's citizens, a suitable site for the Rhode Island Agricultural School was secured near Kingston. The station immediately began its work of preparing an experimental farm under the school's managing board of "practical agriculturists." The doors opened to students in 1890, and four years later the renamed Rhode Island College of Agriculture and Mechanic Arts successfully wrested the land-grant endowment from Brown.[10]

The Southern States

Farmer discontent with the University of North Carolina agricultural program prompted the relocation of the ten-year-old experiment station when Hatch money became available. Although the new Agricultural and Mechanical College at Raleigh became its home, control of the station research program was transferred back and forth between the A & M College and the State Department of Agriculture until the mid-1920s.[11]

Tennessee, Kentucky, and Alabama reorganized their college-attached experiment stations when federal funds appeared. Investigations at these Southern stations were broadened considerably as researchers were relieved of some of the pressure to analyze fertilizers in order to garner financial support. Louisiana's two existing experiment stations, the state station at Baton Rouge and the private Sugar Experiment Station near New Orleans were joined by another one in northern Louisiana in 1888. To make them eligible for aid under the Hatch Act, all three were put under the control of the Louisiana State University and Agricultural and Mechanical College.[12]

South Carolina was on the verge of implementing its own system of experiment stations when the federal-support act was approved. In December of 1886, the state legislature passed a measure to operate two research farms out of fertilizer tax proceeds. The availability of Hatch money allowed the expansion of the plan to include a central station at Columbia's South Carolina College from whence the college president directed work at all three stations. In 1890, the main station was moved to Clemson where an agricultural college had been established in the previous year.[13]

Virginia, too, was ready for the Hatch Act. In March 1886, the state lawmakers anticipated the act's approval by providing for an experiment station under the A & M College at Blacksburg to be established when federal funds arrived. Not until 1905 did the state augment the Hatch support.[14]

Mississippi's Agricultural and Mechanical College in Starkville had engaged in some experimental farm research since its 1880 founding so it was a logical choice as a station location in 1888. The school board of trustees was designated by the legislature to supervise the station work, initially with the advice of representatives from Mississippi's leading farmer organizations. The latter group was largely inactive after 1890. Arkansas and Texas in 1888 and Oklahoma in 1891 located their experiment stations at existing land-grant colleges where they were promptly forgotten for some years by allocators of state revenues.[15]

The experiment stations in both Florida and Georgia fared even less well in their formative years. In 1888, Florida's four-year-old State Agricultural College at Lake City was given responsibility for a new system with the main station located on campus and three substations scattered over the state. Within a year, the system director and entire staff were dismissed and, in 1897, the substations were abandoned. State financial support remained elusive until 1906, when both the college and the station were transferred to Gainesville as the University of Florida. The University of Georgia trustees authorized the formation of the state station in connection with their college of agriculture in 1888, but when the townspeople of Athens failed to provide suitable land, the legislature located the station on donated farmland near Griffin. The inclusion of the university chancellor and a professor on the station board of direction, which was otherwise comprised of a "practical successful farmer" from each congressional district, was the college's only connection with the station for many years.[16]

The Midwestern States

In the Midwest, the Wisconsin State experiment station was made eligible for Hatch funds by a simple acceptance of the measure by the legislature. In Ohio, the process of naming a beneficiary for the Hatch Act revived an old rivalry between the state experiment station and Ohio State University. The station's creation in 1882 had created such controversy that the state legislature had compromised by placing the facility on the university's Columbus campus alongside

Stephen M. Babcock, a chemist with the Wisconsin Station, in 1890 perfected a reliable, inexpensive test for determining the butterfat content of milk, a great boon to the emerging dairy industry. (*National Archives and Records Administration photo*)

the agricultural school's farm, but with a separate board of directors.

When the Ohio station won the contest over the Hatch fund disbursement in 1887, the contending parties negotiated a truce under which the university was reimbursed for the station's use of its facilities and for the service of the school's professor of agriculture as the station director. The arrangement lasted until 1892 when station field work was moved to a newly acquired farm just south of Wooster and its offices took up quarters in downtown Wooster.[17]

Allocation of federal funds for agricultural research intensified the simmering controversy in Missouri and Iowa, too. While both the University of Missouri and Iowa State College maintained schools of agriculture, these divisions were perceived by state agricultural interests as mere token gestures to collect on Morrill grant funds. With the passage of the Hatch Act these sentiments revived, stimulating repeated efforts to move the institutions' schools of agriculture and their connected experiment stations to independent locations.

The colleges held on to the stations, but the successive controversies plagued research efforts for the remainder of the century.[18]

The agricultural experiment stations organized under Kansas State Agricultural College and the University of Minnesota shared another obstacle to development. With rudimentary farm investigations already underway, both institutions simply designated their agricultural faculties as experiment station staffs and appointed the department heads to supervisory councils. While a director was named at each station, the position's occupant was limited to handling correspondence and administrative matters, leaving the researchers to pursue whatever interested them. The result, too often, was unfocused, short-term investigations. The Minnesota station moved to centralize authority in the mid-1890s while Kansas delayed action until 1906.[19]

The conversion of the college farms to experiment stations under the land-grant institutions in Michigan, Indiana, and Nebraska was more orderly. Both the Michigan Agricultural College and Purdue University had some experience with government-subsidized investigation. Since 1881, agricultural faculty at the former had conducted research on farm topics specified by the legislature while chemists at the latter had supervised Indiana's fertilizer control program. Despite changing the name of its school of agriculture to "Industrial College" in 1881, the University of Nebraska agricultural program also was fully prepared to accept the duties thrust upon it when the state assembly accepted the Hatch Act. Illinois University had no such head start. As a land-grant institution it had emphasized the mechanic arts half of the A & M formula. With federal funds after 1888 and a dynamic new director who garnered state financial assistance after 1900, the agricultural experiment station helped elevate the entire university agricultural program.[20]

In one of the two states which had comprised the Dakota Territory until 1889, the Hatch Act actually led to the founding of the state college. A South Dakota Agricultural College had been in existence since 1881 and to this was added an agricultural experiment station in 1887. North Dakota was slower to respond, achieving statehood without a land-grant college to which a station could be attached. Eager to share in the Hatch bounty, the state legislators were convinced by proponents of agricultural education to simultaneously create a North Dakota Agricultural College and an agricultural experiment station in 1890. The school president served concurrently as station director and both organizations were supervised by a board of trustees.[21]

The Western States

In the Far West, California had the only functioning agricultural experiment station in 1887. With federal money to support work at its Berkeley location, it used more local support to expand work onto eight outlying stations between 1888 and 1900. The other states in the region, avid for national aid in promoting economic development, quickly moved to establish their own stations.

Oregon, Colorado, and Nevada, as states with existing land-grant colleges, accepted the Hatch Act offer within the first year that money became available. Oregon's twenty-year-old State Agricultural College appointed its extant staff as station researchers in 1888. In 1891, the school president took over as station director. Colorado State Agricultural College had used its farm for plant variety testing since 1883, so this facility was designated as the experiment station five years later. Two substations were immediately founded by the legislature and two more joined the system in the early 1890s. Nevada also attached its station to the state land-grant institution but added no substations. Initially, the Nevada station did not even add any staff — the University of Nevada president was made the station director and a professor of chemistry became its researcher.[22]

Wyoming established a university in 1887 when it was still a territory, then added an experiment station when it achieved statehood in 1891. The $15,000 annual Hatch grant also was used to support five branch units during the station's first decade of operation. Washington, Montana, and Idaho founded experiment stations soon after becoming states, too. Each was attached to a state college which was created at the same time. Washington did so in 1891, making the station a department of the Washington Agricultural College and School of Science, and placing it under the direction of the president. Idaho's university and experiment station were established in the next year in Moscow. No farm facilities were available there, however, until 1896 when the closing of three distant substations prompted the college town's citizens to purchase a nearby site. The Montana legislature accepted the Hatch Act in 1893, making the station a department of the Montana Agricultural College organized at the same time. The college governing board closely supervised station research put under the direct control of a director.[23]

Utah and New Mexico in 1889, and Arizona in 1890, were still in the territorial stage when their legislatures instituted colleges with allied agricultural experiment stations. Despite the addition of branch stations in the early years of the New Mexico and Arizona stations, all three stations operated limited research programs with no state financial assistance until after the turn of the century.[24]

Courting Farmer Support

Although the Hatch Act provided a stable source of revenue for the agricultural research system, it was a narrow base of support. Like many of the land-grant colleges after the Morrill Act, the experiment stations after the Hatch Act found winning the farmers over to their side to be an arduous task. An emphasis on courting farmer support by discovering solutions to pressing production problems developed at an early date and became an enduring trait in agricultural experiment stations.

It was a time when scientific knowledge about agriculture was scarce, trained scientists were scarcer, and farmer discontent was abundant. The infant years of the state experiment station system coincided with the culmination of nearly three decades of increasing restiveness among the nation's farmers. Indeed, some political support for the creation of a publicly financed system for agricultural research doubtless was founded upon the hope that it might help ease the farm sector's transition into America's industrializing economy, and quiet the clamor for more fundamental economic reforms. In the 1890s the land-grant colleges in Kansas, Iowa, Missouri, and West Virginia suffered through the same types of battles over control which had racked a number of schools in the 1870s and '80s. In this Populist atmosphere, the stations naturally turned to their client-farmers to answer the question of what research was to be.

Most farmers, still suspicious of "book farming", ignored the stations. More enlightened agriculturists, recognizing the potential benefits of experiments but discounting the need for scientists to conduct them, suggested simple enough tasks for the new facilities: test varieties for individual farmers who had neither the time nor money to do so themselves, and disseminate knowledge about the best practices. Legislators in many states added another duty: regulate a broadening array of products that the farmer either bought or sold. By 1899, at least twenty-eight of the stations were required to inspect seeds, fertilizers, feeds, and foods. Practical investigations with immediate payoffs thus came to be expected from the experiment station system.[25]

The development of administrative relations in the colleges with which the stations were connected also encouraged them toward practical work. Still struggling for public acceptance themselves, the land-grant schools often regarded the new stations as little more than federally financed allies in their cause. Encouraged by the vague wording of the Hatch Act, most states simply incorporated the station into the general administration of the college. The college board of trustees usually became the station board of control bringing with it an overriding concern for economy. Common, too, was the naming of college officers and faculty to corresponding positions in the station. As late as 1900, fourteen college presidents were serving concurrently as station directors. At the other institutions, the heads of resident instruction usually filled the station director positions. In most instances, existing departmental structures were retained so that station investigations usually proceeded along a mixture of commodity and disciplinary lines. Too often in these situations, the duty of performing enough research to qualify for Hatch disbursements was imposed upon an agriculture faculty already engaged in full-time instruction.[26]

With few faculty experienced in the methods of scientific inquiry and with pressure coming from college trustees and administrators to run the research programs as inexpensively as possible, the tendency was strong to operate station lands as model demonstration farms which could pay their own way and present an attractive appearance to visitors. "Research" on such a farm might consist only of plant variety trials alternating with plots displaying the effects of differing soil treatments and crop rotations. Whether used for demonstration or for the discovery of new knowledge, a single station farm was limited in its usefulness. Only those who visited the college could learn from its model farm and only those who shared the farm's climate and soils could apply its scientific discoveries. Recognizing these limitations and responding to public demands, the stations expanded beyond their own farms to enlist practicing farmers and more distant lands to broaden the scope of their investigations and the support of their programs.

Some stations, acknowledging the widely shared belief of their farmer clients that research only required patient observation, dispatched seeds, fertilizers, and report forms to farmers scattered over their states. West Virginia's station gave wheat, fruit, and forage seeds along with detailed planting and reporting instructions to each of the university regents to distribute to cooperating farmers. Of those who received wheat seeds in 1889, only one out of 708 cooperators returned useful information while 85 percent returned no information at all. The program was dropped in 1890 after three years and an expenditure of some $2,600.[27]

Substations Introduced

Off-campus research sites staffed by station personnel proved more popular than enlisting the aid of cooperating farmers, though often no more enduring, in the early years. Branch stations could provide opportunities for longer-term, supervised investigations on soil types and under climatic conditions not available at a central station. They also could provide opportunities to disburse precious station funds so broadly as to dilute the entire research effort. With its immense land area of radically different climates and soils, California's research program with eight outlying branches developed the most elaborate system. At least twelve other states operated substations between 1888 and the end of the century. In some states sites were secured from generous townspeople while in others, land was either rented or purchased. Whatever the source of land, most of the substations were overseen by a locally hired farm superintendent who conducted plant variety and fertilizer trials at the direction of the main station staff. Station scientists and budgets often were stretched to the limit by such activities, particularly when state lawmakers mandated branch stations, then provided no additional funds for their operation.

Alabama, which had one branch station in existence in 1888, offered an extreme example of what could happen due to a lack of extra funding. In accepting the Hatch Act the legislature allocated a $2,000 portion of the annual appropriation to the three-year-old Black Belt branch. The state assembly in 1889 began creating a series of secondary-level agricultural schools, designating them at the same time as "branch experiment stations." In 1890, a bill was passed to fund each of three newly created schools with equal parts of a $6,000 share of the $15,000 federal grant for agricultural research in Alabama. Only the governor's veto, strongly backed by friends of the land-grant college at Auburn, saved the main station from having its Hatch support fractioned out to a system of high school-connected demonstration farms.

Few stations faced budget raids of the magnitude in Alabama, but a number of them did have to close down branch operations when local support evaporated in the depression of the mid-1890s. In the early decades of the twentieth century, many branch station systems were revived but they more often were done so in an effort to make programs more applicable to the farm problems of the entire state and less as a concession to popular agitation to share in the federal largesse.[28]

Association of American Agricultural Colleges and Experiment Stations

Difficulties in developing popular research programs and effective station-college relations were anticipated when the Hatch Act was being framed. The 1885 gathering of agricultural leaders had established a committee to plan for a permanent organization to address problems common to the colleges and experiment stations. That committee was the latest in a series involving agricultural teachers, researchers, and administrators who had been unable to create an organization largely because they had failed to solve the question of whether the problems of colleges or of scientific investigation should be their proper concern. Success came only after the passage of the Hatch Act in 1887, when, in October of that year, the Association of American Agricultural Colleges and Experiment Stations was born.[29]

Defining College-Station Relations

Under guidelines suggested by the organizing session's Washington host, Commissioner of Agriculture Norman J. Coleman, the new Association drafted a constitution that neatly sidestepped the troublesome organizational question by giving each college and each experiment station one vote in its business proceedings. While this action implicitly recognized that the stations were something more than "departments" of the colleges in the usual sense, it went no farther in defining the college-station relationship. That task was tackled by two separate committees during the first meeting. One headed by Tennessee station director Charles Dabney interpreted the wording of the Hatch Act for Association members, concluding in a set of advisory propositions that each station should be a distinct department with a single administrator devoting most of his time to the station work. The Dabney committee further suggested that the station maintain separate accounts to better ensure that all Hatch monies were spent in station research rather than in general college operation.

With the Dabney committee report as a philosophical base, a second committee comprised of three experiment station pioneers was asked to prepare a blueprint for station procedures which could be followed by directors setting up institutions under the Hatch Act. Veteran directors Samuel W. Johnson and Wilbur O. Atwater of Connecticut and George H. Cook of New Jersey seemed to realize the impossibility of their assignment from the outset. Their long experience was in conducting research programs largely independent of colleges, a situation which would be uncommon to most new stations. Additionally, each station would encounter challenges and opportunities requiring unique administrative responses. Instead of prescribing a model structure, then, the Johnson-Atwater-Cook report offered a survey of opinions by other station officials on their anticipated work under the Hatch Act. Like the Dabney committee report, the authors could only offer the high-minded suggestion that the stations always remember that they had a mission to both advance science and serve the farmer.[30]

Unable to resolve the issue of college-station relations within the states at this first meeting, the Association was confronted with the related, but more immediate question of college-station relations within the organization itself. In January 1889, at the second annual convention, the delegates met in Knoxville to again consider developing a model for successful station administration. Henry P. Armsby, director of the Pennsylvania station, reoriented the deliberations when he offered an amendment to the Association constitution which would split the body into two sections. In one section, the college presidents would convene to discuss administering teaching programs while in the other, station directors and scientists would meet to share the investigative techniques and results of their research. In this manner, Armsby suggested, the separate spheres of education and experimentation would both advance. Under his proposal, the two sections would continue to convene in brief joint sessions about common concerns. The Armsby resolution framed a cluster of persistent issues in college-station relations into one fundamental question: were teaching and research compatible within a single institution? The problem had challenged the American stations since their beginnings and threatened the unity of their new organization through the turn of the century.

During the time remaining in its 1889 Knoxville sessions, the Association declined to act upon the resolution. Another reorganization plan was adopted at its next annual meeting, dividing the membership into six permanent committees (later designated as "sections") representing the disciplines of agriculture, botany, chemistry, entomology, horticulture, and college management. While this structure recognized that Association members had diverse interests and that college administration was a separate field, it implicitly denied that teachers and researchers had distinct concerns. The annual sessions through the 1890s considered the issue repeatedly as a succession of land-grant college leaders used the occasion to advance their views. The principal positions that emerged from these discussions were perhaps best presented by three Association spokesmen in that decade.

In the fall of 1889, George W. Atherton, president of Pennsylvania State College, articulated what might be termed the college presidents' position in his presidential address to the third convention of the Association. Atherton argued that the framers of the Hatch Act wisely had intended to connect research to teaching in a unified program to advance the land-grant mission of placing practical knowledge in the hands of the public. As Atherton phrased it, "Let the college investigate that it may teach well, and the station teach that it may investigate, . . ." with each activity complementing the other.[31]

Challenging Atherton's contention was Whitman H. Jordan, director of the New York station at Geneva. Advancing the opinion of many career directors toward the specious doctrine that teaching was an inducement to better research, Jordan labeled the assertion "an unmitigated, though perhaps comfortable, fallacy." The New York director insisted that under the arrangement prevailing in the colleges, experimental investigation inevitably was slighted as teaching took precedence. Only the complete separation of activities could ensure the advance of both endeavors, Director Jordan maintained.[32]

With Atherton's and Jordan's positions representing the extremes, most Association members' views fell somewhere between wanting the stations to be completely subservient to or completely independent of the colleges. Henry Armsby, ten years after he had first proposed to split the Association, became its president and a spokesman for conciliation. He had spent that decade as the director of the Pennsylvania station, in conjunction with the state college. In evolving a working relationship with the college president, George Atherton, Armsby developed a comprehensive position which gave equal weight to instruction and research in the land-grant mission. In his 1899 valedictory, Armsby told the Association members, "The ideal experiment station should be as fully separated as possible from the details—the daily grind—of undergraduate instruction, while retaining its general supervision and inspiration." The college, then, must embrace the station as the discoverer of new knowledge and as the trainer of graduate students from whose ranks would emerge succeeding generations of teachers and scientists. Furthermore, the station must be directed by a professional scientist who could offer the staff inspiration, not by a college president who could only give them partial attention.[33]

While Armsby presented an attractive synthesis of viewpoints held by Association members, practical considerations delayed the adoption of one of the crucial features of his vision. A resolution urging that colleges reduce researchers' teaching loads was tabled in the sessions of 1901 and 1902. Still, a consensus in favor of Armsby's attitude had emerged by 1903 when the Association, apparently no longer afraid that the move would tear apart the organization, voted to adopt a new structure similar to that first proposed in 1889. Dropping the awkward six-section arrangement, the Association was reconstituted into two sections, one comprised of college presidents

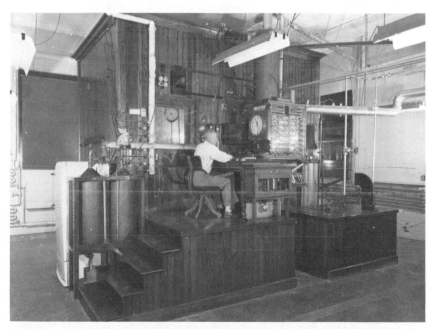

The Armsby Calorimeter, developed in 1902 by Pennsylvania Experiment Station Director Henry Prentiss Armsby, was used to measure the energy and metabolism of large animals until the mid-1950s. *(Pennsylvania A.E.S. photo)*

and the other of station workers. An executive committee with three members from the presidents' section and two members from the stations' section assured overall control by the colleges but recognized the importance of the stations. The reorganization, significantly, provided for annual gatherings of station researchers where they could concentrate on developing effective approaches to common problems.

Office of Experiment Stations

Just as the Association evolved a structure to better address problems in college-station relationships, the United States Department of Agriculture developed an effective agency to fulfill federal obligations under the Hatch Act. Created in 1888, the Office of Experiment Stations was begun as a center for the exchange of information between the stations and grew to become an equal partner with the experiment station section of the Association in formulating research policy for the nation's agricultural experiment station system.

Atwater Sets Standard of Excellence

Wilbur O. Atwater, early station pioneer and, in 1888, director of the Storrs School Agricultural Experiment Station in Connecticut, was selected as the first head of the Office of Experiment Stations. Atwater brought a reputation for rigorous scientific inquiry and independence which stood him well with state stations that were sensitive to any hint of federal control. Accordingly, Atwater strictly adhered to the limited role assigned the USDA by the Hatch Act: assisting the stations in working together and suggesting how they might best approach their research to ensure its quality.

Envisioning its primary duty as facilitating communication between the stations, Atwater's office initiated a series of publications to keep them abreast of each other's work and of the latest scientific developments. Between 1889 and 1913, a total of 256 *Bulletins* and 118 *Circulars* on specific topics of general interest to the stations were issued by the Office of Experiment Stations. Begun in the same year and continuing until 1946, the monthly *Experiment Station Record* published a compilation of abstracts from American and foreign station research reports. Both of these journals were printed in close cooperation with the Association, whose annual deliberations were published by the Office of Experiment Stations until 1909.

From his position as director of the experiment station office, the Connecticut chemist did much to shape the concept of the proper focus of research under the Hatch Act. In an address to the Association in 1889, Atwater prescribed successive steps in the research process: listen to the farmer to determine his needs; select a specific problem on the basis of the station's potential for finding a solution with available facilities and resources; plan experiments carefully; complete the experiments according to the plan, arriving at definite conclusions; and, finally, publish the findings in such a way that the farmers could use them. Because Atwater was convinced that the support of farmers ultimately could be won only by discovering principles of agriculture that were long-term solutions to their problems, he cautioned against straining resources in an effort to find a cure for every new problem the farmers encountered. In an era when the tendency was to do anything to garner farmer loyalty, Director Atwater's advice, backed up by his personal reputation and the prestige of his position, was a valuable reminder that the demands of the scientific discipline should be the guide and the advancement of knowledge should be the standard of success for the stations.[34]

Atwater chose to return to Connecticut and his full-time direction of the Storrs station in 1891, leaving the work of encouraging the state stations to adopt his standard of excellence to capable successors. The

Wilbur O. Atwater was the first director of the Office of Experiment Stations, 1888 to 1891, and a pioneer in nutrition research. (*USDA photo*)

Abram W. Harris was the second director of the Office of Experiment Stations, 1891 to 1893, and, subsequently, president of the University of Maine. (*National Archives and Records Administration photo*)

first of these was Abram W. Harris, a Wesleyan-trained teacher of history and mathematics who had served as Atwater's assistant director in the Office of Experiment Stations. When Harris resigned in 1893 to become the president of Maine State College, another of Atwater's proteges from the Wesleyan humanities program assumed the post. Alfred Charles True had followed his colleagues to Washington when the Office of Experiment Stations was created, becoming an assistant to the director. He emerged as the pivotal individual in the development of the public agricultural research system during the next thirty years.

True and the Atwater Standard

Under True's leadership the Office of Experiment Stations became much more than the "clearinghouse" of information which he claimed it to be; it succeeded in convincing the state experiment stations to put Atwater's theories into practice. The station representatives in the Association actually formulated the policies to attain Atwater's noble goals but, buffeted by local pressures, they relied on the federal office to help put them in effect. Although True was not a scientist, he was a careful, rigorous administrator with a diplomatic

Alfred Charles True, director of the Office of Experiment Stations from 1893 to 1915, initiated a series of policies and procedures which shaped state-federal relations in the public agricultural research partnership to the present day. (*National Archives and Records Administration photo*)

personality well-suited to his delicate mission. His special talent was to gain increasing adherence to regulations of the Office while maintaining the trust of state stations suspicious of federal directives.[35]

The legal basis of the federal agency's influence stemmed from its oversight of expenditures under the Hatch Act, a power delegated to the Office of Experiment Stations in 1894. Framers of the Hatch Act had refused to require federal fiscal review because they feared opposition to that control. The executive committee of the Association could, and did, investigate rumored delinquencies but had no power to withhold federal funds. Beginning in 1890, they proposed accounting forms for congressional consideration. Both Congress and True resisted the imposition of federal authority until they were forced into action by a new Secretary of Agriculture, J. Sterling Morton. Morton was already famous for his distaste of government extravagance when he became secretary at the beginning of a national economic depression. When the proposed budget of the Department of Agriculture came before him in 1894, Morton struck out the request for money under the Hatch Act because his office had no way of accounting for the expenditures of the state stations. The Association, representing the stations, quickly came to terms with the Secretary, who restored the sums for 1895 in return for the authority to institute fiscal review through the Office of Experiment Stations.

Station Reviews Introduced

Content with his victory of principle, Secretary Morton left the development of accounting procedures to the Association. With the cooperation of Director True, a policy that went increasingly beyond the mere annual reporting of expenditures was decided upon by station leaders. The Office was urged to institute personal visits to the stations, thus linking its new fiscal review responsibilities with the advisory functions inherent in the words of the Hatch Act. In this manner, True's office would be able to examine not only accounting procedures but also management, college-station relations, and entire research programs in light of local circumstances. The policy, initiated with thirty-five station "visits" in 1895 (True scrupulously avoided the word "inspections"), became the foundation of the federal partner's contribution to the state agricultural experiment station system. From these review trips True and his associates learned of the constraints under which the stations labored and offered suggestions for improvements. The visits also gave True an overall picture of the entire national system of stations, placing him in an ideal position to formulate procedures to improve that effort on a national scale.[36]

Hatch Funds Reserved for Research

True shared his predecessors' belief that the primary mission of the experiment stations was to discover scientific truths rather than to serve as bureaus of information. With this ever in mind, True embarked on a policy course which inexorably narrowed the range of activities permissible under federal funding. At the same time, he was careful to respect the cardinal principle implied by the Hatch Act that each station was to decide its own research agenda according to the needs of its own state. True's aim was not to dictate research priorities but only to reduce the educational duties placed on stations, enabling their scientists to devote themselves to scientific investigation alone. Although most directors would have agreed that their financial and professional resources were spread thinly over too varied a program, they were unable to consolidate and concentrate their work for fear of alienating hard-earned local support. With the power to decide the eligibility of state stations for Hatch funds after 1894, True had an implicit threat of his own to counter that fear.

The maintenance of branch experiment stations was one activity which, as usually operated in the nineteenth century, drained money and personnel while contributing little to the station mission of discovery. Between 1889 and 1894, the number of substations had grown from fourteen to forty. Convinced that most of the auxiliary station work was only peripherally related to research, True ruled in 1894 that federal funds could no longer be expended in the support of branch experiment stations. Within three years the number of substations fell to eleven as state legislatures were loathe to substitute more local appropriations in the depths of the economic depression of the 1890s.[37]

Dr. True moved to end the almost universal practice of using Hatch money to support college teaching. The Office of Experiment Stations, backing the station directors' position in the Association, had discouraged the application of federal money to pay teacher salaries since its creation in 1888. Still, at those many institutions where educational dollars were short and commitment to research was weak, the temptation was strong to use whatever funds were available to keep teaching going. In 1899, the United States Attorney General ruled in favor of True's stand that Hatch funds could not be applied to any expenses related to academic instruction. Abuses continued into the twentieth century, because when station scientists were employed as college teachers (as half were in 1905), it often was

The Kjeldahl nitrogen apparatus used by the Connecticut station (New Haven) typified state-of-the-art laboratory equipment in the early 1900s. (*Connecticut A.E.S. photo*)

impossible to guarantee that their time devoted to each activity matched the portion of their salaries paid from each account. The best the Office of Experiment Stations could do was to urge administrators to recognize the value of research and insist that separate accounts were strictly maintained.[38]

True was largely successful in his efforts because he adroitly wielded the powers of his office and earned the respect of the leaders of the nation's agricultural research. In the decentralized system, True was the link between stations. He labored to encourage stability in the nation's programs, promoting equality of rewards and opportunities to discourage turnover in scientific personnel and acting as a placement service for stations in need of excellent scientists. Perhaps most importantly, Dr. True was perceived by the state research administrators as their official protector against unreasonable local pressures. Armed with Office of Experiment Stations rulings threatening the withdrawal of federal support, state directors could fight off raids on their station finances while remaining in the good graces of local powers.[39]

USDA Scientific Standards Expanded

By acting as the system's advocate in counsels within the USDA, the Office of Experiment Stations managed to maintain good relations with the stations even as other Department of Agriculture agencies began to threaten the state experiment station monopoly on federal research dollars. James "Tama Jim" Wilson became the Department secretary in 1897 and remained in the position until 1913, serving in the cabinets of three presidents. Capping a career as a farmer, state and national legislator, professor, and experiment station director, the Iowan personally supervised the USDA scientific program. He built a system of bureaus within the Department that soon competed with the state stations for appropriations and scientists. Wilson was an enthusiastic advocate of scientific investigation and Congress proved a responsive audience. General economic prosperity and public demand for government regulation of food and drug ingredients during this "Progressive Era" encouraged Congress to grant ever more money and more extensive inspection duties to the bureaus.

During Wilson's tenure as secretary, annual funds for the USDA jumped from barely $3 million in 1898 to well over $24 million in 1913. Additional money allowed the employment of additional personnel and by 1904, USDA scientists outnumbered those at the state experiment stations. New facilities for research by these federal scientists also were provided. In 1901, a 300-acre experimental farm in Arlington, Virginia, was founded and, in 1910, a 475-acre compound for research in animal and dairy husbandry was purchased in Beltsville, Maryland. Nor was the increased activity of the federal investigators confined to the Washington, D.C., region. By 1913, the Department's Bureau of Plant Industry was operating eighteen field stations in nine states while the Bureau of Entomology had thirty-five field laboratories scattered over the country. By that time, even the Office of Experiment Stations was directing its own corps of agents out in the states.[40]

True's own office staff grew from 38 to 209 members between 1897 and 1912 as agency responsibilities broadened as an outgrowth of its earlier work. Even before Secretary Wilson's administration, Congress appropriated special funds to the USDA to investigate the nutritive value of foods. Wilbur O. Atwater, who had resumed his nutrition studies at the Storrs station in Connecticut upon his retirement from federal service, was recruited in 1894 to supervise the work as a special agent to the Office of Experiment Stations. Over time the program expanded to include an increasing number of collaborators and cooperators at the state stations.

A similar development occurred with the Office's agricultural engineering work. Responding to demands from settlers in the arid West, Congress in 1898 gave the USDA $10,000 to collect and publish information on irrigation. The administration of the modest program was given to the Office of Experiment Stations which already compiled research results and which now added a Division of Irrigation with field agents to locate artesian wells. The responsibility for a similar effort in the drainage of swamplands was mandated in 1902. Several state experiment stations cooperated by furnishing laboratory equipment and housing for resident agents employed directly by the Office of Experiment Stations. True's office also began direct administration of experiment stations when a series of them was created for America's far-flung territorial accessions in this period. Congress began providing direct appropriations for federal agricultural stations in Alaska in 1899, in Hawaii in 1900, and in Puerto Rico in 1901. Stations were added in Guam in 1908 and in the Virgin Islands in 1918.[41]

As the congressionally commissioned scientific activities of USDA bureaus expanded, the state experiment stations became concerned lest they become mere substations to perform local field experiments for a research system controlled in Washington. In appropriating funds, Congress encouraged cooperation with the existing state experiment stations. Consequently, much of the Department-directed work actually was carried out by station scientists using station facilities and equipment under various forms of ad hoc agreements. Ideally, the plans were drawn up between the leader of a bureau in Washington and a state director so that a concerted effort was made to address a problem with both local and national implications. Too often, however, a scientist in one of the national bureaus simply suggested to an investigator in a state station that they collaborate on a particular project of mutual interest. Because the chance to work with federal scientists free from the oversight of local farmers could be a strong lure, such informal agreements were anathema to state directors concerned with organizational loyalty and mission.

The developing array of informal agreements also was unwelcome to Secretary Wilson, who was designated by Congress to supervise the bureaus. In 1899, he declared his intention of bringing order by insisting that all proposals for cooperative investigations be reviewed in the Secretary's office. If approved there, the plans then would be channeled through the Office of Experiment Stations to the states for ratification.

In the same year, the Association initiated a study of the situation, releasing a report in 1900 which recommended agreements better specifying the responsibilities of each cooperator. The report's provisions emphasized the autonomy of the stations, characterizing them as equal partners in "joint experimentation." Both the USDA bureaus and the state stations, the report insisted, should be free either to propose or reject a project. If a joint project was undertaken, a formal agreement must be negotiated between the agencies involved, not individuals. The written agreement would specify the financial obligations of each party as well as publication rights upon completion of the project. Although neither partner had to guarantee its continued cooperation, the report urged that each give "reasonable assurance" that the work would be completed. Furthermore, the report urged that the Department of Agriculture was obligated to confer with the state station even if it was engaged in independent work within the state. Neither Secretary Wilson's memorandum nor the stations' proposals solved the emerging problems of overlapping research that arose when federal research bureaus and state experiment stations pursued what each viewed as its proper assignment.[42]

The stations rightfully claimed that the Hatch Act charged them to "conduct original researches or verify experiments" on an unlimited range of subjects related to agriculture. Thus, they saw the USDA as an interloper who, by exploiting its more direct access to Congress to secure funds, was inexorably taking over the stations' work. With equal accuracy, the Department answered that it too had a congressional mandate to investigate questions of general concern to the nation's farm sector as well as to undertake specific projects at specific places. Because the stations were oriented toward immediate, local problems, the federal bureaus argued that their own investigations were necessary to address the long-term needs of all American farmers.

Experimentation and Specialization

Undoubtedly, the early work of the state agricultural experiment stations was parochial in scope and overpractical in execution. Given the demands for the immediate proof of their value, it could hardly have been otherwise. Yet the stations accomplished much in the two decades following the Hatch Act.

The initial work of almost every station consisted of compiling data on the agricultural resources of the state and presenting the findings to the farm population. Surveys of native plants, insects, soils, and climate filled the stations' early publications along with the results of the chemical analyses of fertilizers, feed, and produce. In

Edwin S. Good, head of the Department of Animal Husbandry from 1906 to 1942, brought fame to the Kentucky Station for his work on the problem of contagious abortion in cattle and horses. (*Kentucky A.E.S. photo*)

the earliest years, studies of crops often meant rudimentary testing of varieties of a state's most important crop but grew into the science of agronomy. The same process occurred in horticulture where investigations of breeding and selection, orchard management, and fruit storage and preservation investigations followed simple variety trials. Early animal research concentrated on finding the best feeding regimes for beef and dairy cattle, swine, sheep, poultry, horses, and even mules. As these feeding trials developed, they came to include ever greater numbers of livestock to make their findings more relevant to commercial producers of meat and dairy products. Beginnings were made in animal health studies as well, with about half the state stations employing veterinary scientists by the early 1900s.[43]

Adams Act of 1906 Boosts Research

The addition of animal health experts to stations was evidence of an important trend. Specialization in the agricultural sciences paralleled the maturation of research at the state agricultural experiment stations. Where the staffs of the agricultural colleges and experiment stations often initially had consisted of an "agriculturist" and, possibly, a chemist on loan from another of the school's divisions, by the turn of the century horticulturists, botanists, plant pathologists, entomologists, bacteriologists, dairymen, and animal husbandmen commonly were listed on station rosters.

Between 1889 and 1905, the number of workers employed in the system more than doubled, leaping from 402 to 845. Of course, not every state station expanded equally; staff sizes ranged from thirty-five in California to only six in Delaware. Wherever the location, station researchers were more likely to be better trained than were the pioneer investigators of twenty years earlier when only a few leaders were trained in European laboratories. By the turn of the century, more and more of them had been taught in the burgeoning graduate programs of the agricultural colleges, where they had worked under established investigators in the experiment stations. While they doubtless absorbed much of the mission orientation that was part of their institutions' land-grant heritage, the new crop of more specialized agricultural scientists also emerged with a heightened sense of themselves as professionals deserving of the same respect as their fellow scientists and academicians. Identifying themselves more as practitioners of science than as servants of farmers, a growing number of station scientists challenged the prevalent assumption that their research must cater to the whims of their local farm supporters. When led by directors with the skill to join scientists' interests with farmers' needs, the state stations slowly began to build a base of knowledge for continued advances at the same time that they won over the farmers with immediately useful findings.[44]

The state agricultural experiment station system was flexible enough to welcome more intellectually rigorous studies but additional money was necessary to allow the stations to embark upon paths of more innovative research. While overall state support increased sixfold between 1888 and 1905 (from about $89,000 to about $540,000), the stations benefited unevenly. In 1905, for example, fourteen stations received no state aid at all, while another five were assigned only the proceeds from performing inspection duties. A handful of the remaining state experiment stations were generously endowed. In 1905, Indiana appropriated nearly $85,000 to its station and New York split over $110,000 between its two stations. Few, however, received as much annually from their states as they did from federal coffers. Even when state money was available it seldom afforded much flexibility for research because lawmakers often earmarked money to study successive local farm "crises" or to pay expenses of politically popular branch stations. Although the Hatch Act did provide a stable source of $15,000 per station annually, its once-generous sums were inadequate by the turn of the century.[45]

By 1903, some leaders of the state agricultural experiment stations were convinced that an infusion of new federal funds was necessary if the system was to compete with the USDA research bureaus, advance its staffs professionally, and emerge from its dependence on farmer goodwill. Finding the Association absorbed in matters of internal reorganization, William A. Henry of the Wisconsin station took it upon himself to initiate movement toward securing more federal aid. Director Henry asked his friend, Wisconsin representative Henry Cullen Adams, to test sentiment for such a proposal in Congress. Encouraged by the response of his fellow members of the House Agriculture Committee, Adams approached Dr. True of the Office of Experiment Stations to help him frame suitable legislation.

The resulting Adams bill followed the simple call of the Hatch Act "for the more complete endowment and maintenance of agricultural experiment stations" with an additional $15,000 annually to each state, but it included two important variations. First, the bill restricted the use of new appropriations "only to paying the necessary expenses of conducting original researches or experiments . . . ." Gone were those phrases justifying all manner of teaching, demonstration, and extension work pursued under the Hatch Act's sanctions to "verify experiments" and for "printing and distributing the results." While the new bill proposed to double federal grants to the state stations, it would do so gradually over several years. In the first year, each state would be entitled to a $5,000 increase over its normal $15,000. Then every year thereafter an additional $2,000 over the previous year's sum would be given until each station received $30,000 annually. In this way its authors hoped to make the bill more appealing to economy-minded Congressmen while encouraging expansion in research at the stations.[46]

The tactic was successful only after two years of effort following Adams' introduction of the proposal in Congress in January of 1904. There, despite the absence of expected opposition from USDA bureau chiefs (who apparently refused to cooperate with each other in many matters), the bill languished. Although Adams was an ardent champion, he was also a freshman representative pushing a revenue measure through a chamber dominated by House Speaker Joseph G. Cannon, an implacable foe of continuing appropriations in general and "book farming" in particular. Proponents for augmented endowments to the stations needed more than vague congressional sentiment in favor of science and progress to overcome such entrenched conservatism.

The Association threw the full weight of its influence behind the Adams Bill only after congressional action on a related matter galvanized it into battle. When Adams introduced his measure, the Association's first legislative priority was further federal endowment for the land-grant colleges; thus enthusiasm for another funding bill was lukewarm. However, since it did favor the measure's aim, the Association helped Congressman Adams clarify the wording and solicited letters of support from station directors when the bill was resubmitted in March of 1904.

In the meantime, the House approved an appropriations bill for the USDA that directed the Department to coordinate the nation's agricultural research into a unified and more efficient whole. The Association's executive committee quickly reacted to the threat to the state stations' independence, convincing congressional leaders to strike the offending proviso from the final version of the appropriation act. Because the House had considered the measure, and even passed it without debate, the Association realized that it must take the offensive in educating Congress about the value of the state agricultural experiment stations. State directors who had so assiduously cultivated the loyalty of agriculturists and politicians during the previous two decades now turned to them for help. Congress was deluged with letters demanding increased subsidies for the station system. In March 1906, the Adams Act became law.

The Adams Act had an impact on public agricultural research far beyond a doubling of funds. Congress reaffirmed its commitment of national support for locally directed experimentation in connection with the land-grant institutions. Furthermore, by requiring that the new proceeds only be expended for "original researches," Congress endorsed the station leaders' call for relief from duties unrelated to the search for new knowledge. These victories did not come without cost, however. Whereas the USDA, through the Office of Experiment Stations, had been evolving an ever more stringent policy of fiscal review of the stations since 1894, the Adams Act gave it the duty to certify annually each state's eligibility for continued support according to compliance with legislative requirements. Upon this legal base, fiscal review was transformed into performance evaluation.[47]

Exhibits like the one at the Montana State Fair in 1911 were one method of communicating the fruits of research to farmers. (*Montana State University photo*)

Experiment Stations Committee on Organization and Policy

Some problems associated with the Hatch Act were avoided in implementing the new legislation because Dr. True's Office of Experiment Stations and the state experiment stations were committed to improving administrative procedures. The issues raised during consideration of the Adams Bill convinced the stations that they needed a more permanent group than the various ad hoc committees and concerned individuals who had formulated policy in the past. The Experiment Station Committee on Organization and Policy thus was created within the Association in December of 1905, just four months before the signing of the Adams Act. ESCOP, as the committee was known, initially brought six veteran station directors together to monitor the system and act for the stations in developing new administrative mechanisms.

Together, ESCOP and the Office of Experiment Stations formulated and implemented a plan to administer the Adams Act in such a way as to improve the quality of scientific research in the experiment stations. Dr. True, with the concurrence of the Committee, was quick to define the legislation's "original researches" clause, insisting that investigations address specific problems whose solutions would have broad applicability to agriculture.

Project System Adopted

The expenditure of Adams funds for routine administration, station maintenance, general information dissemination, and for demonstration or verification experiments was discouraged when True required each station to submit for approval a written plan of work, with all activities grouped into distinct "projects." Each project proposal was to state a general area of concern, the central problem to be addressed, and the specific experiments which, taken together, would yield information toward its solution. An itemized budget was to accompany each project proposal. Under the project system, True's office more easily could monitor adherence of the stations to the intent of the federal legislation which subsidized agricultural research. Whereas in the past it could only withhold future support from a station which it felt had misused Hatch money, the Office of Experiment Stations now could work with the station to remedy any

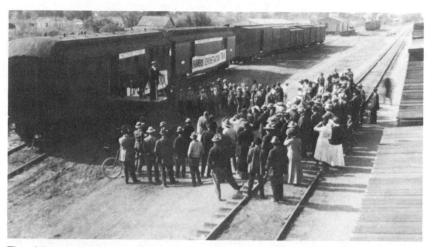

The Arizona Agricultural Experiment Station, like many other stations before the cooperative extension services were operating, used a demonstration train to share the discoveries of agricultural science with its clients. (*University of Arizona photo*)

problems before they required punitive action. The project system was not adopted overnight, but it was steadily expanded to include work undertaken with Hatch and even state funds. Nor did it magically dispel the tensions inherent in the federal-state research partnership. True's project system did provide a mechanism by which inherent conflicts between theory and practice, research and teaching, and decentralization and concentration could be more closely monitored, if not entirely reconciled.[48]

Further encouragement of mission-directed, fundamental research of the type suggested in the Adams Act's "original researches" clause came with a new publication launched by the Office of Experiment Stations in cooperation with the Association. Most bulletins and circulars of the state stations reported the most practical, applied research projects presented in non-scientific language which farmers could readily understand. Indeed, if results of the more fundamental scientific investigations were published in general circulation bulletins they likely would "be ridiculed and bring the station into disrepute with certain classes of their constituents," in the words of one station scientist.[49]

An expanding professional societies' press provided one means of reporting the activities of station scientists engaged in the less obviously applied areas of research, but these periodicals generally were read only by other specialists in these fields. Thus, the *Journal of Agricultural Research* was created to provide an interdisciplinary forum for agricultural scientists to present their best work as determined by an editorial panel of USDA and Association representatives. From its inception in 1913 until its discontinuance in 1949, the *Journal* strove to keep station scientists abreast of innovative work in the system, to enhance the credibility of the agricultural experiment stations in the larger scientific community, and to justify continued support from the national treasury.[50]

Increased Support, Expanded Service

With its more generous money reserved entirely for the conduct of research, the Adams Act contributed mightily to an expansion of the experiment station programs. Encouraged by congressional endorsement of the stations and by continuing economic prosperity, state legislatures loosened their pursestrings. From 1906 to 1920, annual state appropriations for the stations rose from less than $710,000 to over $3,590,000. Similarly dramatic increases of facilities were added to station physical plants: in 1906, building additions were $170,000 whereas in 1914, they equalled about $609,000. Station staffs continued to grow as well, from 950 in 1906 to 1,968 by 1920. While additional money in the first years after the passage of the act apparently acted to reduce the percentage of station workers who were also required to teach from 50 percent in 1905 down to 37 percent in 1911, a greater share than ever before were engaged in the dual capacity by 1920 (58 percent). Still, there probably were fewer occasions when research money was used to defray academic program expenses because of federal auditors' increased power to withhold disbursements and the greater availability of federal funds expressly for instruction made possible by the passage of the Nelson Amendment in 1907.[51]

Extension Beginnings

In many cases, new state funds went to establish or rebuild branch station systems which had been casualties of the 1890s depression and Dr. True's 1894 ruling against the use of federal grants for their support. Always popular with state legislators, substations became more acceptable to experiment station directors after the Adams Act placed their main stations on firmer foundations. From a low of eleven in 1897, the number of outlying experimental stations had risen to twenty-eight in 1904, but many of these were located on temporarily secured, donated land. More permanent facilities followed the passage of the Adams Act in rapidly rising numbers. By 1914, about seventy substations were in operation and by 1920 there were 130 branch stations spread over thirty states.

As in previous years, administration of the branches varied between the states. Larger states with vastly different geographical and climatic conditions found the substations most useful for replicating investigations done at the main station on a larger scale and under differing environmental circumstances. Montana, Mississippi, North Carolina, Idaho, and Wisconsin were among the states which founded permanent facilities of this type in the decade after 1906.

Edith M. Patch of the Maine Agricultural Experiment Station became a leading authority on aphids with her research and extension efforts to control the pest in the first three decades of the twentieth century. (*University of Maine at Orono photo*)

Massachusetts, a smaller state, developed another substation model which concentrated on specific farm commodities. In 1912, for example, asparagus research was pursued at one branch and cranberry experiments undertaken at another.

By maintaining substations with state and local money, station directors avoided the censure of Washington overseers but not the burden of additional administrative duties. The director of the Kansas experiment station reported to a 1912 gathering of his colleagues that, "We have more branch stations than we know what to do with . . . ." Out of five substations mandated by the state assembly, he found only two useful. Only tenuously connected to the central station, the others only incited the hunger of legislators for similar stations in their districts. North Dakota's research director voiced a similar complaint about two of its five outlying experimental locations. He succeeded in blocking the creation of additional substations only by scattering demonstration farms over the state with the aid of the Great Northern and Northern Pacific Railways.[52]

The operation of demonstration farms had been a common answer by the experiment stations since their beginnings to public demands for practical information. And, despite Office of Experiment Stations rulings in 1904 and 1909 which first restricted then forbade Hatch support for such work, many continued to function in the early twentieth century. More popular by that time, however, was another form of extension activity, the farmers' institutes. These traveling lecture programs, which featured expert speakers on farm practices, originated in the 1860s and 1870s. In New England, they evolved from state-subsidized meetings of local agricultural societies, while in the Midwest they were pioneered by the new land-grant colleges in the form of short courses at the colleges during inactive seasons on the farm. Itinerant educational programs were conducted by nearly half of the agricultural divisions of the land-grant colleges by the turn of the century, while station researchers served as cooperating lecturers in those states where farmers' institutes were sponsored by state agencies. In 1902, even the Office of Experiment Stations became involved in the movement with an appropriation of $2,000 to develop course outlines, train lecturers, and suggest speakers for farmers' institutes. As the institutes matured and their audiences became more sophisticated in their demands, an ever increasing amount of the station scientists' time was spent out of the laboratory and on the lecture circuit. In 1914, for example, 8,858 institutes were held across the country involving 590, or nearly one-third, of the station scientists.

Supplementing the lectures of the farmers' institutes in many parts of the country were county agents who traveled from farm to farm to lend firsthand advice to agriculturists. Begun in Texas in 1904, the idea of dispatching resident agents who could convince leading farmers to use a portion of their acreage for demonstration was adopted by Seaman Knapp in an effort to help cotton growers cope with the boll weevil invasion. With the financial support of the USDA, private philanthropic foundations, and local governments, cooperative extension expanded to improve diversification in the South and farm management in the North. In this effort, too, the experiment stations were called upon to discover and disseminate useful information; in some cases, the stations administered the programs.[53]

Smith-Lever Act of 1914

The various extension programs, which included demonstration farms, farmers' institutes, and itinerant adult education instructors, had become so popular that national legislation was passed to provide funds for rural extension activities. The Smith-Lever Agricultural Extension Act established a national system for rural adult vocational education with state administrators in the land-grant college and agents out in the counties.

Seaman A. Knapp, while professor of agriculture at Iowa State Agricultural College, authored the original version of what became the Hatch Act and later became the leader in the movement that created the national cooperative extension network in 1914. (*USDA photo*)

Like the legislation funding experiment stations, the Smith-Lever Act allowed each state to operate its own program. Unlike the Hatch and Adams Acts, however, each state was required to match every dollar over an initial $10,000 of the annual federal grant. Nor did the states share equally in the federal largesse: a state's entitlement was determined by its proportion of rural residents in the total rural population of the United States. Both the matching requirement and the apportionment formula would be adopted in subsequent legislation concerning support of the state agricultural experiment stations.[54]

USDA Scientific Agencies Reorganized

A 1915 reorganization of the USDA had a more immediate effect on the stations. The Office of Experiment Stations found itself with a new director and a more sharply defined mission. To administer the expanded federal-state agricultural programs, a State Relations Service was created within the Department and A.C. True was placed at its head. Joining the Office of Experiment Stations in the new agency were two new Offices for Extension Work, which consolidated the farmers' institutes promotion with extension work formerly undertaken in the Bureau of Plant Industry, and an Office of Home Economics, which took over nutrition investigations. By also relinquishing its irrigation and drainage research to the USDA's Office of Public Roads, the Office of Experiment Stations concentrated entirely upon assisting the state, territorial, and insular agricultural experiment stations. Edwin West Allen, a chemist trained in Germany and employed by the Office since 1890, succeeded his longtime associate as director while True concentrated on establishing the federal extension agency.[55]

Office of Experiment Stations Tightens Reins

Allen, who had worked closely with his predecessor in implementing Office of Experiment Stations policies, continued Dr. True's close watch on expenditures of federal research grants for research. Together, they continued to contract the range of permissible expenses after the passage of the Adams Act. On at least three occasions before the end of World War I, they were compelled to invoke the powers of their office to prompt stations to correct long-standing abuses.

Edwin West Allen was an assistant to A.C. True before becoming chief of the Office of Experiment Stations from 1915 to 1929. (*National Archives and Records Administration photo*)

Since its founding following the Hatch Act in 1888, the Nevada agricultural experiment station had indiscriminately applied its federal proceeds to pay salaries of teachers at Nevada State University, buy instructional materials, and even provide a livestock herd for the college. Into the twentieth century, the university president still was agricultural dean and station director while the state was providing little money for education, perpetuating an atmosphere ripe for financial improprieties. When repeated suggestions to mend its ways were ignored, the Office of Experiment Stations in 1912 threatened the Nevada station with an interruption in federal funding. During the next year, Nevada responded agreeably. A new director was employed for the experiment station and the college of agriculture got a new dean. To ensure the separation of experiment station and college activities, field research was moved from college lands onto those of cooperating farmers and ranchers. The state legislature even appropriated $5,000 to the station in return for transferring title to the cattle herd to the college. Only offices and laboratories were retained on the Reno campus.[56]

Problems at the Oklahoma station during this same period proved less amenable to solution. Although the positions of college president and experiment station director were separated in 1899, real power over the college and station was retained by a board of agriculture with a popularly elected chairman and a politically appointed membership. Thus, the Oklahoma station was peculiarly subject to political strife afflicting the young state.

Two successive years of board unrest so disrupted research in Oklahoma that the Office of Experiment Stations ominously warned in 1912 that "the Oklahoma station must be regarded as in an unfortunate and unsatisfactory condition." The situation continued to deteriorate in the following year, culminating in the abrupt dismissal of the station director in July and a popular referendum that turned out the board of agriculture in August. The governor of Oklahoma immediately commissioned a new board but the ejected members secured a court injunction blocking the appointment of their replacements.

Convinced that no research could be pursued effectively during the legal wrangling, the Office of Experiment Stations withheld Hatch and Adams funds to Oklahoma for the first nine months of 1914. Only after the furor died down and the state legislature appropriated $5,000 to support the station (for the first time ever) were Washington administrators persuaded to resume quarterly payments to the Oklahoma station. Even then the Office of Experiment Stations forwarded only enough of the overdue income to cover the actual expenses incurred by experiments in those three quarters— only $8,667 of the $22,500 to which the station was entitled. Apparently relieved to be functioning at all under the circumstances, Oklahoma did not challenge the decision of federal auditors.[57]

The trustees of the Georgia station were less tractable when federal monies were withheld from their institution on similar grounds in 1917. The agricultural experiment station in Griffin had only tenuous connections with the land-grant college in Athens, and it had been largely neglected by state legislators in their budget deliberations. Consequently, the station concentrated on generating sales income by operating a model farm and dairy, restricting experiments to variety tests and fertilizer analyses.

In 1913, a temporary suspension of federal funds by the Office of Experiment Stations prompted some reforms: the station's board of directors promised to seek state money to operate the demonstration units and employed a scientist to direct the research program. But no new state funds followed and repeated legislative efforts to join the station more closely to the agricultural college of the University of Georgia failed.

When the station's scientist-director resigned in late 1916 only to be replaced by the ex officio president of the station's board of control who had failed reelection as State Agriculture Commissioner, the Washington office again stepped in to hold up Hatch and Adams payments. Hoping to put to rest the recurring problems which it largely attributed to the Georgia station's isolation from the agricultural school and its consequent exposure to the vagaries of state politics, the Office of Experiment Stations in 1917 declared the Georgia system illegal by the terms of the Hatch Act which, in its opinion, allowed no stations independent of colleges unless those stations had existed prior to the passage of the act. As a prod to state authorities to place the station under college control, the suspension of funds by the USDA initially seemed successful when both the out-going and in-coming governors put their support behind legislation to "reattach" the station to the university (thus restoring the original form voted by the legislature in 1888 but never implemented).

When the Georgia lawmakers delayed action on the proposal and made plans to appeal to the United States Congress to force the release of funds, Georgia's governor and USDA representatives agreed to a compromise. In return for assurances by the state's chief executive that he could push the reattachment bill through the legislature when it reconvened, USDA administrators supported a congressional resolution directing it to release past- and currently-due federal research money to the station in Griffin, but channeling the grants through the agricultural college in Athens.

The settlement, however, fell apart in Congress as Georgia's delegation instead secured an amendment to the appropriations bill naming the Georgia Agricultural Experiment Station at Griffin as the sole recipient of all federal disbursements under the Hatch and Adams Acts without reference to the college in Athens. To complete the rout, legislators back in Georgia concurrently refused to affiliate the station more closely with the university's agricultural programs. For 1918, they did make $8,000 available for station repairs but at the same time created a competing research facility near the town of Tifton. This Georgia Coastal Plain Experiment Station received the bulk of state appropriations for agricultural research ($25,000 to match local contributions its first year alone) and was administered by a governor-appointed board with no connection to the university. Both the Georgia station near Griffin and the Coastal Plain Station near Tifton retained their virtual independence from the University of Georgia for thirty years more.[58]

Although few stations encountered the trials suffered by those of Nevada, Oklahoma, and Georgia, the entire agricultural experiment station system underwent substantial administrative changes during an era that featured the beginnings of the national agricultural extension service, war in Europe, and farm prosperity in America. First came a reduction in the amount of state support for the stations as the new and highly visible extension services competed for public money. Although six more states were appropriating money to their experiment stations in 1915 than were doing so in 1914, total state contributions to the research effort were $445,000 less than in the year before the Smith-Lever Act. The decline was about three-fourths of that amount required from the states as matching funds for extension, suggesting that legislators simply shifted funds to qualify for new federal dollars. The reduced funding period was short-lived, however, as state appropriations surpassed 1914 levels and resumed their upward climb within three years.[59]

Growing Pains in World War I

World War I similarly disrupted the stations. The need for abundant food and fiber for American and allied armed forces intensified the stations' concentration upon experiments that looked toward immediately increasing production. The pursuit of long-term investigations also suffered from a reduction in the hours devoted to research. Many scientists were called away to military duty, while leaders were needed on wartime mobilization boards. Following the armistice, war-induced farm prosperity prompted a flood of new enrollments in the agricultural colleges, inevitably increasing teaching loads of those scientists who held dual appointments. As was earlier the case when state funding increases were briefly interrupted, the demands for teaching upon station staffs soon returned to their more usual levels.

Of more lasting impact on the station system was the enormous turnover in seasoned administrative personnel. According to the Office of Experiment Stations, over one-half of the state stations changed directors in the six years after 1914. At nine stations, research directors were given additional duties as extension directors, college deans, or university presidents. Continuity in the stations' research efforts was threatened too by the resignations of over 400 department heads between 1914 and 1920. A booming wartime and immediate postwar economy beckoned station scientists and administrators into private business at about the same time that many members of the first generation of station generalists retired. New positions in the stations also opened up; the number of investigators more than doubled between 1905 and 1920, going from 845 to 1,968. Consequently, the experiment stations emerged from the First World War era with a younger, less experienced, and more specialized corps of scientists.[60]

Balancing Demands

The investigators may have been younger but the public research system in which they served had matured by the end of the war, having shed its extension duties at the same time as it added new scientists in a broadened range of disciplines. As institutions with allegiance both to farmers and to science, the state agricultural experiment stations fashioned programs which ranged along a continuum from basic, to applied, to developmental research. Agricultural scientists engaged in a continuous process of searching out problems, discovering facts related to their cause, and developing these facts into improved technologies that could then be further developed into economically feasible solutions. By producing an ever widening stream of practical knowledge, and by appealing to the principles of academic freedom and free scientific inquiry when political interference threatened, successful station administrators promoted an atmosphere in which scientists were kept aware of larger research needs so

Donald F. Jones of the Connecticut Agricultural Experiment Station was a pioneer in the development of hybrid corn, demonstrating the practical producing hybrid-corn seed without detasseling. (*Connecticut A.E.S. photo*)

that they could apply their knowledge and skills to meet them. In this unique climate agricultural science began to flourish as the stations succeeded in building a critical mass of basic knowledge and collecting a critical array of scientists to exploit it.

The state agricultural experiment stations were confronted by a whole new set of challenges beginning in the postwar period. By the 1920s more and more farmers were looking to the land-grant institutions to educate their children, discover solutions to their farm problems, and advise them how to increase their production. To be sure, suspicions of "book farming" lingered in the minds of many farmers. As late as 1913, 44 percent of farmers in a national survey reported that experience alone was valuable.[61] Still, as agriculture became more specialized, less self-sufficient, and more oriented to the market, those farmers who hoped to remain prosperous depended increasingly on the knowledge discovered by agricultural science. Unfortunately, in the two decades that followed World War I, few farmers realized their hopes as American agriculture endured an era of unrivaled economic depression. Overproduction of some products in the face of declining domestic consumption combined with a shattered world economy to send commodity prices plunging from their wartime highs. With other segments of the economy booming, the difference between what the farmer had to pay for goods and what he received for his produce steadily grew, making his position especially onerous.

The agricultural depression of the 1920s actually helped reverse an earlier trend which had placed such demands on investigators' time. Responding to lowered economic prospects, enrollments in agricultural courses ebbed and larger numbers of scientists were freed to pursue research. Between 1921 and 1929, the percentage of station scientists who also taught in their colleges fell from 52 percent to 45 percent. As the extension services matured, a similar lessening in the demand upon station staffs occurred. In 1921, 22 percent of the researchers at the stations had their time divided between investigation and extension duties, but at the end of the decade only 14 percent were so employed. In the 1920s, too, many experiment stations were relieved of regulatory functions as state departments of agriculture responded to the urgings of land-grant colleges and the USDA to take over these services.

Even as their non-research obligations declined, the stations received more support from state legislatures. From 1920 to 1924 alone, state appropriations for the system rose from $3,594,000 to $6,115,000. In 1925 and again in 1927, money from the states dipped, only to rise again to over $8,000,000 in the last two years of the decade. By 1929, every experiment station was benefiting from some state support, ranging from $1,000 in North Dakota to $916,000 in Ohio.[62]

Economics and Sociology Gain a Foothold

Although it seems to have had little effect on the dollars for the stations, the early years of the 1920s farm crisis did have an impact upon the experiment stations' research programs. With overproduction generally identified as the chief culprit in persistently low farm incomes, the need for further research to increase crop yields was questioned. The erosion of support for this traditional research emphasis combined with a growing concern about rural economic and social problems to prompt the public agricultural research system to broaden its interest. Studies of production costs were joined by studies of the cost of marketing; home economics began with nutritional surveys; and some beginnings were made in sociology with studies of rural standards-of-living.

Many of these newer projects were pursued in cooperation with scientific agencies of the USDA like the Office of Farm Management and Farm Economics, the Office of Home Economics, and the Bureau of Markets. Joint projects in the more traditional lines of inquiry continued, too, between the stations and Department agencies. Collaborative work had progressed to the point in 1920 that a member of the Experiment Station Committee on Organization and Policy suggested that the state stations simply be subsumed under the USDA, with state directors reporting to deans of agriculture and the Secretary of Agriculture.

Administrative Oversight Revives State-Federal Tensions

Determined to retain the stations' autonomy, ESCOP rejected the plan after lengthy consideration at its 1921 meeting. Yet, hoping for a better system to coordinate the work undertaken between the stations and the various federal bureaus, the directors pressed the Department to create an office with enough power to oversee all scientific activity. As part of a general plan to reorganize along functional lines, the USDA created in 1921, and filled in 1923, the position of Director of Scientific Work. In 1923, the short-lived States Relations Service was dissolved and its home economics and extension offices given independent status. The Office of Experiment Stations was attached to the office of Director of Scientific Work and its chief, still E.W. Allen, was named concurrently as Assistant Director of Scientific Work.[63]

Under the new arrangement, the Office of Experiment Stations continued reviewing station programs, approving research proposals, and encouraging communication between the stations. It also watched over local administrative relations to promote the general welfare of the national system. In the 1920s and early 1930s when economic hardship spawned political turmoil which disrupted station programs, the task sometimes proved difficult. In four instances during those years, Dr. Allen's office withheld federal funds from state stations whose efforts were impaired by staff dismissals or unqualified appointments.

In 1923 and again in 1928, the Oklahoma Agricultural Experiment Station experienced a revival of its earlier troubles. The first episode closely followed the scenario of 1913-1914. The station director, the tenth man to hold that position in the preceding twenty-three years, resigned in protest when the college and station governing board replaced the Oklahoma A & M president and many of his faculty supporters. As a consequence of their actions, the board members themselves were unseated in favor of a new group which promptly removed the *new* president, whereupon the temporarily retired station director resumed his post. For a brief period before the director's return in 1924, the Office of Experiment Stations stopped payments to the station. In 1928, federal funds were again withheld from the Oklahoma station following the summary discharge of the director and many of his support staff. Again, payments were resumed after a short hiatus.[64]

In Arizona, trouble arrived with a new university president in 1922. In addition to circumscribing the powers of the station director to administer the research program, the University of Arizona president also diverted to the use of other college divisions some $2,000 worth of experiment station equipment purchased with federal money. While that practice had been common in the early years, by 1926 it was aberrant enough to provoke the Office of Experiment Stations to suspend federal money on two occasions after investigation revealed serious lapses. A new university board of regents was installed in 1927, which, after accepting the president's resignation, restored amicable relations with the station's Washington partner.[65]

The Mississippi station was also denied its share of federal research money over the summer of 1930 when its director and many of its scientists were discharged in a purge of the faculties of all four state-supported colleges by a new governor. When the dismissals were announced, the Office of Experiment Stations immediately stopped funds to the Mississippi station and dispatched a representative to meet with the governor and the state education board. The meeting caused the appointment of a capable director recommended by the Office and the reemployment of many dismissed scientists and teachers. Funding resumed immediately.[66]

In each of these cases, the Office of Experiment Stations intervened to shield station research programs or personnel from threats from outside the station. But, in Rhode Island, it was the station administration itself which prompted censure from Washington. The Office interrupted regular disbursements to the Rhode Island station in 1927 following years of disagreements about poor accounting procedures and vague projects. Alarmed at the cut off of what was then the station's only source of support, the Rhode Island College trustees removed the recalcitrant director and ordered a new acting director to initiate rapproachement with the federal agency. Negotiations in 1928 led to an agreement to repay all the withheld money, excepting a $3,000 "disallowance."[66]

The rarity of cases in which the Office of Experiment Stations suspended federal research grants to compel station adherence to expected standards attested to the success of administrative policies evolved since the passage of the Hatch Act. Using on-site reviews and the project system implemented following the Adams Act to monitor station research, the Washington staff worked closely with the individual stations who submitted their programs of work as discrete projects for Office of Experiment Stations approval. The Office rejected a relative few projects: in 1928, for example, only twenty-three of the nearly 400 proposals were turned down. Yet in that same year, Washington reviewers insisted upon substantial modifications in another 105 of those proposed projects in an attempt to promote scientific productivity in the state agricultural experiment stations.[68]

Nearly three-quarters of the proposals approved in 1928 were funded under legislation enacted three years earlier. In 1919, a movement began within the Association of American Agricultural Colleges and Experiment Stations to increase national support to encourage research into new concerns like economics and sociology.

Farm economics had been emerging since the Populist tumult and interest in adjustment to social change among rural people rose after the appointment by Theodore Roosevelt of a Country Life Commission in 1908. From these beginnings, agricultural economics and rural sociology expanded in a few state stations and in the USDA Office of Farm Management and Farm Economics which, in 1919, included a section for Rural Life Studies.

Purnell Act of 1925 Broadens Research Horizons

Recognizing the need to prompt the states into support for these subjects, a group of agricultural leaders proposed to their fellow Association members in 1920 that an amendment to the Hatch Act be framed which would provide federal money specifically for economic and sociological investigations. Following the Smith-Lever lead, they urged that states be required to match federal contributions. The executive committee of the Association agreed to push for new support legislation but decided to broaden eligibility to include research on production of crops and animals and to drop the state matching requirement.

A bill incorporating the Association ideas was introduced in Congress in January of 1921 by Representative Fred S. Purnell of Indiana. With provisions calling for an immediate appropriation of an additional $15,000 to each station with increases of $10,000 per year until each state station received $85,000 annually above their $30,000 from the Hatch and Adams Acts, the bill was deemed too expensive by the House Agriculture Committee. There, it died twice only to be resubmitted in December 1923 at the same time as an identical bill was presented to the Senate by Edwin F. Ladd, a former agricultural college president who had become a North Dakota senator. The House Committee on Agriculture in May of 1924 reported an amended version, reducing the initial grant to each station to $10,000 with annual increases of only $5,000 until the additional yearly support equalled $30,000. Seeking the assistance of a broad spectrum of interests, the Association presented its case for the Purnell Bill to a President's Agricultural Conference in January 1925. So convinced were the conference delegates that they urged Congress to pass the measure at double the House committee recommendations. Both the House and Senate complied in time for President Calvin Coolidge to sign the act into law on February 24, 1925.[69]

The Purnell Act provided additional annual appropriations amount-

Liberty Hyde Bailey, dean of the College of Agriculture at Cornell University and director of the university's agricultural experiment station from 1903 to 1913, chaired President Theodore Roosevelt's Country Life Commission which studied rural social and economic problems in 1908 and 1909. (*New York State College of Agriculture and Life Sciences at Cornell University photo*)

ing to $20,000 for 1926 with stepped increases to $60,000 in 1930 and thereafter for each state agricultural experiment station. The legislation did more than triple funds available from the national treasury; it specifically encouraged attention to the economic and social problems unique to farm life. In the process, the Purnell Act explicitly stated goals for the stations: "the establishment and maintenance of a permanent and efficient agricultural industry, and . . . the development and improvement of the rural home and rural life . . . ." The first object, of course, had been the implicit guide to investigations since the time of the Hatch Act. The second, which legitimized efforts to expand research programs to serve broader needs than only agricultural production, was entirely new to many stations.[70]

Since the Purnell Act contained no new administrative procedures, the Office of Experiment Stations and the Experiment Station Committee on Organization and Policy simply agreed to extend the existing project system to cover the new funds, urging the stations to undertake no more work than they could effectively pursue. The warning was necessary because, despite the incremental nature of the increase, state stations rather suddenly could afford to double their research financed by federal dollars within two years.

Expanding the Scope of Service

Most susceptible to the problems which could arise from inadequate planning were those projects which sought to heed the Purnell Act call for agricultural economics, rural sociology, and home economics investigations. Many stations eagerly expanded into the new subjects. In the first year alone, 234 agricultural economics and ninety-six home economics projects were initiated by the stations. However, few trained scientists were available to the experiment stations to undertake the new research.

The Social Science Research Council, prior to launching a fellowship program for graduate training, determined that in that first year only forty-one of the 288 persons engaged in experiment station social science projects held doctoral degrees. Those agricultural economists, rural sociologists, and home economists in the experiment station system who were trained adequately often faced another obstacle in planning their studies. Many agricultural scientists, including directors, were reluctant to accord the social scientists equal status. The belief that the problems of rural America were essentially economic and could be solved by discovering and convincing farmers to adopt more efficient production practices persistently discounted alternative approaches. This tenet translated into proportionately less financial and staff support for social science research in agriculture. Home economists investigating nutrition perhaps fared best since their experiments were closest to those of traditional biological science, but even they had to overcome early challenges posed by college chemistry departments.

The first task facing investigators in the newer disciplines was defining rural problems in terms that could be addressed by research. Toward this end, the Association, meeting in April of 1925, proposed six major subjects on which to concentrate Purnell-funded research. At its subsequent annual conclave, the organization's executive committee named standing committees comprised of six to twelve experiment station and USDA scientists to suggest lines of research on a national scale within each subject. In agricultural economics, a Committee on Distributing and Marketing Farm Products and another on the Problem of Surpluses of Farm Products shared the same members. Committees on Factors Which Influence the Quality and Palatability of Meat and on Vitamin Content of Food in Relation to Human Nutrition were convened to formulate an agenda for foods and nutrition research. In the broader areas of home economics and rural sociology, a Committee on Rural Home Management Studies and another for Rural Social Organizations and Agencies Essential to Effective Agriculture were formed. Although they functioned for only about five years, the Purnell advisory groups were important as the first in a succession of later attempts to create a common national agenda for new phases of agricultural research.[71]

The Great Depression and the Experiment Station System

Economics and social distress among rural residents only worsened in the 1930s, a decade in which the entire country began to share the farmers' adversity. The Great Depression, because of its severity and longevity, prompted new attitudes toward the role of government, with profound effects on every public institution. Nowhere was this more evident than in the United States Department of Agriculture which metamorphosed under Secretary Henry A. Wallace into one of the major "action agencies" of Franklin Roosevelt's New Deal.

To the USDA's traditional research, education, and regulatory duties were added price support, commodity loan, acreage and marketing allotment, rural electrification, crop insurance, flood control, and soil conservation programs. In implementing these new services, federal agencies became more directly involved with the farmer, sometimes encroaching upon what traditionally had been considered the domain of the land-grant colleges. The state cooperative extension services were affected most directly as many were enlisted in beginning the agricultural adjustment programs, but the experiment stations often were called upon to undertake supporting research.[72]

An exchange of reports between an Association Committee on Federal-State Relations in Research and the USDA in 1931 and 1932 revealed tensions between the two even before the Department increased its presence on the local scene during the New Deal. The Association committee suggested that the USDA confine its research to gathering results of state experiment station investigations and translating them to a national scale. The Department responded that it had a mandate to pursue research to fulfill its regulatory duties and, furthermore, that it had an obligation to search for solutions to specific problems which the stations were ignoring. The two organizations could only agree to continue communicating to minimize the inevitable jurisdictional conflicts, the same conclusion reached between 1935 and 1944 by a series of committees on federal-state relations.[73]

Despite the wariness with which the stations eyed the USDA, relations with the Office of Experiment Stations remained civil because the agency managed to maintain its tradition of appearing to side with the stations in disputes with federal policymakers. Doubtlessly it helped, too, that a former station director was selected in 1931 to fill the position left vacant by E.W. Allen's death two years earlier. James T. Jardine, the brother of a former Secretary of Agriculture, came to the post of chief of the Office of Experiment Stations from the Oregon Agricultural Experiment Station. There, he had served as director for eleven years. Thus, he invested the office with a sensitivity to the directors' point of view, an important asset in the hard times of the Depression.

Working closely with the Experiment Station Committee on Organization and Policy, a group which he had chaired for the three years prior to his call to Washington, Jardine concentrated on maintaining quality research in the midst of financial adversity. Administrative strictures against spreading federal dollars over many projects were relaxed in some instances, allowing state stations to maintain projects and staff which were threatened by the withdrawal of state money. On other occasions, Jardine came to the stations' defense against efforts to shift from research the proceeds from the sale of products from experiment station investigations. These sales could be considerable: in 1934 nearly 10 percent of the money available to the stations was in the category "sales of farm products." While responding to emergencies with specific suggestions, Jardine and his associates reiterated that placing all research of the stations in a project system was the most effective means of scrutinizing research and justifying expenditures to tightfisted legislatures and a sometimes suspicious public.[74]

With state finances in dire straits as the Depression deepened and the public questioning the need for agricultural research in an era of excess farm production, appropriations for the agricultural experiment stations dwindled. After reaching a high of $9,501,097 in 1932, combined state funding fell to $7,740,248 in 1933, then to $6,704,470 in the next year. In the remaining years of the 1930s, state support

James T. Jardine, brother of USDA Secretary William M. Jardine, came from the Oregon Station in 1931 to serve as chief of the Office of Experiment Stations until 1946. (*National Archives and Records Administration photo*)

slowly rose each year but not until 1941 did it surpass 1932 levels. The continued availability of federal funds allowed the agricultural experiment stations in general to hold on to station scientists: only once did the total of scientists decline, from 3,620 in 1933 to 3,567 in 1934.[75]

Bankhead-Jones Act of 1935 Establishes Formula Funding

Federal action also was responsible for prompting the states to resume increasing support to the stations. In 1935, Congress enacted legislation giving the public agricultural research system more money, but only if the states provided matching amounts. Passage of any new funding bill, especially for increases for agricultural research in the midst of farm surplus, was due largely to two men. One was the member of the House Committee on Agriculture, James P. Buchanan of Texas, who was determined to erect a lasting monument to his career of service to farming interests, and the other was Secretary Wallace, who successfully justified increased basic research to solve current and future problems. Accordingly, the Bankhead-Jones Act of 1935 provided new money for:

> research into laws and principles underlying basic problems of agriculture in its broadest aspects; research relating to the improvement of the quality of, and the development of new and improved methods of production, distribution of, and new and extended uses and markets for, agricultural commodities . . .; and research relating to conservation, development, and use of land and water resources for agricultural purposes.

The act called for an additional $1 million for 1936 with annual incremental increases of $1 million until the total reached $5 million in 1940 and subsequent years. Only 60 percent of this new money was to go to the state experiment stations. The Secretary of Agriculture was given the remainder of the funds as a "Special Research Fund" to be used at his discretion. The new money for the state stations was to be distributed on the basis of each state's proportion of the rural population of the United States, and then only when the state matched the federal contribution out of its own treasury. Both of these features were borrowed from the Smith-Lever Act which had financed extension work during the last two decades. When the forty-eight states, the territories of Alaska and Hawaii, and Puerto

Field Days, like this one held in 1936 at the Texas Station's Sonora branch to discuss livestock, linked farmers' needs with research opportunities. (*Texas A.E.S. photo*)

Rico divided the $600,000 appropriated for the first year, the Texas station received the largest share ($37,341) and Alaska got the smallest ($559).[76]

The state experiment stations also benefited from the other 40 percent of the Bankhead-Jones money mandated for the USDA. The act itself required that one-half of the Special Research Fund to be used to establish and maintain research laboratories in the nation's major agricultural regions. In implementing the provisions, Secretary Wallace located some of the regional research facilities near land-grant colleges and experiment stations where they could serve as focal points for cooperative research projects between neighboring states. The appointment in 1936 of Office of Experiment Stations chief J.T. Jardine to serve concurrently as USDA Director of Research further ensured that the state stations would have a prominent role in decisions about national research.

In the five years following the passage of the Bankhead-Jones Act, nine regional research laboratories were founded. A Charleston, South Carolina facility concentrated attentions on vegetable crops in the southeastern states while a laboratory located in Auburn, Alabama focused on diseases which plagued the region's poultry and livestock. In the north central states were a swine breeding station in Ames, Iowa, a poultry laboratory in East Lansing, Michigan, and a soybean utilization installation in Urbana, Illinois. State College, Pennsylvania was the location for a pasture improvement laboratory for cooperating stations in the northeastern states. At Cornell University another facility served as a regional center for the study of the relation of soils to plant, animal, and human nutrition. The Western states benefited from a sheep breeding laboratory in Dubois, Idaho and an irrigation station in Riverside, California.[77]

The Bankhead-Jones Regional Research Laboratories were soon joined by four other regional facilities with the passage of the Agricultural Adjustment Act of 1938. Responding to Republican demands to discover new industrial uses for farm commodities in surplus and to Mississippi Senator Theodore K. Bilbo's insistence on a facility to concentrate on cotton products, Congress included in its price support bill a provision to fund four regional utilization laboratories. Located in New Orleans, Louisiana; Wyndmoor, Pennsylvania; Peoria, Illinois; and Albany, California, each was to encourage cooperative USDA and state experiment station investigations on the major surplus crops of the region. The New Orleans Utilization Laboratory, for example, was to concentrate on new uses to expand the markets for cotton products, sweet potatoes, and peanuts. When war broke out in Europe, all the regional laboratories constructed since 1935 turned from regional to overriding national concerns.[78]

Firm Foundations

The Second World War brought the United States out of the economic doldrums and reoriented agricultural experiment station programs toward finding ways to increase production with less manpower and to meet specific military mobilization needs. By 1940, the public agricultural research system was prepared to meet this challenge. Over the previous half-century it had evolved from a string of poorly funded, understaffed, and publicly disparaged campus outposts into a loosely coordinated collection of land-grant college-based institutions which could respond to immediate practical needs of their local farmers while contributing to scientific knowledge. Forced by local circumstances to heed farmer opinion and encouraged by federal legislation and Office of Experiment Stations policies to address broader issues, the state agricultural experiment station system succeeded in building the popular support and scientific expertise which would contribute much of the knowledge base underlying the postwar revolution in agricultural technology.

Notes

[1] Roland R. Robinson, *Administration of Federal Agricultural Research Funds by the Science and Education Administration/Cooperative Research* ([Washington]: USDA, Science and Education Administration/Cooperative Research, September 1978), p. 4.

[2] True, *Agricultural Experimentation*, pp. 129-131.

[3] A.C. True and V.A. Clark, *Agricultural Experiment Stations in the United States* (Washington: USDA, Office of Experiment Stations Bulletin 80, 1900), pp. 164-167, 171-174; Knoblauch et al., *State Agricultural Experiment Stations*, pp. 152-153; Ernest M. Law, "The Agricultural Experiment Station Movement in Connecticut, 1840-1900: A Case Study of Tax-Supported Scientific Discovery" (Ph.D. dissertation, Yale University, 1951), pp. 183-191.

[4] Harold Whiting Cary, *The University of Massachusetts: A History of One Hundred Years* (Amherst: University of Massachusetts, 1962), pp. 72-73; Frank P. Rand, *Yesterdays at Massachusetts State College: 1863-1933* (Amherst: Massachusetts State College, 1933), pp. 84-85.

[5] Hedrick, *History of Agriculture in New York*, pp. 422-424; R.E. Krauss, "About the Experiment Station—A Centennial Celebration," New York State A.E.S., Geneva *Special Report* 48 (May 1983): 3; Gould P. Coleman, Pioneering in Agricultural Education: Cornell University, 1867-1890," *Agricultural History* 36 (October 1962): 205-206.

[6] Woodward and Waller, *New Jersey's Agricultural Experiment Station*, pp. 53-54, 61-62.

[7] True and Clark, *Agricultural Experiment Stations*, pp. 242-244.

[8] True, *Agricultural Experimentation*, pp. 116-117; George H. Callcott, *History of the University of Maryland* (Baltimore: Maryland Historical Society, 1966), pp. 189-190; True and Clark, *Agricultural Experiment Stations*, pp. 180-181.

[9] True and Clark, *Agricultural Experiment Stations*, pp. 310-311.

[10] Herman F. Eschenbacher, *The University of Rhode Island: A History of Land-Grant Education in Rhode Island* (New York: Appleton-Century-Crofts, 1967), pp. 17-19, 23-27, 45-69.

[11] North Carolina Agricultural Experiment Station, *A Century of Service*, p. 7.

[12] True, *Agricultural Experimentation*, pp. 130-131.

[13] Ibid., p. 117; G.H. Aull, "South Carolina Agricultural Experiment Station: A Brief History, 1887-1930," South Carolina Station *Circular* 44 (December 1930): 16-18.

[14] Harold N. Young, *Virginia Agricultural Experiment Station: 1886-1966* (Charlottsville: University Press of Virginia, 1975), pp. 11, 52.

[15] John W. Bailey, *Mississippi Agricultural Experiment Station: An Historical Sketch* (A & M College: Mississippi A.E.S. Bulletin 216, March 1923), pp. 3-4, 8; Marie L. Lavallard, ed., "Arkansas Agricultural Experiment Station: The First Forty Years," in *Agricultural Progress in Arkansas* (Fayetteville: Arkansas A.E.S., May 1976), unpaginated; True and Clark, *Agricultural Experiment Stations*, p. 414.

[16] Janos Shoemyen, "History of the Florida Agricultural Experiment Stations," *Sunshine State Agricultural Research Report* 20 (Summer 1975): 13; Samuel Proctor, "Early Years of the Florida Experiment Station, 1888-1906," *Agricultural History* 36 (October 1962): 213-215, 219-221; Nancy J. Bunker and Tom Dupree, *100 Years: A Century of Growth Through Agricultural Research* (Athens: University of Georgia College of Agricultural Experiment Stations, 1975), pp. 6-7; True and Clark, *Agricultural Experiment Stations*, pp. 186-187, quotation from p. 191.

[17] Alexis Cope, *History of Ohio State University*, pp. 499, 510-511; William E. Krauss, "History: 1882-1982," *Ohio Report on Research and Development in Agriculture, Home Economics, and Natural Resources* 67 (May-June 1982): 35.

[18] Frederick B. Mumford, *History of the Missouri College of Agriculture* (Columbia: Missouri A.E.S. Bulletin 483, 1944), pp. 73-74; Earle D. Ross, *The Land-Grant Idea at Iowa State College: A Centennial Trial Balance, 1858-1958* (Ames: Iowa State College Press, 1958), pp. 91-96.

[19] Julius T. Willard, *History of Kansas State College of Agriculture and Applied Science* (Manhattan: Kansas State College Press, 1940), pp. 67-69; Joseph C. Fitzharris, "Science for the Farmer: The Development of the Minnesota Agricultural Experiment Station, 1868-1910," *Agricultural History* 48 (January 1974): 206-207.

[20] True, *Agricultural Experimentation*, pp. 74-75, 108-109, 111-112, 115, Charles Hardin, *Freedom in Agricultural Education* (Chicago: University of Chicago Press, 1955), pp. 67-68.

[21] True and Clark, *Agricultural Experiment Stations*, p. 403; William C. Hunter, *Beacon Across the Prairie: North Dakota's Land-Grant College* (Fargo: North Dakota Institute for Regional Studies, 1961), pp. 15-16, 18.

[22] True and Clark, *Agricultural Experiment Stations*, p. 375; A.T. Steinel and D.W. Working, *History of Agriculture in Colorado* (Fort Collins: State Agricultural College, 1926), pp. 541-542; Samuel B. Doten, *Nevada Agricultural Experiment Station, 1888-1943: An Administrative History, With Comment Upon It* (Reno: University of Nevada A.E.S. Bulletin 163, March 1943), pp. 10-11.

[23] True and Clark, *Agricultural Experiment Stations*, pp. 197, 293-294, 461-462; Enoch Albert Bryan, *Historical Sketch of the State College of Washington: 1890-1925* (Pullman: State College of Washington, 1928), pp. 486-487; C. W. Hungerford, *An Historical Review of the Idaho Agricultural Experiment Station* ([Moscow]: Idaho Agricultural Research Progress Report 36, 1960), p. 4.

[24] True and Clark, *Agricultural Experiment Stations*, pp. 136-138, 326-327, 420.

[25] James T. Bonnen, "Some Observations on the Organizational Nature of a Great Technological Payoff," *Journal of Farm Economics* 44 (1962): 1281; Charles E. Rosenberg, "Science, Technology, and Economic Growth: The Case of the Agricultural Experiment Station Scientist 1875-1914," *Agricultural History* 45 (January 1971): 2; David B. Danbom, "Publicly-Sponsored Agricultural Research in the United States from an Historical Perspective," unpublished paper [1984], pp. 13-14; Willard, *Kansas State College of Agriculture*, pp. 93-125; Ross, *Land-Grant Idea at Iowa State*, pp. 91-96; Hardin, *Freedom in Agricultural Education*, pp. 65-66; William D. Barnes, "Farmers Versus Scientists: The Grange, the Farmers' Alliance, and the West Virginia Agricultural Experiment Station," *Proceedings of the West Virginia Academy of Science* 37 (1965): 197-201; True and Clark, *Agricultural Experiment Stations*, pp. 465-466.

[26] True and Clark, *Agricultural Experiment Stations*, p. 48.

[27] Kerr, *Alabama Agricultural Experiment Station*, pp. 24; Hills, *Five and Fifty Years*, p. 19; John A. Myers, *Bulletin 7 of the West Virginia Agricultural Experiment Station* (Charleston, West Virginia: Moses W. Donnally, 1890), p. 223.

[28] True and Clark, *Agricultural Experiment Stations*, pp. 145-148; Kerr, *Alabama Agricultural Experiment Station*, pp. 20-23.

[29] The Association underwent a succession of name changes as its membership broadened to reflect the changing focus of its concern: Association of Land-Grant Colleges in 1920; Association of Land-Grant Colleges and Universities in 1926; American Association of Land-Grant Colleges and State Universities in 1955; Association of State Universities and Land-Grant Colleges in 1962; and National Association of State Universities and Land-Grant Colleges (NASULGC) in 1965. Vivian Wiser and Douglas E. Bowers, *Marketing Research and Its Coordination in USDA: A Historical Approach* (Washington: USDA Agricultural Economic Report 475, August 1981), p. 7n.

[30] Knoblauch et al., *State Agricultural Experiment Stations*, pp. 55-58, 63-65.

[31] Ibid., pp. 67-73; Association of American Agricultural Colleges and Experiment Stations, *Proceedings of the Third Annual Convention, Held at Washington, D.C., November 12-15, 1889* (Washington: USDA, OES Miscellaneous Bulletin 2, 1890), p. 76. The accounts of the land-grant college association meetings hereafter will be cited as NASULGC, *Proceedings* followed by the date.

[32] NASULGC, *Proceedings, July 13-15, 1897*, pp. 23-24.

[33] NASULGC, *Proceedings, July 5-7, 1899*, pp. 21-28.

[34] Knoblauch et al., *State Agricultural Experiment Stations*, pp. 78-88, 146-148.

[35] Charles E. Rosenberg, "The Adams Act: Politics and the Cause of Scientific Research," *Agricultural History* 38 (January 1964): 3-4; Margaret Rossiter, Preface to *Alfred True on Agricultural Experimentation and Research*, by Alfred C. True (New York: Arno Press, 1980); "Abram Winegardner Harris," *Experiment Station Record* 72 (April 1935): 433-434.

[36] Knoblauch et al., *State Agricultural Experiment Stations*, pp. 89-92; Gladys L. Baker, "The Face of the Bureaucrat: A Profile of USDA Leadership," in *Farmers, Bureaucrats, and Middlemen: Historical Perspectives on American Agriculture*, ed. Trudy Huskamp Peterson (Washington: Howard University Press, 1980), pp. 65-67; Conover, *Office of Experiment Stations*, pp. 57-58, 104.

[37] Knoblauch et al., *State Agricultural Experiment Stations*, pp. 94-95; True, *Agricultural Experimentation*, p. 131.

[38] Wiser and Bowers, *Marketing Research*, p. 9; United States Department of Agriculture, Office of Experiment Stations, *Annual Report of the Office of Experiment Stations: 1905* (Washington: Government Printing Office, 1906), p. 181. Hereafter cited as OES, *Report on the Experiment Stations*.

[39] Conover, *Office of the Experiment Stations*, p. 105; Rosenberg, "Adams Act," p. 4n.

[40] True, *Agricultural Experimentation*, pp. 186-191, 197-198, 203; Ernest G. Moore, *The Agricultural Research Service* (New York: Praeger, 1967), pp. 16-17; Paul E. Waggoner, "Research and Education in American Agriculture," *Agricultural History* 50 (January 1976): 240.

[41] Conover, *Office of Experiment Stations*, pp. 62-65, 89-90, 95-96; Moore, *Agricultural Research Service*, pp. 39-40. In 1929, Alaska's station came under the provisions of the regular station-funding acts with Hawaii and Puerto Rico stations admitted as full partners after 1955. USDA, Science and Education Administration-Cooperative Research, *Administrative Manual for the Hatch (Experiment Station) Act as Amended* (Washington: USDA Agriculture Handbook 381, November 1980), p. A8.

[42] Wiser and Bowers, *Marketing Research*, p. 9; Knoblauch et al., *State Agricultural Experiment Stations*, pp. 123-124.

[43] True, *Agricultural Experimentation*, pp. 141-159.

[44] Ibid., p. 137; OES, *Report on the Experiment Stations: 1905*, pp. 176-181; Ronald L. Nye, "Federal vs. State Agricultural Research Policy: The Case of California's Tulare Experiment Station, 1888-1909," *Agricultural History* 54 (October 1983): 436-437; Bonnen, "Some Observations on a Great Technological Payoff," p. 1284; Rosenberg, "Adams Act," pp. 7-8.

[45] OES, *Report on the Experiment Stations: 1905*, pp. 182-183.

[46] Adams Act, 34 Stat. 63 (1906); Knoblauch et al., *State Agricultural Experiment Stations*, pp. 96-97.

[47] Rosenberg, "Adams Act," pp. 6-12; Knoblauch et al., *State Agricultural Experiment Stations*, pp. 96-100, 107, 159-160.

[48] Knoblauch et al., *State Agricultural Experiment Stations*, pp. 106, 160-163; Rosenberg, "Adams Act," pp. 11-12.

[49] H.J. Webber, "A Plan of Publication for Agricultural Experiment Station Investigations," *Science* 26 (October 18, 1907): 510.

[50] True, *Agricultural Experimentation*, p. 211; Knoblauch et al., *State Agricultural Experiment Stations*, pp. 148-149.

[51] True, *Agricultural Experimentation*, p. 212; OES, *Report on the Experiment Stations: 1920*; Waggoner, "Research and Education in American Agriculture," p. 247; Nelson Amendment, 34 Stat. 1256, 1281 (1907).

[52] True, *Agricultural Experimentation*, pp. 210, 138; H.L. Russell, "Branch Experiment Stations," in NASULGC, *Proceedings: November 13-15, 1912*, pp. 179-183 (quotation on p. 183); Bailey, *Mississippi Agricultural Experiment Stations*, pp. 18-31; Hungerford, *Historical Review of the Idaho Agricultural Experiment Station*, pp. 7-8; Hunter, *Beacon Across the Prairie*, pp. 53, 230.

[53] True, *Agricultural Experimentation*, pp. 210-212; G. L. Baker, *The County Agent* (Chicago: University of Chicago Press, 1939), pp. 6, 26-36; Scott, *Reluctant Farmer*, pp. 64, 67-72, 92-93, 106; Knoblauch et al., *State Agricultural Experiment Stations*, pp. 112-113.

[54] Smith-Lever Agricultural Extension Act, 38 Stat. 372 (1913-1915).

[55] Conover, *Office of Experiment Stations*, pp. 52, 59-60; Rosenberg, "Adams Act," p. 4.

[56] Doten, *Nevada Agricultural Experiment Station*, pp. 21-23, 25, 38; OES, *Report on the Experiment Stations: 1912*, p. 156.

[57] OES, *Report on the Experiment Stations: 1911*, p. 181; *1912*, p. 186 (quotation); *1913*, p. 72; and *1914*, p. 191; Francis Richard Gilmore, "Historical Study of the Oklahoma Agricultural Experiment Station" (Ed.D. dissertation, Oklahoma State University, 1967), pp. 114-115, 117-119.

[58] OES, *Report on the Experiment Stations: 1913*, p. 17; *1915* p. 94; *1917*, pp. 94-95; and *1918*, p. 6; Georgia File in Suspension of Funds Cases, Miscellaneous Records Relating to the Administration and Allocation of Federal Funds: 1887-1956, Records of the Office of Experiment Stations, Record Group 164, National Archives, Washington, D.C.; Georgia Experiment Station, *Thirtieth and Thirty-First Annual Reports: 1917 and 1918* (Experiment: Georgia AES, 1919), pp. 3-4, 7-8; Georgia Coastal Plain Experiment Station, *Annual Report: 1919-1920* (Tifton: Georgia Coastal Plain A.E.S. Bulletin 1, 1921), pp. 4-5, 21; Bunker and Dupree, *100 Years*, pp. 8-10.

[59] OES, *Report on the Experiment Stations: 1914*, pp. 256-257 and *1915*, p. 288-289; Hardin, *Freedom in Agricultural Education*, p. 98.

[60] True, *Agricultural Experimentation*, pp. 236-237.

[61] C. Beaman Smith and K. H. Atwood, *Relation of Agricultural Education Agencies to Farm Practices* (Washington: USDA, Bureau of Plant Industry Circular 117, 1913), p. 22.

[62] True, *Agricultural Experimentation*, p. 273; OES, *Reports on the Experiment Stations: 1920-1929*; Knoblauch et al., *State Agricultural Experiment Stations*, p. 114.

[63] True, *Agricultural Experimentation*, pp. 251-252; Knoblauch et al., *State Agricultural Experiment Stations*, pp. 116-117.

[64] OES, *Report on the Experiment Stations: 1923*, p. 3 and *1928*, pp. 17-18.

[65] OES, *Report on the Experiment Stations: 1926*, p. 13.

[66] OES, *Report on the Experiment Stations: 1931*, p. 10.

[67] OES, *Report on the Experiment Stations: 1928*, p. 17; Mississippi File in Suspension of Funds Cases, Miscellaneous Records Relating to the Administration and Allocation of Federal Funds, Records of the Office of Experiment Stations.

[68] OES, *Report on the Experiment Stations: 1928*, pp. 4, 6.

[69] Lowry Nelson, *Rural Sociology: Its Origin and Growth in the United States* (Minneapolis: University of Minnesota Press, 1969), pp. 10, 32-33; True, *Agricultural Experimentation*, pp. 275-277.

[70] Purnell Act, 43 Stat. 970 (1925); Robinson, *Administration of Federal Agricultural Research Funds*, p. 9.

[71] Wiser and Bowers, *Marketing Research*, pp. 27-30; John M. Gaus and Leon O. Wolcott, *Public Administration and the United States Department of Agriculture* (Chicago: Public Administration Service, 1940), p. 232; Association of Administrators of Home Economics, *National Goals and Guidelines for Research in Home Economics: A Study* (East Lansing, Michigan: AAHE, 1970), p. 78; NASULGC, *Proceedings: 1926*, pp. 201-203.

[72] Hardin, *Freedom in Agricultural Education*, pp. 40, 47-49.

[73] Knoblauch et al., *State Agricultural Experiment Stations*, pp. 127-128; Hardin, *Freedom in Agricultural Education*, p. 144.

[74] OES, *Report on the Experiment Stations: 1934*, p. 152; R.W. Trullinger, "An Appraisal of the Policies and Procedure Involved in the Hatch Act from the Standpoint of an Efficient Way of Administering Productive Research Work," in NASULGC, *Proceedings: 1937*, pp. 144-147; "Selected Short Abstracts of Cooperative State Research Policy Including Rulings and Opinions on Federal-Grant Fund Research," Cooperative State Research Service-Office Document-1125 Revised, January 1, 1966.

[75] OES, *Reports on the Experiment Stations: 1930-1941*.

[76] Carroll W. Pursell, Jr., "The Administration of Science in the Department of Agriculture, 1933-1940," *Agricultural History* 42 (July 1968): 232-235; Bankhead-Jones Act, 49 Stat. 436 (1935); OES, *Report on the Experiment Stations: 1936*, p. 182. Bankhead-Jones also increased support for resident instruction at the land-grant colleges with $980,000 for 1936 rising to $2,480,000 in 1940 and thereafter, distributed on the basis of a State's percentage of the nation's total population. State extension services were granted an extra $8,000,000 in the first year and $12,000,000 in 1940 and subsequent years, with each share based upon farm-resident population.

[77] Wiser and Bowers, *Marketing Research*, p. 36; OES, *Report on the Experiment Stations: 1939*, pp. 3-4.

[78] Pursell, "Administration of Science in the USDA," pp. 238-239; Wiser and Bowers, *Marketing Research*, pp. 37-38.

CHAPTER III
War, Prosperity, and the Golden Age of Science: 1941-1961

The state agricultural experiment stations, like American agriculture itself, embarked upon great changes as the Depression ended. Past trends in the nation's farming sector accelerated—fewer farmers, larger farms, and more specialization and heightened susceptibility to market fluctuations. The increased substitution of biological and mechanical technology for manpower characterized a "Second Agricultural Revolution" which began in the mid-1940s.

The public agricultural research system generated much of the knowledge that fueled the increases in productivity prompting these changes. The state agricultural experiment station provided an administrative mechanism which grouped together scientists from an array of disciplines concerned with overcoming the problems confronting its farmers. By the 1940s agricultural science had moved beyond the largely descriptive work of the past so that its practitioners began to cooperate in attacking obstacles to productivity advances in a systems approach. Incremental advances to knowledge from agronomists, entomologists, engineers, and plant and animal breeders, physiologists, and pathologists began to be combined synergistically into production and market enhancing technologies specific to a state's major agricultural commodities, contributing to increasingly rapid gains in farm production in selected areas. With these advances as evidence of its value, a station often was able to secure additional support for its entire program of research, promoting agricultural science on a broad front within the state.

As the experiment stations were rewarded with expanded budgets, they were also confronted with increasing demands for new answers to new problems that threatened sustained abundance of farm production in the United States. The combination of local direction and national coordination embodied in the institutional structure of the state experiment stations lent the system a flexibility that allowed its scientists the opportunity to meet these expectations.

With the eruption of World War II, all segments of the American economy rather suddenly were called upon to resume full production after years of retrenchment. Any uncertainty the experiment stations may have held about their traditional priorities was dispelled by the emergency and they returned to the task they perhaps did best: finding ways for agriculture to produce more with less.

Agricultural Research Aids War Effort

In an effort to focus the agricultural research system on wartime needs, the United States Department of Agriculture in early 1942 created a new Agricultural Research Administration over the Bureaus of Plant Industry, Agricultural Chemistry and Engineering, Animal Industry, Dairy Industry, Entomology and Plant Quarantine, and Home Economics, as well as the Office of Experiment Stations. Thus, for the first time, all the scientific activities of the Department and, through the Office of Experiment Stations, the state research institutions were the sole interest of a single agency, at least in theory. In practice, the administrator did little to exercise his authority to reorder the fiercely independent component bureaus under his direction.[1]

The new office did coordinate the considerable wartime agricultural research in the Department and encouraged the state stations to address pressing needs. The entire system cooperated in compiling past research results to set realistic farm production goals. The stations responded energetically to the challenge, concentrating on making the most of their state's agricultural characteristics to benefit the country. The Office of Experiment Stations estimated that over 40 percent of the 3,472 federally funded projects undertaken by the stations in 1942 were specifically designed to aid the war effort.

On a broader scale, station programs in every discipline set out to free from America's farms the manpower needed for industrial and military service. Agronomists, pathologists, entomologists, and agricultural engineers cooperated in developing the biological, chemical, and mechanical technology which could provide bountiful harvests with minimum labor. Additionally, researchers sought to increase supplies of or find substitutes for commercial fertilizers, feed, and insecticides whose major ingredients were needed in war production, and for rubber, petroleum, and seed stocks when supply sources were interrupted by the war.

Other investigators aided the military effort more directly. Station scientists were enlisted to discover ways of maintaining vegetative cover for airfields and to combat lice, ants, roaches, flies, and mosquitoes that plagued military camps. The range of activity undertaken by the stations in support of the war effort was illustrated by the Alabama station which, in 1942, studied the influence of tractor-tread design on military vehicle mobility (in cooperation with staff of the USDA neighboring tillage research laboratory). Scientists here also developed an inexpensive, nutritional dog ration for the Army K-9 corps.[2]

Of perhaps more lasting significance were *human* nutrition experiments begun to maintain the vitamin and mineral content of foods preserved as concentrated field provisions. At the suggestion of the National Research Council, a national cooperative study was launched in 1942 under the direction of a committee consisting of an Office of Experiment Stations representative and four regional coordinators drawn from the experiment stations. By 1943, forty-four state stations were studying preservation techniques and nutritional values of over sixty different foods.[3]

The state agricultural experiment stations expanded into these research areas with fewer scientists and relatively little additional money. Military service drained the stations of many scientists while the again prosperous private sector beckoned others to leave. Between 1942 and 1945, the number of station workers declined more than 11 percent, not including those on military leave. Appropriations from state legislatures increased the budgets of the experiment stations at the steady but unspectacular pace begun in 1935. In the fiscal year before the United States entered the war, total state appropriations were $9,907,865. By 1945, they equalled $11,557,221 having risen in every year except 1943. Federal funds for the stations remained stationary during the war, with the Hatch, Adams, and Purnell Acts contributing $90,000 annually to each station and the Bankhead-Jones Act splitting just over $2,400,000 among them.[4]

ESCOP Expands Spokesman Role

Total Bankhead-Jones appropriations had been scheduled to rise to $3,000,000 in 1940. Beginning with the 1939 fiscal year, however, annual increases began to lag behind mandated sums, reaching $2,100,000 rather than the scheduled $2,400,000. Concerned over the shortfall in a period when the stations were still recovering from successive years of lessened state support, ESCOP welcomed an opportunity to plead the case for more money. In 1940, the directors' committee got its chance when representatives of the Bureau of Budget accepted an invitation from ESCOP chairman Robert E.

Buchanan to attend a meeting at the Iowa station which he directed. At the ensuing Ames Conference, station representatives stressed their independence from the USDA and convinced the visitors from the budget office to allow ESCOP to present budget testimony directly to the bureau and Congress. Bankhead-Jones grants did not suddenly jump to the previously legislated level, but they did increase—to $2,463,708 after 1941, to $2,663,708 after 1945, and to $2,863,708 after 1948.[5]

Earl O. Heady, associated with the Iowa Experiment Station since 1940, earned international acclaim for his contributions in developing theory, experimental designs, quantitative analyses, and economic interpretation for interdisciplinary research between economists and technical scientists. *(Iowa State University photo)*

Perhaps the most important outcome of the Ames Conference was the recognition of the Experiment Station Committee on Organization and Policy of the Association of Land-Grant Colleges and Universities as the national spokesman for the state agricultural experiment stations. Two years after this de facto designation at Ames, ESCOP absorbed the Joint Committee on Projects and the Correlation of Research, in effect becoming an executive committee for the Section on Experiment Work within the Association. To broaden its representation, the constitution of ESCOP was amended at the same time. Membership on the committee after 1942 consisted of three directors chosen from each of the four regions with the secretary of the Association's Section on Station Work and the chief of the Office of Experiment Stations appointed as ex officio members. Furthermore, a Subcommittee on Home Economics was created, comprised of one home economist from each region, with the chief of the Bureau of Home Economics and the principal administrator for the discipline within the Office of Experiment Stations acting for the USDA.

In the 1940s, the parent body of ESCOP, the Association of Land-Grant Colleges and Universities, also moved to establish closer ties to the sources of federal power, placing a secretary in a Washington, D.C. office at the beginning of the decade and elevating the position to secretary-treasurer in 1945. With the national government becoming more active in research and education, the experiment stations and the colleges found it imperative to have more effective voices in policy making.[6]

Research and Marketing Act of 1946

ESCOP soon was called upon to represent the stations' opinion in efforts to enact a new federal-funding bill which began with the close of the war. As the conflict wound down, fears rose that continued high production levels in the absence of wartime markets would usher in a new agricultural depression. Anxious to avoid the unpopular and stringent controls on farm production, congressional attention turned toward expanding markets. By the end of the war, Congress was considering numerous proposals to harness agricultural research to marketing in the same effective manner that it had approached production. From the various suggestions, two pieces of proposed legislation emerged by 1946. A bill introduced by Congressman John Flannagan of Virginia sought to expand the capacity of the state experiment stations by increased appropriations, with a portion reserved for investigations to discover new uses and markets for farm products. Another, offered by Congressman Clifford R. Hope of Kansas, would provide funds to be dispensed at the USDA's discretion to promote research in marketing and distribution. In August 1946, both proposals became law as separate titles in a three-part package generally known as the Research and Marketing Act of 1946.[7]

Framed as an amendment to the 1935 Bankhead-Jones Act, Title I of the new legislation actually went much further, beginning with the statement of the goals of Congress in funding agricultural research from the national treasury. While the Purnell Act of 1925 had declared the intention to improve rural life, the 1946 act explicitly linked rural conditions to the nation's welfare, acknowledging "a sound and prosperous agricultural and rural life as indispensable to the maintenance of maximum employment and national prosperity." Thus, Congress encouraged agricultural research to maintain a balanced farming and industrial economy.

Section 9 of Title I authorized new funds for the effort: $2,500,000 for 1947, an equal addition for 1948, and $5,000,000 additional annual increases for 1949, 1950, and 1951 with "such additional funds . . . as the Congress may deem necessary" for subsequent years. This last, open-ended authorization was new to research subsidy, as was the particular formula adopted to allocate the funds to the state experiment stations. The stations would receive equal portions of 20 percent of each year's appropriation and split another 52 percent on a formula basis: one-half according to relative rural population and the other half according to relative farm population. Every dollar of these formula allocations appropriated after the enactment of the new authority had to be matched by the states, and one dollar out of every five was earmarked "for conducting marketing research projects approved by the Department of Agriculture." Another 25 percent of the Section 9 allocations for each year was reserved for a "Regional Research Fund" to sustain investigations undertaken cooperatively by two or more states on a problem of regional significance, with a nine-member committee representative of the station directors recommending which projects to support. The remaining 3 percent of Section 9 money was delegated to the Office of Experiment Stations to administer programs specified in the section.

The state experiment stations only indirectly benefited from Section 10 of Title I, which provided discretionary funds to the USDA to encourage research in two broad categories. Section 10(a) authorized the USDA to encourage the search for "new, and extended uses of agricultural commodities and products thereof" with annual grants scheduled to rise from $3,000,000 in 1947 to $15,000,000 after 1950. "So far as practicable," the new utilization research was to be carried out in USDA laboratories, but the Secretary of Agriculture could contract "with such public or private organizations or individuals as he may find qualified" to perform supplementary work. Section 10(b) more directly effected the stations, authorizing the Department to support cooperative federal-state research into questions unrelated to farm product utilization. For 1947, $1,500,000 was appropriated for the purposes of this subsection, with equal additional yearly amounts for 1948, 1949, and 1950 until the total was continued annually at no less than $6,000,000. This fund was in addition to a similarly administered $2,000,000 annual Special Research Fund provided for in the Bankhead-Jones Act of 1935 and reauthorized in Section 10(d) of the 1946 legislation.

Title II of the 1946 legislation provided the Secretary of Agriculture with additional cooperative funds amounting to $2,500,000 in 1947 and increasing to $20,000,000 yearly after 1950. Reserved wholly for "research and service work in connection with the preparation for market, processing, packaging, handling, storing, transporting, distributing, and marketing of agricultural products," the money was to be disbursed by the USDA to support cooperative projects not only in research, but in extension and inspection as well. Again, "to the maximum extent practicable," the research funded under this title of the act was to be carried out cooperatively with the state experiment stations under contract, but other public and private institutions were also eligible for support. Unlike the cooperative discretionary funds provided in Title I, Section 10, however, this money for marketing research had to be matched with an equal amount by the contracting institution. Finally, to police the distribution of these grants, Title II included authorization for the Secretary of Agriculture to create a single administrative agency for marketing work.

The last of the three titles included in the 1946 Research and Marketing Act called for a national advisory committee to assist the USDA in developing an agenda for research and in securing the cooperation of research institutions, industry groups, and farm organizations in the process. Chaired by a USDA official, the eleven-member committee was to include no other federal employees and at least six representatives of producers of commodities. Title III also authorized the Secretary to convene any other committees which might help implement specific provisions of the act.[8]

The Research and Marketing Act introduced a series of innovations which required new administrative policies. Developing guidelines for implementing the complex research provisions largely fell to the new chief of the Office of Experiment Stations, Robert W. Trullinger, and to ESCOP. Since Dr. Trullinger had been with the office since 1912, his succession to the position upon James Jardine's retirement in 1946 signalled no sudden break with past policies.

Funds Reserved for Marketing Research

The immediate business facing those entrusted with new administration was to determine how the Title I proviso about marketing research would be enforced. Even though the specified 20 percent was interpreted to apply to the aggregate of stations, Trullinger's office monitored expenditures at each state station to simplify accounting and to encourage adherence to the aims of the lawmakers. For the first year in which appropriations were available, the experiment stations as a whole were required to spend a total of $720,000 in federal and matching funds upon "marketing research projects." Deciding what experiments could qualify for earmarked funds was difficult. After initial confusion in translating the words of the act into researchable topics, the USDA and an ESCOP subcommittee released an interpretation in 1951 which sanctioned studies into three main areas: packaging, transportation, and storage; grading and distribution; and marketing institutions and financing. Later, it was necessary to broaden the definition because some stations found it increasingly difficult to meet the escalating dollar amounts to satisfy the 20 percent requirement, but the beginnings of sound research were established upon the 1951 guidelines.[9]

Regional Research and the Committee of Nine

To fulfill the other earmarking clause in the Research and Marketing Act that set aside 25 percent of Title I, Section 9 appropriations for regional research, an elaborate administrative structure evolved. While the act specified that a committee of nine representatives of the station directors was to recommend projects worthy of support, ESCOP and the Office of Experiment Stations had to decide how to select these representatives and how to allocate the money. Most of the existing interstate cooperative projects centered around the Bankhead-Jones regional laboratories which relied upon the four existing regional associations of directors to plan and supervise investigations. A similar regional orientation was adopted to administer the new joint work. The Committee of Nine immediately was chosen on a regional basis with each of the regional associations of directors nominating two members from among its ranks and the home economists in the national land-grant college association proposing the ninth member.

Meeting in 1946, the nine formulated a priority list of nine areas eligible for support, appropriately headed by "marketing." They considered twenty-five projects submitted for funding with the $625,000 that was scheduled for 1947. By 1950, some seventy proposals were vying for $1,224,100 in funds, prompting the Committee of Nine to turn to the regional organizations of station directors for help in allocating money and screening prospective projects.

Robert W. Trullinger, who came to the Office of Experiment Stations in 1912, was elevated to chief in 1946 and served until 1955. *(National Archives and Records Administration photo)*

Informally at first, then formally by the mid-1950s, the Regional Research Fund was divided between the four regions on a formula basis leaving it to the directors' associations to recommend the distribution of funds between projects. Scientists in the stations submitted proposals through their directors to the regional committees who then appointed an Administrative Advisor to gather a Technical Committee of scientists from each of the stations interested in the project. The Technical Committee drew up specific plans for experiments, assigning responsibilities among cooperating members who would meet periodically to review progress. The Committee of Nine functioned as national reviewers to recommend worthy projects for Office of Experiment Stations funding. However, even after delegating much of its work to the regional associations of directors, the national committee frequently was overwhelmed by review duties which impaired its potential as a group of scientists contributing a national perspective.[10]

Research Advisory Committee Developed

The idea of seeking a broader perspective in shaping public agricultural research also was embodied in the Research and Marketing Act's Title III, which called for a national committee to advise the USDA on research programs under the act. The producer-dominated

National Advisory Committee first convened in October of 1946 and soon after changed its name and its scope of concern. As the Agricultural Research Policy Committee (and later still as the National Agricultural Research Advisory Committee), its interests widened beyond marketing and it evolved into a sounding board for all federally financed research in agriculture.

Employing authority given the Secretary of Agriculture by Title III to create whatever other advisory groups would be helpful, the Committee in 1948 established twenty-two subcommittees for specific commodities or marketing processes. The parent group and all its subcommittees consisted of eleven members, six of them representatives of producers. From time to time, the advisory committee system was restructured to reflect new interests and broadened concerns but its basic operation remained fairly constant.

Prior to each advisory group's annual meeting, a corresponding USDA group compiled a list of research problems and submitted them to the commodity advisory committee which ranked them by priority. Each list was forwarded to the national committee which used the data to suggest funding priorities to the Secretary of 'Agriculture. The advisory system inaugurated by the Research of Marketing Act did little to inject new ideas for study in the public agricultural research institutions but it did enhance communication between scientists and agricultural business.[11]

Various advisory committees which proliferated on the state level produced the same outcome. Station councils had long been utilized by several experiment stations to exchange information between scientists and producers. World War II, with its plethora of mobilization boards and planning committees, further encouraged the trend toward organizing to address shared problems. With the passage of the Research and Marketing Act, the Association advocated the formation of advisory councils, suggesting that their structure parallel the national system of commodity committees. By 1952, three-fourths of the stations had done so, generally finding the various commodity producer organizations eager to cooperate with one another to increase the political clout of the agriculture sector.[12]

Funding Promise Unfulfilled

While the Research and Marketing Act introduced a series of far-reaching features into the administration of public research, the failure of Congress to appropriate the sums promised in the Act limited its impact. As after the passage of the Bankhead-Jones Act in 1935, national lawmakers provided none of the dollars pledged in 1947, and consistently underfunded every section of the act each year thereafter. Funds were first made available in 1948, equalling the $2,500,000 called for in the previous year for direct payments to the state experiment stations and for regional research. For the next year Title I, Section 9 appropriations increased to about $3,250,000 and Title II, Section 204 money for cooperative research into marketing problems were forwarded for the first time, with the USDA contracting with thirteen state stations at a cost of $60,500.

In the four years beginning with 1950, direct Research and Marketing Act money for the stations remained at $3,600,000 despite the act's call for appropriations to rise from $10,000,000 to $20,000,000 over that period. Increases in the next two years raised Section 9 totals to just over $11,000,000 for 1955. In that year, too, thirty-eight stations split $500,000 provided them under contract with the Department upon the recommendations of an ESCOP subcommittee called the Experiment Stations Marketing Research Advisory Committee. The experiment stations were not singled out for support at less than that pledged; in 1952, appropriations for all the provisions of the act amounted to less than $19,000,000 compared to the promised $61,000,000.[13]

Congress proved reluctant to meet its commitments made in 1946 for a variety of reasons. Perhaps foremost was the expected surplus of commodities failed to materialize after the war, making research to discover ways to dispose of stockpiles irrelevant. Without a crisis, Congress looked carefully at what they were paying for and, in the case of the USDA's administration of Research and Marketing Act requirements, were not entirely satisfied with what they saw. Most galling was the Department's refusal to reorder its bureaus (which it had done just four years prior to the RMA's passage) to bring all marketing work together. Instead, a single Research and Marketing Act Administrator was named to coordinate scattered marketing research in the Department, with a Research and Marketing Advisory Committee of agency heads as a consultative council. Even the office of Research and Marketing Administrator was discontinued when its incumbent stepped down in 1949. Supervision of the act then fell to the Agricultural Research Administration which retained the intra-department advisory committee as the Research Council. With the singular administrative post abolished, the apparent need for marketing research less pressing, and the various advisory committees more broadly interpreting their duties, Congress was less and less inclined to treat Research and Marketing Act funds separately from more regular USDA appropriations. By the early 1950s, separate budget hearings for agricultural marketing research were abandoned.[14]

The disparity between what had been pledged and what was delivered was so great that the House Committee on Agriculture commissioned a committee to investigate what deficiencies in public agricultural research caused the House Committee on Appropriations to curtail scheduled funding increases. In the summer of 1950, Representative Stephen Pace of Georgia convened hearings and D. Howard Doane of the Doane Agricultural Service headed an eleven-member panel representing agribusiness, farm journals, national farmer groups, and state experiment stations. Their Pace/Doane Report cited overly complex administrative arrangements within the USDA and excessive accounting requirements upon the state agricultural experiment stations as impediments to organizing research more efficiently. To address these shortcomings the report urged the Secretary of Agriculture to place all departmental research activity under a single administrator, and called on Congress to consolidate the jumble of existing research-funding into a single authority.

Golden Age of Science

Although neither suggestion was new, the fact that they were stated by a citizens' panel representing a broad spectrum of the public gave the recommendations greater force in an era that was emerging as a "golden age" for agricultural science. With the war won and the Great Depression behind it, America faced the future with renewed optimism, secure in its belief that many of the world's problems could be solved or at least lessened by scientists and the technological miracles which streamed forth from their laboratories. Congress merely reflected the public's high regard for scientific research when it chartered the National Science Foundation in 1950 to develop science policy and encourage basic research through project grants.[15]

Agricultural research shared in the glory as hybrid crops and new pesticides came into use, seeming to promise an end to hunger. The Research and Marketing Act of 1946 showed congressional confidence in the skills of agricultural scientists to discover principles of efficient commodity marketing, just as they had done for commodity production. The congressional investigation four years later was less an expression of diminished faith in the capacity of scientists than evidence of pique over delays in getting the effort underway.

The esteem accorded agricultural science directly benefitted the state experiment stations in two major ways: a whole new generation of young scientists was attracted to public research and public financial support increased dramatically. Between 1947 (when the stations returned to full strength) and 1955, the number of professionals employed in the experiment stations increased from 5,290 to 7,892, a jump of nearly 50 percent in less than a decade.

Funding from states grew more spectacularly over the same period, far outstripping increases required by matching provisions in the Research and Marketing Act. State appropriations in 1948, for example, totalled nearly $25,000,000, an increase of more than $5,000,000 over the year before whereas only an $1,800,000 addition was required by the act. Yearly incremental gains continued unabated even as scheduled federal Research and Marketing Act increases stopped from 1950 through 1953. In the latter year, state support equalled more than $42,300,000. By 1955, the agricultural experiment stations received over $51,000,000 from their state governments as compared to just over $19,000,000 granted under the five different federal acts.[16]

As more tax dollars flowed into subsidizing agricultural investigations, calls grew more frequent for reforms to make the system more efficient. A year before the Pace/Doane Report recommended realigning the USDA, a Hoover Commission Report on the organization of the executive branch did the same, characterizing the Department unfavorably as "a loose confederation of independent bureaus and agencies." When the Eisenhower administration arrived in Washington in 1953, a major effort was begun to reorganize the USDA.

Reorganization in Washington

The reorganization instituted by Secretary Ezra Taft Benson went straight to the heart of the Hoover Commission criticisms, replacing the old system of independent bureaus with an arrangement featuring four assistant secretaries. Under the Assistant Secretary for Federal-State Relations was placed an Agricultural Research Service (ARS), taking the place of the Agricultural Research Administration. The ARS retained its predecessor's responsibilities of supervising federal research and allocating research funds to the states.

The Office of Experiment Stations lost its title, as did the other long-standing bureaus, but it was recreated as the State Experiment

Stations Division within the Agricultural Research Service. With the new title came new positions filled by veterans of the old agency. R.W. Trullinger, who had been named Assistant Administrator for Experiment Stations under the ARS when the reorganization became effective, stepped down in 1955. He was succeeded by his former deputy, Erwin C. Elting, whose title was changed to Deputy Administrator. Dr. Elting had been with the Office of Experiment Stations since 1936, just four years longer than Harold C. Knoblauch, who became Director of the State Experiment Stations Division in 1954.[17]

Despite the appointment of familiar administrators to new posts, the new USDA structure did not sit well with the state agricultural experiment stations. As early as 1951, when Secretary Benson's predecessor proposed regrouping the Department's components, the Experiment Station Committee on Organization and Policy established a subcommittee to monitor the process. Station directors feared that their independent voice within the Department's councils would be stilled by any changes, a fear that seemed borne out in the plan finally adopted in 1953. The Executive Committee of the Association of Land-Grant Colleges and Universities made known the displeasure of the station representatives in both 1954 and 1955, petitioning the Secretary of Agriculture to restore an Office of Experiment Stations independent of the division which directed the Department's own research. Although the remonstrances of the Association did prompt the USDA to promote the officer administering the stations' federal funds to the rank of deputy administrator when Elting succeeded Trullinger in 1955, he was left under ARS control.

From his new position as coordinator of the nation's public agricultural research, the Agricultural Research Service Administrator in 1958 invited the state stations, through ESCOP, to join ARS in a full-scale review of federal-state relations. An eleven-member Joint Committee on Cooperative Research involved ARS administrators, ESCOP-selected directors, and the ARS Deputy Administrator for Experiment Stations. For two years, they labored to set guidelines for the federal and state partners in agricultural research. In 1960, their report again tried to distinguish the respective roles of the partners, stressing the local responsibilities of the state stations and the broader duties of ARS. Still, the report concluded that neither sphere was mutually exclusive and that both federal and state station scientists had a duty to pursue basic research. Promises to work together more closely in locating research facilities and in undertaking cooperative experiments were made by the conferees. Like previous attempts to standardize policies governing federal-state relations, the Joint Committee on Cooperative Research perhaps was notable more for good intentions than concrete accomplishments. At least it provided USDA and state station administrators with a forum to share their concerns.[18]

Consolidating Funding Legislation

The other national issue confronting the agricultural experiment stations in the 1950s was the consolidation of the federal legislation which subsidized their agricultural research. Paralleling the movement to consolidate research in the USDA, the effort to simplify the legal authorizations for federal allocations originated in the 1940s and culminated in the mid-1950s. In 1941, just one year after the Bureau of Budget informally agreed to work with ESCOP in compiling national budget requests, it asked the station directors' representatives to draft a bill combining the provisions of Hatch, Adams, Purnell, and Bankhead-Jones into single act. Equally desirous of simplifying what was becoming a maze of authorizations, the committee nevertheless was wary of what could happen to mission statements and continuing appropriations when exposed to the vagaries of Congress. Paradoxically, ESCOP drafted a bill but recommended it not be adopted. The idea faded into the background only to reemerge in 1945 with the same results. After three years of operating under the complex provisions of the Research and Marketing Act of 1946, however, the station directors themselves began to urge consolidation. The USDA, responding to sentiment in Congress, drafted a proposed measure in consultation with the committee of station directors in the fall of 1949. In the next year, the Pace/Doane Committee lent its support, submitting the USDA-ESCOP proposal to Congress as part of its recommendations.

When Congress finally considered the subject in 1955, it did so in a form carefully worked out by the representatives of the state experiment stations. The rationale for national support of agricultural research in the state experiment stations which had evolved during the previous seven decades was preserved:

> to conduct original and other researches, investigations, and experiments bearing directly on and contributing to the establishment and maintenance of a permanent and effective agricultural industry in the United States, including researches basic to the

problems of agriculture in its broadest aspects, and such investigations as may have for their purpose the development and improvement of the rural home and rural life and the maximum contribution by agriculture to the welfare of the consumer, as may be deemed advisable, having due regard to the varying conditions and needs of the respective States.

Also retained were the various allocation formulas legislated over the years along with the "open-ended" appropriations feature of the Research and Marketing Act. Thus, although no set annual amounts were established, the yearly funds were to be divided 20 percent equally among the stations, 26 percent according to a state's share of the United States rural population, 26 percent according to a states share of the United States farm population, and 25 percent for support of cooperative, regional research between two or more stations. The remaining 3 percent was to cover costs incurred by the Secretary of Agriculture in administering the new legislation. Existing matching requirements were to be maintained, too, as every state had to contribute equal funds excluding an initial $90,000 and the money received for regional projects.

The draft by the stations did not preserve limitations included in the Hatch, Adams, and Purnell Acts on using federal money to purchase or rent land and buildings, and the prohibition in the Adams Act on subsidizing printing. Finally, the consolidated bill would have exempted increases above the amounts available in 1955 from the requirement that 20 percent be reserved for marketing studies.

Congress accepted the arguments in favor of consolidating the many federal accounts into two (formula funds and regional research funds) and agreed to abolish the anachronistic limits on physical plant and publication expenditures. It would not, however, concur in the proposed reduction in the 20 percent for marketing research. The House insisted that the earmarking must apply to all federal appropriation increases to ensure that the stations maintain their efforts toward relieving the recurring problem of farm surpluses. With this requirement restored, the consolidating Hatch Act became law in August of 1955.[19]

Few new administrative procedures were necessary to put the new Hatch Act of 1955 in force. Soon after the bill's passage, Dr. Knoblauch, director of the State Experiment Stations Division, notified the stations that although there was no longer a need to separate project accounts by the source of their authorizing legislation, it was necessary still to keep project accounts distinct from one another and to signify which qualified as regional or marketing research. Additionally, despite the new Hatch Act's failure to continue the requirement in the original Hatch, Adams, and Purnell Acts that the stations annually report their activities to Washington, Knoblauch urged them to continue this traditional communication with the Secretary of Agriculture.

Policy and Procedure Adjustments

The State Experiment Stations Division continued to clarify what money qualified to match or "offset" federal money. Obviously, state appropriations of annual operating funds to the agricultural experiment station best would meet the intent of Congress to stimulate state investments in agricultural science. Nevertheless, Washington administrators recognized a widening array of sources of less direct support. The services of an accountant and a private gift given through the state government were allowed in 1954 and 1955, respectively, in Alaska. Permission was given Wisconsin in 1957 to include publication expenses in its offset totals, while Nevada in 1962 was authorized to apply income from the sale of products of experiments.[20]

The definition of a marketing project also was steadily broadened. In 1948, when the requirement of earmarking first went into effect, about $720,000 was necessary in federal and state matching funds; by 1955, some $3,312,000 had to be spent by the stations on marketing projects. After the experiment stations failed to put a cap on the requirement at 1955 levels, the figure rose with every year, reaching more than $9,764,000 in 1961. The categories of eligible projects established in 1951 by ESCOP and the USDA soon proved too narrow in light of the interest in new research arenas and the growing competence of investigators. Recognizing these trends, committees representing the research partners in 1957 added consumer preference studies and, three years later, marketing and food technology investigations to the list of qualifying subjects.[21]

The Committee of Nine continued to operate the amended Hatch Act, acting as a final review board on projects that vied for a portion of the 25 percent of federal funds reserved for interstate, cooperative experimentation. Included in its duties beginning in the 1950s was the oversight of interregional projects whose scope went beyond the boundaries of the individual administrative regions to encompass programs worthy of national support.

Designated as IR-1, the first of what was to become a series of interregional projects was inaugurated in 1950. Headquartered at one of the branch facilities of the Wisconsin Agricultural Experiment Station, IR-1 coordinated a national effort to collect, evaluate, preserve, and distribute superior potato germplasm. In 1955, a similar program under the title IR-2 provided the same service for virus-free ornamental tree stocks with a repository maintained at Washington State University.

In a further attempt to improve its original role as a scientific council providing a long-range, national perspective on public research, the Committee in 1956 named a project review subcommittee to preview proposals before the whole body met. In the same year, the Committee members' terms were extended from two years to three years to introduce more continuity planning. With the number of active regional and interregional projects reaching 198 and the amount of available funds equalling $5,593,000 from federal sources alone in 1958, these administrative adjustments were necessary just to keep the Committee of Nine abreast of what was being done from year to year.[22]

Increased Support, Increased Expectations

The new Hatch Act departed from previous authorizations in omitting specific dollar figures in favor of "such sums as Congress may from time to time determine to be necessary." Between 1955 and 1961, Congress determined it necessary to increase funding for state agricultural experiment stations by 66 percent, from $19,118,000 in the first year to $31,825,000 in the last. Over $10,000,000 of that gain was legislated in the first two years following the passage of the amended Hatch Act, with more modest increases in every year except 1960. State appropriations made available in the same period rose at about the same rate as federal ones, beginning at $51,151,000 in 1955 and reaching $87,190,000 in 1961. Although the increases were not as dramatic as the ones immediately after World War II when state funding rose 340 percent in a decade, they did allow the continued expansion of research in the state agricultural experiment stations' broadening programs. In terms of funding, then, agricultural research's "golden age" carried through the two decades that followed America's entry into the Second World War.[23]

The twenty years of almost uninterrupted gains in operating

budgets and scientific manpower did not come without costs to the state agricultural experiment stations. As money increased, so did the expectations of those who allocated it in both Congress and state legislatures. Ironically, as the federal proportion of all money available to the stations diminished from 31 percent to 20 percent between 1941 and 1961, congressional concern about the more efficient administration of research grew. Annual scrutiny of budget increases, earmarking requirements, and citizen advisory committees were all institutionalized in the national legislation of the era. Twice the Department of Agriculture was pressed into full-scale reorganizations, at least in part by congressional desire to coordinate public agricultural research for the benefit of the entire country. Additional state support came with the same expectations of serving more regional and local interests. The sometimes irreconcilable demands upon the state stations only intensified in succeeding years as new research topics caught the attention of more and more segments of the American public.

Notes

[1] Moore, *Agricultural Research Service*, pp. 76-77.

[2] OES, *Report on the Experiment Stations: 1942*, pp. 2, 4; Kerr, *Alabama Agricultural Experiment Station*, pp. 70-71.

[3] OES, *Report on the Experiment Stations: 1943*, p. 3.

[4] OES, *Reports on the Experiment Stations: 1935-1946*.

[5] OES, *Reports on the Experiment Stations: 1939-1953*; USDA, Agricultural Research Service, *Reports on the Agricultural Experiment Stations: 1954-1955* (Washington: Government Printing Office, 1955-1956); Knoblauch et al., *State Agricultural Experiment Stations*, pp. 169-170.

[6] Wiser and Bowers, *Marketing Research*, p. 41; Hardin, *Freedom in Agricultural Education*, p. 137; "Minutes of the Committee on Experiment Station Organization and Policy, October 24-30, 1942," unpublished typescripts in USDA, Cooperative State Research Service files. Hereinafter cited as ESCOP, "Minutes."

[7] Douglas E. Bowers, "The Research and Marketing Act of 1946 and Its Effects on Agricultural Marketing Research," *Agricultural History* 56 (January 1982): 251-253; Wiser and Bowers, *Marketing Research*, pp. 46-47.

[8] Research and Marketing Act, 60 Stat. 1082 (1946).

[9] Emerson Babb, *Report to Cooperative State Research Service, U.S. Department of Agriculture on Impacts of Federal Funding Requirements on Marketing Research at State Agricultural Experiment Stations* [Washington: USDA, CSRS, January 1977], pp. 7-8.

[10] Bruce F. Beacher, "Committee of Nine—A Reference History of RRF Policy and Procedures: 1947-1973," draft manuscript, 1973, in CSRS offices, Washington, D.C., pp. 1, 8-11; A.A. Spielman, "Some Biased Observations on the Administration of the Regional Research Fund," paper presented to the Annual Meeting of the New England Economics Council, Amherst, Massachusetts, June 15, 1959, pp. 2-4; Wiser and Bowers, *Marketing Research*, p. 66.

[11] Harry C. Trelogan, "Research and Marketing Advisory Committees," *Journal of Farm Economics* 38 (February 1956): 1-5; Itzhak Arnon, *Organisation and Administration of Agricultural Research* (Amsterdam: Elsevier Publishing Co. 1968), pp. 11-13; Wiser and Bowers, *Marketing Research*, pp. 50-53.

[12] Hardin, *Freedom in Agricultural Education*, pp. 102-103, 106.

[13] OES, *Reports on the Experiment Stations: 1947-1953*; ARS, *Reports on the Experiment Stations: 1954-1955*; Bowers, "Research and Marketing Act of 1946," p. 258; Knoblauch et al., *State Agricultural Experiment Stations*, pp. 179-181.

[14] Bowers, "Research and Marketing Act of 1946," pp. 255-262; Wiser and Bowers, *Marketing Research*, pp. 61, 64.

[15] United States Congress, House Committee on Agriculture, *Federal Agricultural Research: Hearings* (81st Cong., 2nd sess., July 11-21, 1950), pp. 2, 66, 69-73; "The National Science Foundation: A General Review of Its First Fifteen Years," in *The Politics of Science*, ed. William R. Nelson (New York: Oxford University Press, 1968), pp. 140-143.

[16] Danbom, "Publicly-Sponsored Agricultural Research," pp. 23-25; OES, *Reports on the Experiment Stations: 1945-1953*; ARS, *Reports on the Experiment Stations; 1954-1955*.

[17] Wiser and Bowers, *Marketing Research*, p. 62; Moore, *Agricultural Research Service*, pp. 78-80; Knoblauch et al., *State Agricultural Experiment Stations*, pp. 136-138.

[18] Knoblauch et al., *State Agricultural Experiment Stations*, pp. 130-132.

[19] Ibid., pp. 170-173; U.S. Congress, House Committee on Agriculture, *Federal Agricultural Research: Hearings*, pp. 32, 89-92; Amended Hatch Act, 69 Stat. 671 (1955).

[20] State Experiment Stations Division-Station Letter-2135, October 17, 1955; H.C. Knoblauch to Maine A.E.S., December 13, 1955; Knoblauch to Alaska A.E.S., June 4, 1954 and June 12, 1955; Knoblauch to Wisconsin A.E.S., October 9, 1957; and Thomas S. Ronningen to Nevada A.E.S., May 10, 1962 in "Selected Short Abstracts of Cooperative State Research Policy."

[21] OES, *Report on the Experiment Stations: 1948*; ARS, *Report on the Experiment Stations: 1955*; USDA, Cooperative State Experiment Station Service, *Funds for Research at State Agricultural Experiment Stations; 1961* (Washington: Government Printing Office, 1962); Babb, *Impacts of Federal Funding Requirements on Marketing Research*, pp. 7-8.

[22] Wiser and Bowers, *Marketing Research*, p. 67.

[23] OES, *Reports on the Experiment Stations: 1945-1953*; ARS, *Reports on the Experiment Stations: 1954-1959*; CSESS, *Funds for Research: 1960-1961*.

CHAPTER IV

Strengthening the Planning Process: 1961-1971

Farm productivity advances continued their phenomenal post-war growth in the 1960s and became increasingly dependent upon scientific discovery and technological innovation. The growing sophistication of agricultural science prompted the realization that the knowledge it generated was a renewable resource seemingly without limit and that its scope extended far beyond the farmer's field and the rancher's pasture. Coupled with this increased respect for science was a heightened concern that the agricultural revolution which it underlay produced social and environmental casualties along with bumper crops. As the state experiment stations' traditional clientele of farmers dwindled in number and political clout, newly powerful voices emerged to demand a greater share in shaping the agricultural research establishment into a more socially responsive system. A series of administrative adjustments and priority-setting mechanisms to accommodate these interests resulted.

Further USDA Reorganization

A change in presidential administrations prompted the first major organizational restructuring to strengthen the agricultural research policy process. Responding to two decades of pressure from the state experiment station directors and their allies in the Land-Grant College Association, John F. Kennedy's Secretary of Agriculture, Orville L. Freeman, reinstated the agency charged with oversight of the Hatch Act to a position of equality with the federal arm of the research partnership. In September of 1961, a Cooperative State Experiment Station Service (CSESS) was created as a successor to the State Experiment Stations Division, as the old Office of Experiment Stations had been known while it was under the Agricultural Research Service. George A. Selke was tapped as acting administrator of the new agency, reporting to the Secretary through the Assistant Secretary of Federal-State Relations. H.C. Knoblauch, who had been the Director of the State Experiment Stations Division since 1954,

Theodore C. Byerly left the Agricultural Research Service in 1962 to become administrator of the newly independent Cooperative State Experiment Station Service and its successor, the Cooperative State Research Service. He served until 1969. *(National Archives and Records Administration photo)*

became CSESS Deputy Administrator. He continued in that position when a successor to interim head Selke was named.

Theodore C. Byerly, following a twenty-year career with the Agricultural Research Service, was moved over to lead CSESS in May of 1962. In the next year the agency was redesignated the Cooperative State Research Service (CSRS) to reflect a broadening of state clients with the introduction of federal support for research in forestry schools. Coincident with this title change was a USDA reorganization that abolished the division of Federal-State Relations in favor of one for Science and Education. A director was placed at its head when Congress declined to give the Department an additional Assistant Secretary. The new structure gave a higher profile to research and extension activities within the USDA and, thus, was perceived as an encouraging development by directors of the state stations.[1]

While the restructurings of 1961 and 1963 held promise for a new era of cooperation in federal-state agricultural research relations, Byerly's selection as head of CSESS and then CSRS did much to diminish the hope. Coming from the federal side of the partnership, Byerly aroused suspicions from the outset among powerful elements within the experiment station leadership while his decisive personality did little to mitigate initial distrust. Departing from the traditional management style of his predecessors who had relied upon the station directors to formulate policy and procedural positions, Byerly steered an independent course in the promotion of scientific excellence in the public agricultural research system. By scrupulously avoiding the appearance of speaking only for the state experiment stations in Department counsels, he seemed to tip the delicate balance between representing the stations and serving the USDA in the latter's favor. Although the manner in which policy changes were brought about antagonized some state directors, interactions between CSRS administrators and scientists with research counterparts in USDA in-house agencies were improved, strengthening the federal-state partnership as a whole. After nearly seven years of frequently acrimonious duty as administrator, Byerly was elevated to Assistant Director of Science and Education, leaving his former position to be filled by an individual more congenial to the state directors.[2]

Roy L. Lovvorn was the choice of both the stations and the Department of Agriculture to replace Byerly in 1969. Lovvorn had begun his career with the USDA Bureau of Plant Industry and, more importantly in the view of the state stations, had spent the previous thirteen years as the director of the North Carolina Agricultural Experiment Station. While in that position he had served terms on the Committee of Nine and as chairman of the Experiment Station Committee on Organization and Policy. He brought with him to the office of CSRS Administrator a diplomatic personality and the confidence of an overwhelming majority of station directors which went far in repairing strained relations between the research partners.

Enhancing Research Quality

By reflecting renewed sensitivity to state concerns Lovvorn succeeded in gaining the acceptance of a number of his predecessor's initiatives in evolving an expanded role for the Cooperative State Research Service. Under both men the agency sought to become more than a project accounts inspector, instead focusing its efforts on enhancing the quality of science undertaken by the agricultural experiment stations. To implement this concept, CSRS concentrated on upgrading the skills of its scientific staff, utilizing state station expertise to a greater extent, and restructuring on-site reviews to provide more useful evaluations of research programs.

To improve the quality of the agency staff both as scientists and as administrators, opportunities for temporary assignments to state stations in need of experienced research managers were actively sought. Taking advantage of the Intergovernmental Personnel Act provisions, state station scientists were also brought to Washington or temporarily employed on a parttime basis in the field to make use of their special expertise on a national level. In this manner both CSRS scientists and some of the best experiment station investigators could keep abreast of new developments in their disciplines while broadening their perspectives.

Roy L. Lovvorn served as administrator of the Cooperative State Research Service from 1969 to 1976, having previously been director of the North Carolina Station. *(USDA photo)*

Recognizing the impossibility of maintaining a staff of the very best minds in every field of agricultural science, Byerly and Lovvorn instead encouraged their corps of scientists to cultivate networks among their peers working in the federal, university, and experiment station laboratories. Scientists outside the agency were also invited to join CSRS-led review teams which visited the stations periodically to evaluate research programs. The reviews became future oriented, referring to past research agendas and performances as foundations on which to project improvements. Resident scientists and their administrators exposed their concepts for future research programs to outside scientists best able to respond constructively to them.

The review process itself underwent a change. No longer did CSRS scientists sit down with individual state researchers and quiz them on details of project outlines and investigative procedures, followed by hours of pouring over station accounts to spot discrepancies in expenditures. Instead, the stations were encouraged to identify areas in need of objective evaluation and to indicate which individuals in the agricultural research community might best advise them on future directions. Fiscal reviews became the province of separate teams of auditors from the USDA. Freed from much of the onerous routine work which had characterized it as an inspection agency, the Cooperative State Research Service sought to present itself as a facilitator of program improvement, as a repository and broker of scientific and administrative talent available to every state agricultural experiment station at government expense.[3]

The experiment stations, as the beneficiaries of the new policies, welcomed the reorientation of CSRS. Faced with demands for new answers to increasingly complex questions which required the integration of an expanding number of factors in their production and marketing investigations, the stations needed to draw upon a larger pool of expertise. The increasing sophistication of research was reflected in the growing numbers of scientists employed in the stations and by the larger proportion of these researchers which held doctoral degrees in their disciplines. In 1960, the stations counted 9,607 investigators on their staffs and by 1970 that figure had grown by another 2,100. Fully 70 percent of those in the latter year held Ph.D.'s, generally earned at one of the land-grant universities which awarded over 14,000 doctorates in fields associated with agriculture and home economics in the 1960s alone.[4]

Experiment Stations in the University Setting

Part of the reason for enlarged staffs in the experiment stations was the necessity for each land-grant college to maintain an array of scientific talent which could meet not only the farm sector's increasingly complex needs for continuous, comprehensive information but also the university's demand for a broad based academic program. This demand grew in the 1960s as the land-grant institutions strove to leave behind the "cow college" label so often applied to them in the past, a movement with profound implications for the state stations' role in the university context. The days when an institution's agricultural research program was equal to all of its academic activities were passing. The land-grant colleges diversified to become full-fledged universities with research and teaching interests encompassing much more than agriculture. Consequently, agriculture became just another unit on campus, with a corresponding drop in status of the experiment stations in the overall administrative hierarchy of the institutions. As faculty members, station scientists often were valued more as contributors to scientific knowledge and as mentors for graduate programs than for their potential for enhancing state economic development through research findings. Accordingly, promotions in universities increasingly depended upon publications in refereed journals and less upon the agricultural significance of the research. Whereas in the early years of operation the station director often ranked just below the college president, by the 1960s he was more likely to report through the dean of the school of agriculture, who himself was only one of many administratively equal deans.[5]

While the expansion of the land-grant university could mean a diminution of status for the associated experiment stations, it could also mean increased opportunities for interactions with other elements on campus not traditionally connected to agriculture but nonetheless valuable in this era of changing expectations for research. Cross-campus cooperation between scientists of disparate disciplines ranging from basic chemistry to applied home economics was encouraged at many universities, prompting new administrative arrangements that incorporated research, extension, and instructional activities in a number of fields.

Sometimes designated as "Institutes" (University of Minnesota, Washington State University, University of Florida, and University of Tennessee) or "Divisions" (University of California system, and University of Arkansas), these creations provided a formal mechanism for integrating the triad of research, extension, and teaching under a single vice president over separate deans or directors for each unit. In some states, the title of the agricultural experiment station was even modified to indicate its broadened range of concern. Thus, the Iowa station was renamed the Agriculture and Home Economics Experiment Station. The Wooster, Ohio facility became the Agricultural Research and Development Center, and the Washington State University affiliate was transformed into the Research Center.

With the campus-located experiment stations extending their investigations into new areas at the same time as land-grant institutions were requiring more land for university buildings, outlying research centers were called upon in new ways. Substations had long been valued as points of contact between the interests of scientists and the needs of farmers. As soil fertility often declined and pests and diseases evolved to resist new control techniques, site-specific research at the branches continued to be important in maintaining current yields in dissimilar farming areas found in the same state. Branch stations provided a means of demonstrating promising research findings as agricultural "truths" in the areas where they were located, furnishing an essential connection between laboratories and farms. Responding to climatic conditions and market opportunities, many of these areas were devoted increasingly to single, specialty commodities, prompting the outlying facilities to adjust their work to service the agriculturists engaged in these pursuits. By the 1960s, nearly every state experiment station included a system of branch stations, many of them concentrating on basic, applied, and developmental investigations on a single dominant farm enterprise. Most common were beef, horticulture, vegetable, rice, tobacco, and forestry substations but some were devoted to more exotic fare like strawberries (Arkansas) and cranberries (Massachusetts). Whether geographically or commodity oriented, the branch stations functioned to focus research efforts on the diverse components of a state's agricultural sector just as the parent experiment stations of which they were a part did for the nation and its multistate agricultural regions.

McIntire-Stennis Forestry Research Act of 1962

Among the "crops" subject to increased attention by the state agricultural experiment stations were forest products which supplied a significant portion of the natural resource-based income of many states. Public research to support the application of science to forest regeneration and management had begun as early as the 1920s when the USDA Forest Service was authorized by Congress to establish forestry experiment stations across the United States. Twelve of these were completed by the mid-thirties and an attempt was made at the beginning of the next decade to provide a new category of funds to the state agricultural experiment stations to pursue similar work. Since the bulk of the state station funds were distributed according to a formula based on rural and farm population, those states whose primary agricultural pursuit was the exploitation of woodlands received relatively small amounts to support forestry programs. Thus, the 1941 proposal called for new funds allotted according to a modified formula that included "farm woodland" in the equation with farm population. Nothing came of the proposal until two decades later when advances in forest science combined with heightened public concern for natural resource conservation to prompt the enactment of the McIntire-Stennis Forestry Research Act.[6]

The McIntire-Stennis Act of 1962 was designed to encourage forestry research at the land-grant colleges, experiment stations, and other qualified schools of forestry by providing federal money through the Department of Agriculture to each state on a dollar-for-dollar matching basis. These funds were to be disbursed following a formula to be established by an advisory board comprised of seven representatives of the institutions eligible for the annual grants. This formula was to take into account such factors as acreage of non-federal commercial forest land and the volume of timber annually cut in each state, but could include other considerations as well. In addition to creating an allocation advisory group, the act called for the Secretary to convene annually an advisory committee of equal numbers of public agency and private industry representatives to indicate program directions. Lastly, the legislation defined forestry research to include reforestation, woodlands and related watershed management, outdoor recreation, wildlife habitats, wood utilization, and "such other studies as may be necessary to obtain the fullest and most effective use of forest resources."[7]

McIntire-Stennis authorizations were first translated into appropriations for the 1964 fiscal year and placed under Cooperative State Research Service administrative control. Sixty-one institutions shared that and subsequent years' money. The land-grant institutions in fifty states and Puerto Rico and ten additional universities with forestry research programs were made eligible according to a formula determined by the seven-person committee called for in the legislation. The formula allocated $10,000 to each state as a base and distributed 40 percent of the remainder according to a state's proportion of the nation's total commercial forest land, 40 percent according to the value of its timber cut annually, and 20 percent according to its contribution of non-federal forestry research dollars.

In the same year that the grants first became available, a fourteen-member McIntire-Stennis Cooperative Research Advisory Committee was convened to advise the Secretary of Agriculture on program operation. Comprised of seven forest industry representatives, four state forestry officials, two Department of Interior administrators, and one experiment station director, with the USDA Director of Science and Education as non-voting chairman, the Advisory Committee oversaw a forestry research program which experienced steady growth in support over the succeeding twenty years. For each of the years 1964 and 1965, $1,000,000 was appropriated from the federal treasury under the McIntire-Stennis Act, equalling just over 2 percent of the total funds distributed through CSRS in those years. By 1974, federal support increased to $6,203,000 annually, nearly 7 percent of CSRS-managed money. Ten years later, yearly accretions had brought the figure to $12,702,000, about 6 percent of the combined federal research dollars provided to the states for agriculture-related investigations. With state matching funds more than doubling the totals in each year, the McIntire-Stennis Act did much to encourage the expansion of forestry research in a manner that capitalized on the existing framework of locally directed public agricultural research institutions.[8]

Research Facilities Grants

Buoyed by their success in getting national support for forestry research centered in the state agricultural experiment stations, the station directors were encouraged further in 1963 when Congress agreed to forward additional public funds to help upgrade buildings and laboratories at the research stations. By rescinding previous limitations on channeling federal research money into facilities renovation, the Amended Hatch Act of 1955 theoretically had allowed building program expenditures. Yet, because Hatch funds had to be spent entirely within the year they were awarded and because the stations needed every available dollar to meet operating expenses, that source of federal money was unavailable in practice to help with the capital outlays required to refurbish physical plants. To overcome these impediments to national assistance for research facility modernization, the directors proposed in 1960, and the Congress passed three years later, the Research Facilities Act.

The Research Facilities Act directed the Secretary of Agriculture to distribute funds to be matched by the states for the "construction, acquisition, and remodeling of buildings, laboratories, and other capital facilities" on the basis of a formula that resembled that in the Amended Hatch Act: one-third equally to each, one-third according to the proportion of rural residents, and one-third to the proportion of farm population. Recognizing that effective construction programs rarely followed the timetables of fiscal-year accounting requirements, the legislation allowed each station to obligate its annual share over the course of three years.

When it came to actually voting the money under Research Facilities Act authorizations, Congress proved less generous than the stations had hoped. After an encouraging start of $3,242,000 in federal funds for fiscal year 1965, only $2,000,000 was forwarded annually in 1966, 1967, and 1968. No money followed in 1969 and a token $1,000,000 came in 1970 for the last time. Disillusioned by the meagerness of facilities grants in relation to the amount of political capital expended in Congress to secure even these amounts, the directors virtually abandoned subsequent attempts to push for continued support in that category. Still, authorizations were continued in the language of succeeding agricultural research legislation in hopes that the program might someday revive.[9]

Pesticides and Environmental Protection Research

Even in 1965, when the initial appropriation for facilities remodeling was relatively generous, the state stations could not freely apply their portions of the building and equipment grants to construction projects of their choosing. In response to the rather sudden rise of public concern over the effects of pesticides used in agriculture, Congress specified that the new money must be applied to facilities devoted to research in restricting the use of suspected hazardous chemicals used in farming.

Goaded into action by the outcry prompted by the book, *Silent Spring*, in which author Rachel Carson criticized agriculture and its research support system for neglecting ecological concerns, Congress also directed that a part of the 1965 Hatch appropriations be used to study ways to reduce the threat of pesticides to the environment.[10] The agricultural experiment stations, along with the private chemical industry, had pursued much of the research that made DDT and kindred organochlorine and organophosphorus compounds available to farmers for crop and livestock protection in the 1940s and '50s. In the regular course of their efforts to preserve the natural resource base upon which agriculture lay, the stations had also been in the forefront in discovering the potential hazards to wildlife and humans of the indiscriminate use of these chemicals. Thus, when the resulting furor prompted demands to restrict the use of agricultural chemicals, Congress appropriately called upon the stations to contribute their considerable expertise in helping to regulate the use of pesticides. The state agricultural experiment stations had an existing organizational structure to gather pertinent knowledge on a national scale and the array of scientific disciplines necessary to address the issues on a broad front. And, recognizing that many of the gains in farm productivity so valued by the American consumer relied upon the careful application of pesticides, they were aware that decisions on the fate of agricultural chemical use must be made only after carefully balancing social risks and economic benefits.

As the federal government developed a system for registering pesticides, the state stations fulfilled a significant role from the outset. The agricultural chemical companies concentrated their attentions on certifying the safety of those pesticides with high market potential, often finding the regulatory process too expensive to develop many of the compounds used only on a limited number of acres. Yet these "minor use" pesticides were vitally important to many isolated groups of specialty crop farmers. To meet the needs of these farmers, the state agricultural experiment stations developed an interregional project to gather the information necessary to clear a number of the minor use pesticides.

Designated IR-4, the "National Program of Clearances of Pesticides for Minor and Specialty Uses" was launched in 1963 to coordinate the compilation of data at the stations on pesticide tolerances with a New Jersey station laboratory at Rutgers University as the headquarters. Over the next twenty years information gathered under IR-4 auspices was instrumental in clearing over 2,000 pesticides and the project itself became the centerpiece of subsequent research efforts dealing with the whole range of pest and disease management issues.[11]

Special Grants for Special Problems

In earmarking the Research Facilities grants and a portion of the regular Hatch funds in the 1965 budget, Congress expressed its desire to direct research attention at specific problems it felt the stations were neglecting. It had done the same thing three years earlier when the House Appropriations Subcommittee on Agriculture had reserved part of 1962 Hatch funds for weed investigations. From that date sentiment continued to grow in Congress for the enactment of some formal legislative mechanism to address specific areas of constituent concern or problems of interstate magnitude.

The Regional Research Fund set-aside was originally intended to encourage work in the latter category but it had evolved an allocation formula that in practice confined most cooperative research to that between states in the standard regions. To lessen the annual combat for those funds within each region and to give each station the opportunity to concentrate its regional investigations on projects in which it truly had an interest, the Committee of Nine in 1964 began disbursing the money on a state by state basis. The new policy allowed station directors to better integrate their regional efforts into on-going program planning and was a necessary step in reducing the administrative nightmares long associated with regional research. Still, the regional programs often remained, in the words of the CSRS regional coordinator, mere "groupings of station projects" and was ill-suited to addressing the changing special interests of Congress.[12]

While the state experiment stations preferred retaining the discretion allowed them by formula allocations, they realized the limitations inherent in the Regional Research Fund administrative procedures and that Congress was becoming increasingly enamored with earmarking regular appropriations. Bowing to the inevitable in 1965, they supported, albeit hesitantly, the passage of legislation that authorized additional funds through the USDA to support new investigations in the public agricultural research system.

Designed to complement the institutional grant program embodied in the Amended Hatch Act, Public Law 89 - 106 authorized "Specific Research Grants" (later called "Special Grants") for selected projects which would run for a maximum of five years. As the Secretary's representative, the Cooperative State Research Service annually called for proposals in areas singled out by Congress for special attention and established review committees in each category to select the best of the projects for funding. For 1966, a total of $1,600,000 was offered in a range of areas that reflected the catholic interests of Congress and the potentials of agricultural science: cotton and soybean production cost reduction, water resources development, new product uses, human nutrition, air pollution, and cooperative marketing were among them.[13]

Since the appropriations amounted to less than 3 percent of the total funds delivered to the state experiment stations from the federal treasury and were in addition to a $3,000,000 increase in Hatch money in 1966, the station directors harbored few objections toward the Specific Grants program in its first year. That abruptly changed when the deliberations for the 1967 budget began with a proposal by President Lyndon B. Johnson to cut Hatch allocations by $8,500,000 while increasing Specific Grants by nearly $3,000,000. Stung by the implication that federal administrators could select projects worthy of support better than they themselves, the station directors were only partly mollified when Congress restored the cuts and the former balance between institutional and project grants that had existed in the previous year. For the remainder of the decade, the directors virtually abandoned support for Special Grant increases. The program's level remained constant at $1,717,000 for designated research projects from 1967 through 1970.[14]

1890 Land Grant Colleges Join the System

Appropriations under Specific Grants authority actually totaled $2,000,000 for each of those years, but $283,000 of the annual grants were reserved for a new program of institutional support designed to incorporate an additional source of potential scientific talent into the public research establishment. Responding to President Johnson's call for the federal government to take the lead in breaking down barriers of discrimination encountered by black Americans during this turbulent era of civil rights activism, the USDA proposed to Congress that the system of predominantly Negro land-grant institutions receive subsidies to foster the development of agricultural science expertise. Congress concurred in the request, using Specific Grant authority beginning in the 1967 fiscal year to provide support for the theretofore minimal research programs undertaken at the sixteen so-called 1890 Institutions.

Since their creation with federal support under the Second Morrill Act, a few of the 1890 colleges had developed agricultural research programs. Virginia State College at Petersburg had been designated an experiment station in 1937 and was given some state dollars for research. Prairie View Agriculture and Mechanical College of Texas was accorded similar status in 1947 and even received a small portion of the state's Hatch money for a few years. Tennessee State University in Nashville inaugurated some agricultural investigations with privately donated funds in 1960, as did North Carolina Agricultural and Technical State University in 1964. However, none of the sixteen employed a full-time staff of scientists engaged in research to complement their programs of instruction. The infusion of federal support beginning in 1967 did little to immediately change the situation. Distributed to the 1890 Institutions on the basis of a formula derived from the Hatch model and suggested by a National Academy of Sciences advisory group impaneled for the purpose, the new funds were only a beginning.

The agricultural research programs of the 1890 colleges started virtually from scratch and faced many of the same problems that had confronted the Hatch-founded experiment stations some eighty years earlier. They had to convince college administrators of the value of research to free scientists from teaching duties, court local constituent support and state funds, and secure adequate scientific talent and equipment. The effort was to prove especially arduous given the late start of the program and its relatively low level of financial support.[15]

The Special Grants legislation, in both its specific project funding orientation and its inclusion of a new set of actors in the public agricultural research system, was perhaps an indication that the days of virtually unrestricted federal block grants to the state agricultural experiment stations were passing. An increasing number of demands in the 1960s for accountability in the form of planning committees provided further evidence. While much of the concern that prompted the formation of these groups was directed toward the federal component of the research partnership, the state stations were inevitably included in the calls for better coordination to reduce what was perceived as duplication and inefficiency in the system.[16]

The idea of gathering research administrators and research users to help chart the course of investigations was not, of course, new. The Experiment Station Committee on Organization and Policy had impaneled six advisory groups in the wake of the Purnell Act of 1925 to suggest lines of work in agricultural economics, home economics, and rural sociology.

Following the dictates of the Research and Marketing Act, the USDA had formed a system of producer-dominated councils in a number of commodity areas, capped by an Agricultural Research Policy Committee to monitor the federal research effort under the Act of 1946. In 1961, that group was rechristened the National Agricultural Research Advisory Committee. Two years later the number of commodity-oriented councils was reduced from twenty-five to eleven and their deliberations were opened to the public in an effort to include other voices in the policy formulation process. These advisory groups were abandoned altogether in 1970 and replaced by a series of USDA-sponsored regional workshops to elicit public opinion on government science and education programs.[17]

Agricultural Research Planning Committee

State experiment station and Department of Agriculture administrators took part in all of these efforts and in another one, called the Committee on Agricultural Science, created in 1962 for university scientists to counsel the Secretary on improving the quality of federal research. Still, no national forum existed for those actually engaged in research to articulate their needs and coordinate their activities. A step towards filling this gap was made in 1964 with the naming of an Agricultural Research Planning Committee under the chairmanship of the USDA Science and Education Director. Designed primarily as a joint USDA and state agricultural experiment station effort, the research planning committee also included a land-grant president and representatives from the National Academy of Science and the President's Office of Science and Technology among its fifteen members.

The Agricultural Research Planning Committee was subdivided into five subcommittees (long-range planning, program development, facilities, scientific manpower, and financial resources) that indicated the breadth of its concerns. Meeting only twice annually to advise the Secretary of Agriculture who only had control over the federal research establishment, its actual power belied the ambitious scope of its responsibilities.[18]

The "Long-Range Study" and Research Classification

Spurred by a USDA proposal to eliminate a host of Agricultural Research Service installations and cooperative projects, the Senate Committee on Appropriations issued a call in the spring of 1965 for the USDA and the state agricultural experiment stations, with industry advice, to develop a plan for "systematic and continuous review of research programs" to weed out duplication and inefficiency in the public agricultural research system.

Neither the Committee on Agricultural Science nor the Agricultural Research Planning Committee had the stature or staff support to undertake such a delicate and time-consuming task, so an ad hoc group representing the USDA research agencies and the state experiment stations was called into being. They, in turn, consulted with over 500 agricultural leaders from public research institutions and private industry in compiling a report issued in the fall of 1966. The fruits of their labor, popularly known as the "Long-Range Study," broke new ground by not only suggesting ways to promote coordination within the system but also by indicating future goals and the manpower needed to meet them. Most importantly, it devised a research inventory scheme whereby efforts toward the goals could be monitored.

Recommendations for enhancing coordination in the research system included the elevation of the Science and Education Director to Assistant Secretary status within the USDA; the formation of ad hoc subcommittees in the various subject matter areas to report on needs to the Agricultural Research Planning Committee; the extension of grant eligibility to institutions outside the land-grant community; the joint planning of future national and regional laboratories between the Agricultural Research Service and the state stations; and the implementation of a projects inventory on an annual basis.

The continuing inventory was to be based upon a classification system that included ninety-one research problem areas related to ten goals denoting the objectives of agricultural research: 1) resource conservation and use, 2) protection of forests, crops, and livestock, 3) efficient production of farm and forest products, 4) product development and quality, 5) efficiency in the marketing system, 6) expand export markets and assist developing countries, 7) consumer health, nutrition, and well-being, 8) raise level of living of rural people, 9) improve community services and environment, and 10) basic research.

Each project was then to be identified by activity, indicating its purpose; by commodity or resource, indicating its principal subject of interest; and by field of science, indicating the disciplines involved in its execution. Once a project was characterized in the first two dimensions it could then be related directly to one or more of the research problem areas and, thus, tied explicitly to the goals. The Long-Range Study also included an inventory of current (1965) research reflecting expenditures of scientist-man-years and financial resources to serve as a benchmark for the future. By this method, agricultural research administrators for the first time were given a standard tool for collecting data for use in planning and evaluation, as well as for presenting the scope of their activities to those demanding an accounting of their efforts.[19]

The Long-Range Study classification scheme, with some refinements, fulfilled the intention of its authors to provide a standard of measurement for the public agricultural research partners. Within a year, a series of thirty-two federal-state research task forces were being assembled to conduct in-depth analyses of the problem areas identified in the report. The eighteen commodity (fruit, swine, etc.) and fifteen functional (farm prices, rural development, etc.) groups that resulted were comprised primarily of state station and USDA scientists but included a handful of consultants from industry and academe.

In each of their areas of responsibility the joint task forces sought to evaluate the current situation, visualize the technology necessary to overcome existing problems, develop research approaches, identify and quantify potential benefits, predict probabilities of achieving objectives, and recommend manpower commitments to meet the goals. One of the first products of their work was a consensus to add five new Research Problem Areas to the ninety-one originally identified.[20]

Current Research Information System Established

The research problem areas-based classification model had the potential to provide scientists and administrators with a standard frame of reference in describing their work but the need remained for a system whereby that data could be effectively compiled and retrieved. Keeping track of the research projects at the state agricultural experiment stations and within the USDA had proved a daunting task from their beginnings.

A.C. True of the Office of Experiment Stations had begun a card index of station-issued publications in 1891 which reflected much of the research effort out in the states. A better indication of activities was possible after the widespread adoption of the project system early in the twentieth century. Project descriptions were enrolled into a manual card file that, by the 1950s, included Agricultural Research Service projects along with those of the stations. Alternately known as the "Green Goddess" or "Green Monster," depending on the degree of frustration encountered in retrieving data from the enormous drum holding the files, the system was ill-suited either to keeping scientists abreast of the latest efforts in their fields or to meeting the growing accountability demands upon administrators.

In the 1960s, information management reached the computer age, holding promise that an automated system could take over the role of the cumbersome manual filing system. First proposed in 1964, and in the development stage by the time the Long-Range Study was issued to provide it with a ready-made classification scheme, the Current Research Information System (CRIS) was operational by the end of the decade. CRIS included a description of each project according to its objectives, approach, and relation to research problem areas. Manpower and financial support levels were included as well as a listing of publications resulting from the work, with new data added annually. Thus, the agricultural research partners were provided with a system for reporting, accounting, and management in addition to a library of current and past research projects.

Although problems inherent in collecting, classifying, and retrieving timely information tended to make the system's claim to be "current" somewhat suspect, the Current Research Information System was an enormous improvement on its forerunners. It introduced a common vocabulary and structural arrangement for describing investigations and provided benchmark data whereby projections for future research directions could be measured by actual performance.[21]

Facilitating Communications: The Directors at Large

Even as CRIS was in the planning phase the station directors realized that a staff would be needed to set standards for the gathering of data and to translate that information into a form that could be readily understood by policymakers. Concurrently, the activities of the Long-Range Study commission highlighted the need for better communication within the experiment stations and with the federal agricultural research agencies. The Experiment Station Committee on Organization and Policy, made up of three directors chosen from each region, a delegate from its home economics subcommittee, and the CSRS Administrator, represented the state stations on national issues but did not have the continuity of membership to lend to CRIS the sustained attention it required. The four regional associations of directors were better organized in this regard but their infrequent meetings and regional orientations limited their effectiveness in responding quickly to interregional and national issues.

In 1960, before either CRIS or the Long-Range Study plans were underway, the North Central Regional Association of Experiment Station Directors reflected its concern for the same need by proposing a single individual to represent its membership on a full-time basis. While nothing immediately came of the suggestion, by 1966 the other regional directors' groups were considering similar measures. Encouraged by ESCOP at its April gathering, the North Central Association designated George M. Browning, Associate Director of the Iowa station, as regional research director. The Southern Directors Association soon followed the lead by naming Director Louis E. Hawkins of Oklahoma as its director-at-large prior to the November, 1966 ESCOP meeting. By February of the next year, Director Mark T. Buchanan of

Washington was serving in the same position for the Western Region directors. More cautious in conferring "at large" status on one man, the Northeastern Regional Association of Directors appointed Henry R. Fortmann, Associate Director of the Pennsylvania station, as a regional coordinator in the fall of 1967.

The different titles bestowed on these regional representatives reflected the variety of expectations among the station directors who had chosen to create the positions. Some desired the incumbents to act only as facilitators of communication and cooperation between the regional associations. Others envisioned them as a standing council of "super directors" to monitor developments within the USDA and Congress and to serve as spokesmen on emerging issues affecting the entire system.

While the exact nature of their role remained undefined as they assumed their posts, the regional representatives concentrated their initial activities on the immediate task of collecting the data necessary to put the Current Research Information System in operation. Working closely with the Cooperative State Research Service in this effort, the regional directors functioned as a national resource group for the Washington bureaucracy and the stations because of their wide knowledge and availability to policymakers in the capital and to directors in the states. Thus, their sphere of interest naturally expanded to include the whole range of issues in the federal-state partnership so that they evolved into de facto liaisons for the state agricultural experiment stations.[22]

Agricultural Research Policy Advisory Committee

With the directors-at-large developing into an effective, if informal, sounding board for problems confronting the stations and CSRS, the search continued for an improved means of representing the many voices concerned with formulating public policy related to agricultural research. The Long-Range Study had encouraged the expansion of the Agricultural Research Planning Committee to incorporate a broader membership and a 1968 Joint Task Force on Federal-State Relations that followed suggested an entirely new group to replace it.

When the co-chairman of the Joint Task Force, Clifford M. Hardin, became Secretary of Agriculture in 1969, the Agricultural Research Policy Advisory Committee (ARPAC) was born. Like its predecessor, ARPAC was charged to recommend measures for more effective joint planning and coordination in the public agricultural research partnership. And, like the Agricultural Research Planning Committee before it, ARPAC included an equal number of federal and state representatives as voting members. However, the new version of the advisory council added a new category of ex officio, non-voting delegates to incorporate the viewpoint of agribusiness (National Agricultural Research Advisory Committee and Agricultural Research Institute representatives) and that of the President's budget framers (Bureau of Budget delegate) in the policy process.[23]

Separation Between Planning and Budget Processes

The addition of a budget office representative to the agricultural research advisory council was an attempt to scale what research administrators perceived as the major obstacle to serious participation in previous planning exercises: priority-setting was not translated effectively into annual federal appropriations. Congress repeatedly called for allocation requests supported by documentation as to needs and opportunities, but the final product rarely reflected the effort after traveling through the budget-passing labyrinth.

The Experiment Station Committee on Organization and Policy presented a budget proposal developed by its legislative subcommittee to the Cooperative State Research Service. Through the mid-1960s, the annual proposals usually consisted of a modest increase to support continuing base programs and new funds to concentrate attention in a few broad priority areas from lists submitted by the state experiment station directors.

Beginning with the 1968 fiscal year budget, the first considered after the release of the Long-Range Study, ESCOP tied suggested increases to discrete "research packages" related to the research problem areas identified in the 1966 report. CSRS then took that request through the Science and Education office to the Secretary of Agriculture who negotiated with the President's Bureau of the Budget for inclusion in the executive budget that went to Congress. At every step adjustments in the original proposals could be made before ESCOP was able to reenter the process to advocate its position to the lawmakers. By that time the original requests for base program support were often reduced or redirected to different priority areas in the executive budget.

House appropriators often restored the cuts, with small increases added in areas of special interest to their constituents, while the Senate would direct substantial increases for core programs and excise some of the new initiatives. Once a conference committee agreed to a compromise that the President would sign, the agricultural research budget that resulted likely bore little resemblance to ESCOP's original submission in either program direction or overall level of support.[24]

The special grants legislation in mid-decade gave Congress an outlet to support program thrusts outside of the ESCOP budget figures for formula funds, while the Long-Range Study and the new ARPAC advisory group that followed helped the agricultural research partners articulate their needs in a more coordinated manner. Still, the outcome of the budget formulation process remained frustrating to research planners convinced of the need for a substantial infusion of federal funds to address new problems and exploit new opportunities.

Federal money available through CSRS administration of the Hatch Act rose from $32,303,000 in 1961 to $61,550,000 in 1971, a 91 percent increase as compared to a 153 percent gain in the previous decade. The uneven rate at which the increases came during the 1960s seemed to contradict the justification for improved planning efforts but were due rather to increasing fiscal restraint on the part of the President and Congress. Prior to the Long-Range Study, annual increases ranged from a high of 14 percent (for fiscal year 1965) to a low of 6 percent (for 1963, 1964, and 1967), for an average of nearly 10 percent yearly from 1961 through 1967.

Gains for the four years after budget requests were based on the Long-Range Study projections averaged only 5 percent annually, with a range of between 0 percent (for 1968) and 11 percent (for 1971). In the first of these years, Congress originally passed a 7 percent increase for Hatch funds, then froze spending at 1967 levels. In 1969, a 4 percent increase was legislated, then reduced to 3 percent by subsequent law. No budget reduction bill followed in 1970 and the state agricultural experiment stations received the entire proceeds from another 4 percent increase in formula funds. While the next year produced an 11 percent addition in Hatch money, clearly the effects of a stagnating national economy, to say nothing of a spiraling rate of inflation, were beginning to tell on the level of support for agricultural investigation from the federal treasury.[25]

Despite a decade of activity concerned with their more efficient allocation, federal funds still comprised only about 20 percent of publicly appropriated money for the state agricultural experiment stations in 1971, just as they had in 1961. Grants from private industry and producer organizations and proceeds from the sale of station products furnished a roughly equal percentage, so state appropriations undergirded most of the research programs in the stations. Fortunately for them, this category of support rose more rapidly than did federal contributions. State legislators advanced more than $195,000,000 in 1971 as compared to just over $87,000,000 in 1961, with yearly increases averaging 12 percent. Gains in research funds from state sources were not, of course, spread equally throughout the system. The health of the state economy, particularly that of its agriculture sector, as well as the political astuteness of farm producer organizations played a large part in determining the degree of state support. The agricultural experiment stations were, after all, primarily concerned with discovering ways to foster economic development at the local level. Those that could best relate their activities to income protection and enhancement reaped the most benefit from state lawmakers in the 1960s, much like they had in past decades.[26]

Shifting Research Thrusts

As might be expected, then, the state stations devoted most of their efforts to solving problems constraining crop and animal production. Yet, the growing public sentiment for the stations to widen their research universe did have an effect during the late 1960s as measured in shifts in federal research dollars among broad program thrusts.

In both 1966 and 1971, the categories of Crop Resources and Animal Resources subsumed a majority of the federally funded investigations but their dominance lessened over those years from 64.5 percent to 60.7 percent of total expenditures. Traditional economics and marketing research also declined, from 10.6 percent to 8.3 percent.

Natural Resources programs concerned with soil, water, environmental pollution, and wildlife were the chief beneficiaries of research shifts, rising from 8.2 percent to 11.2 percent of the effort as reflected in expenditures. The closely allied Forest Resources work was also better endowed by 1971, receiving a 6.4 percent share of dollars compared to 5.8 percent in 1966.

Nutrition, food safety, and rural development investigations included in the category of People, Communities, and Institutions experienced the second largest gain, garnering a 7.5 percent share in 1966 and a 9.9 percent share in 1971.[27]

These shifts toward research related less to producers and more to consumers were slight but they did indicate that the agricultural experiment stations were sensitive to the calls for more socially responsible investigations. Their own planning activities sought to incorporate these broadened concerns in projections for future work and their subsequent performance demonstrated that they took the pledges seriously.

The Long-Range Study suggestions for areas deserving refocused attention, while not up to the overall levels desired, were closely observed in the actual redirection of resources that were available. National legislation earmarking funds for specific areas and new rescarch institutions, combined with their own efforts to bring in a wider spectrum of opinion in research planning, helped spur these program adjustments. The increasing sophistication in methods and a heightened sense of obligation to the wider public among investigators in the disciplines traditionally included among the agricultural sciences doubtless played a part as well. The process of change was to quicken in succeeding years as the state agricultural experiment stations continued to adapt their programs to the frequently diverging demands of producers and consumers.

Notes

[1] USDA, "Secretary's Memorandum No. 1462, July 19, 1961"; "USDA Press Releases, September 1, 1961 and November 22, 1963."

[2] Interview with Thomas S. Ronningen, retired Director-At-Large, Northeastern Region, Washington, D.C., February 28, 1985; interview with R. Dennis Rouse, Director Emeritus, Alabama Agricultural Experiment Station, Auburn, Alabama, April 16, 1986; interview with Theodore C. Byerly, retired Administrator, USDA, Cooperative State Research Service, Beltsville, Maryland, April 10, 1986.

[3] Interviews with T.S. Ronningen, February 28, 1985 and February 10, 1986; interview with Roy L. Lovvorn, retired Administrator, USDA, CSRS, Raleigh, North Carolina, April 22, 1986; "Cooperative State Research Service-Station Letter-2299, October 9, 1962", ESCOP, "Minutes, October 14-16, 1965 and October 13, 1966"; USDA, CSRS, "Office Memorandum 1149" in CSRS Office of the Administrator, Washington, D.C.

[4] Wallace E. Huffman, "Institutional Development of the Public Agricultural Experiment Station System: Scientists and Departments," unpublished manuscript, May 1985, p. 26; W.E. Huffman, "Production of Scientists for U.S. Agriculture by Land-Grant Universities: 1920-1980," Iowa State University Department of Economics Staff Paper No. 138, March 1984, p. 22.

[5] Keith A. Huston, "Priority Setting Processes in the State Agricultural Experiment Stations," in *An Assessment of the United States Food and Agricultural Research System*, vol. 2, pt. B, *Commissioned Papers*, ed. U.S. Congress, Office of Technology Assessment (Washington: OTA, 1982), pp. 10, 51; Agricultural Research Policy Advisory Committee, *Research to Meet U.S. and World Food Needs* (Kansas City, Mo.: ARPAC, 1975), p. 57.

[6] G.L. Baker, Wayne D. Rasmussen, Vivian Wiser, and Jane Porter, *Century of Service: The First 100 Years of the United States Department of Agriculture* (Washington: USDA, 1963), pp. 129-130, 236; ESCOP, "Minutes, September 5-12, 1941."

[7] McIntire-Stennis Forestry Research Act, 76 Stat. 806 (1962).

[8] "CSRS-Station Letter-2445, May 14, 1965"; CSRS, "Cooperative State Research Service Appropriation History," summary chart prepared by Program Development and Budget Office, CSRS, 1984.

[9] Research Facilities Act, 77 Stat. 90 (1963); U.S. Congress, House Committee on Agriculture, *Miscellaneous Hearings: Additional Facilities for Research at State Agricultural Experiment Stations* (87th Cong., 2nd sess., March 1962), pp. 62-64, 85, 113; ESCOP, "Minutes, April 23-24, 1968"; CSRS, "Appropriation History."

[10] CSRS, "Office Memorandum 3247, February 10, 1967"; ESCOP, "Minutes, April 30-May 1, 1964."

[11] "National Program of Clearances of Chemicals and Biologics for Minor or Special Uses" file in Regional Research Office, CSRS; ESCOP, "Minutes, November 10, 1963."

[12] Interview with R.L. Lovvorn, April 22, 1986; Beacher, "Committee of Nine," p. 202; interview with T.S. Ronningen, February 10, 1986; Marshall Harris and R.J. Hildreth, "Reflections on the Organization of Regional Research Activities," *American Journal of Agricultural Economics* 50 (November 1968): 820-822; interview with Donald W. Barton, Director Emeritus, New York State Agricultural Experiment Station (Geneva), Ithaca, New York, June 18, 1986; ESCOP, "Minutes, November 13, 1966" (quotation).

[13] ESCOP, "Minutes, April 25 and November 10, 1963"; "CSRS-Station Letter-2492, January 10, 1966."

[14] "CSRS-Station Letter-2513, April 25, 1966"; "CSRS-Station Letter-2530, August 31, 1966"; Moore, *Agricultural Research Service*, p. 163; ESCOP, "Minutes of the Legislative Subcommittee, July 1-2, 1969" and "Minutes, November 9, 1969."

[15] B.D. Mayberry, ed., *Development of Research at Historically Black Land-Grant Institutions* (N.p.: Association of Research Coordinators, Land-Grant 1890 Colleges and Universities, 1976), p. 41, 43; interview with Benny D. Mayberry, retired Research Director, Tuskegee Institute, Tuskegee, Alabama, April 15, 1986; interview with T.S. Ronningen, February 10, 1986.

[16] U.S. Congress, Senate Committee on Appropriations, *Report on the Proposed Elimination of Agricultural Research Stations and Lines of Work* (89th Cong., 1st sess., Report No. 156, April 1965), pp. 3-4.

[17] ESCOP, "Minutes, April 27-28, 1961"; USDA, "Secretary's Memorandum No. 1706, September 19, 1970"; Wiser and Bowers, *Marketing Research*, p. 71.

[18] Beacher, "Committee of Nine," p. 161; National Association of State Universities and Land-Grant Colleges and the U.S. Department of Agriculture, *A National Program of Research for Agriculture* ([Washington: NASULGC and USDA], 1966).

[19] ESCOP, "Minutes, April 28-29, 1965"; NASULGC and USDA, *National Program of Research for Agriculture.*

[20] ESCOP, "Minutes, May 10-11, 1967 and November 12, 1967."

[21] True, *History of Agricultural Experimentation*, p. 132; interview with T.C. Byerly, April 10, 1986; Agricultural Research Policy Advisory Committee, CRIS Subcommittee, *Current Research Information System: Report of a Study* ([Washington]: USDA and NASULGC, 1975), p. 1; American Agricultural Economics Association Committee, "Report by the AAEA Committee on the Current Research Information System," paper submitted to the AAEA Board of Directors, July 1983, p. 2; James E. Halpin, Director-At-Large, Southern Region, to author, December 16, 1985.

[22] ESCOP, "Minutes, April 28-29 and November 13, 1966; November 12, 1967; and April 29-May 1, 1969"; interview with T.S. Ronningen, February 10, 1986; interview with R.L. Lovvorn, April 22, 1986.

[23] NASULGC and USDA, *Federal-State Experiment Station Relations in Agricultural Research: Report of a Task Force Jointly Sponsored by the National Association of State Universities and Land-Grant Colleges and the U.S. Department of Agriculture* ([Washington: NASULGC and USDA], 1968), pp. 9-10; USDA, "Secretary's Memorandum No. 1657, June 16, 1969."

[24] ESCOP, "Minutes of the Legislative Subcommittee, July 27, 1964" and "Minutes, April 23-24, 1968"; USDA, Science and Education, *Paradox of Success: The Impact of Priority Setting in Agricultural Research and Extension* (Washington: USDA, Science and Education, 1984), pp. VI-8, VII-9.

[25] CSRS, "Appropriation History."

[26] CSESS, *Funds for Research: 1961*; CSRS, *Funds for Research at State Agricultural Experiment Stations: 1971* (Washington: USDA, 1972); W.E. Huffman and J.A. Miranowski, "Economic Analysis of Expenditures on Agricultural Experiment Station Research," *American Journal of Agricultural Economics* 63 (February 1981): 116-117.

[27] U.S. Congress, House Committee on Appropriations, Subcommittee on Agriculture-Environmental and Consumer Protection, *Agriculture-Environmental and Consumer Protection Appropriations for 1974: Hearings*, pt. 3 (93rd Cong., 1st sess., March 1973), p. 558. Interviews with a number of former and present state directors and USDA administrators indicated that programs at the stations differed little according to soures of funding, thus research thrusts identified as federally funded should essentially reflect the entire station effort.

CHAPTER V
The Paradox of Success: 1972-1976

The critical scrutiny of the public agricultural research system that had begun in the 1960s only intensified in the 1970s. Productivity of the major farm commodities had doubled and sometimes quadrupled since the Second World War, so that less than 5 percent of the population remained on farms to furnish the food and fiber needs of the United States in 1970.

Once the transformation of agriculture from a labor-intensive to a knowledge-intensive industry was nearly complete, a growing number of Americans who attached special reverence to their agrarian past were having second thoughts about the process that had produced unprecedented abundance at the cost of depopulating the farms. This "paradox of success," as one study aptly termed it, prompted new challenges from outside and inside the scientific establishment and produced a new round of evaluative studies and priority-setting exercises which absorbed the attention of national policy makers and research administrators for years to come.[1]

Demand for a New Agenda

From its beginnings in the United States, agricultural science operated on the general belief that increasing efficiency of production was the primary means of improving rural society. Over the years, due to perceived client interests and science's claim to neutrality, this basic assumption, expanded to include the goal of cheaper food and fiber for consumers, became an end in itself.

The critics who emerged in the 1970s charged that this narrow focus on applying more technology to produce ever greater amounts of commodities with less labor had made farming more capital intensive while contributing to economic concentration and environmental degradation. In the process, the populist critique continued, the state experiment stations became allied with agribusiness who transformed scientific discoveries into profitable commercial technologies at the expense of the farmers who the land-grant programs had been created to serve.

Furthermore, agricultural research was alleged to be the monopoly of a small segment of the American scientific community, its members overwhelmingly white, male products of the land-grant institutions themselves. They, of course, shared their institutions' devotion to the short-term problems of production agriculture and, thus, were heedless of consumer needs and the long-term consequences of technological innovations.

A "new agenda," then, was demanded of the public agricultural research establishment, one which considered the social and environmental effects of technology adoption and opened research opportunities to a broader spectrum of investigators. The two main tenets of the New Agenda critique—the experiment stations failure to meet farmers' needs by serving corporate agribusiness and their failure to serve science by being overpractical—were most dramatically articulated in two studies completed in 1972. One was a social justice indictment of science for being too successful while the other faulted the research system for doing too little.[2]

Hard Tomatoes, Hard Times

The Agribusiness Accountability Project led by Jim Hightower focused on the labor-displacing farm mechanization investigations of the California station as an example of how far agricultural research had strayed from its original mission of improving rural life and the welfare of the consumer. Instead, investigations were more often geared to turning out standardized farm commodities designed to meet the demands of machine harvesters and food retailers, an injustice to the consumers who had to eat the products and to the farm laborers who were denied their livelihood. *Hard Tomatoes, Hard Times*, as the report was titled, was the result.

The sensational report was followed by hearings before a Senate subcommittee on migrant labor and a lawsuit to forbid the USDA from releasing research dollars to the state stations. While neither legislation nor an injunction resulted, the agricultural research stations were put in the position of countering charges by showing that their activities were aimed at directly benefiting all farmers by keeping their production costs down. In the midst of compiling this defense against external attack, the agricultural research establishment came under assault from within the scientific community for being *too* wedded to the concerns of farmers and neglecting its responsibility to science.[3]

Pound Committee Report

The National Academy of Sciences, at the invitation of the Secretary of Agriculture in 1969, initiated a study of the quality of research undertaken with federal appropriations. Chaired by Glenn S. Pound of the University of Wisconsin, the committee organized into a series of discipline-oriented study panels that sampled the research activities of the federal-state partners as represented in the brief, descriptive entries in the Current Research Information System. Emphasis was placed on the Agricultural Research Service effort.

The Academy's findings, released as the Pound Report in 1972, characterized much of the research as overly practical in concept and pedestrian in execution. Such assertions as "there is an unwarranted duplication of effort . . . [and] an inexcusable amount of mediocre and duplicative research" were widely circulated in the public and scientific press. So, too, was the report's charge that the blame rested on administrative procedures that stifled free scientific inquiry.[4]

Scores of more moderately worded studies by government agencies, congressional committees, and private foundations followed in the remaining years of the decade, but the conclusions of the Hightower and Pound reports tended to frame the debate over the functioning of the public agricultural research system. Nearly every subsequent review applauded the federal-state partnership for its flexibility in marshaling scientific expertise that returned high dividends on its public investment in the past. Nearly unanimous, too, was the opinion that the system could be made more relevant to society in the future if the priority-setting process was opened to a larger set of advisors and if more financial support was directed toward less traditional fields of activity than production agriculture.[5]

New Administrative Arrangements in the USDA

Agriculture had become increasingly subject to off-farm forces, leading even the traditional supporters of agricultural research to demand a broader agenda. Responding to these new concerns, the USDA and the state experiment stations repeatedly reordered their planning and administrative structures and sought new funding sources to expand the scope of their research.

Coinciding with the furor engendered by the release of the Pound Report but largely unrelated to its call for the streamlining of management within the USDA was the transfer of oversight responsibility for the Forest Service and Soil Conservation Service to the Science and Education office. To reflect better the Department's concern for environmental issues which were drawing much public attention, an Assistant Secretary for Conservation, Research, and Education was named in 1973 to head the rearranged division that still included the Cooperative State Research Service, the Agricultural Research Service, the Extension Service, and the National Agricultural Library.

CSRS, thus, reported through an Assistant Secretary, a goal long sought by the state station directors who desired a higher profile for station research within the USDA. The Department's preoccupation with the more immediate and more politically sensitive concerns of the Forest Service and the Soil Conservation Service, however, tended to limit the expected benefits of the reorganization.[6]

Review Procedures Adjusted

The Cooperative State Research Service continued under the leadership of Dr. Lovvorn until his retirement in 1976 when Richard J. Aldrich came from his post as Associate Director for the Missouri station to serve as CSRS Administrator. On-site reviews remained the primary activity of the agency under both men as they continued working with the station directors to develop better procedures to strengthen the quality and relevance of investigations.

Special reviews that included outside experts who joined station scientists and administrators to consider options for research improvements became the dominant form of assistance. Only thirty-four of the ninety-three review teams CSRS led to the stations in 1975 were of the more traditional subject-matter review type that assessed past program performance.

Temporary staff appointments in CSRS increased during the same period, contributing to a shift in the agency's operations in Washington. CSRS scientists routinely had reviewed each project outline sent to them by the stations to assess its scientific merit and feasibility. The available professional staff, even with the help of leading scientists from state and USDA laboratories who were detailed for one-year periods to CSRS, found it more and more difficult to effectively perform this laborious task in the face of mounting project submissions of increasing methodological sophistication.

Following the recommendations of a CSRS-sponsored study on how to overcome the growing dissatisfaction with the value of this service to the state stations, new Administrator Aldrich in 1977 began limiting individual project examinations to a simple determination of its appropriateness for federal funding. The state agricultural experiment stations were asked to develop in-station peer review processes for the consideration of each project proposal, the report of which would accompany the project outline to CSRS for final approval.

Richard J. Aldrich left the Missouri Agricultural Experiment Station in 1976 to become administrator of the Cooperative State Research Service and its successor, the Cooperative Research/Science and Education Administration, where he served until 1978. *(USDA photo)*

A number of states already were well acquainted with peer review procedures in their quest for grant funds from organizations like the National Science Foundation and the National Institutes of Health. Others initially resisted what seemed to be yet another administrative hurdle to getting investigations underway, but most welcomed the opportunity to expose their programs to the critical scrutiny of a wider audience of scientists.[7]

"Regionalization" of the Agricultural Research Service

Another product of the persistent calls for a more coordinated system of public agricultural research was the wholesale reorganization of the Agricultural Research Service in the early 1970s. Since the 1950s, the federal partner in the system had gained increasing financial support from Congress by locating the majority of its new laboratory facilities across the United States, often in association with the state land-grant institutions. This development more closely allied federal scientists with their counterparts at the state stations but engendered concern among some Washington-based ARS administrators that their professional corps was becoming absorbed into the state agricultural research system.

In an effort to reassert control over the ARS programs while retaining the advantages of close contact with the state scientists, the agency was restructured on a regional basis in 1972. Deputy Directors of Research were named to oversee all investigations within four regions whose boundaries were coterminous with those observed by the state experiment stations. National Research Investigation Leader positions were discontinued as part of the management decentralization plan, although a National Program Staff of technical experts was soon added in an attempt to reclaim some of the agency's lost leadership role in the agricultural sciences.

Whatever the effects of the ARS regionalization on the federal bench scientists in the field, the state stations generally welcomed the decentralization because it decreased the perception of rivalry between the partners in public agricultural research. As intended, it placed federal managers in closer contact with state administrators, allowing them to work more closely together in the many planning efforts underway in the 1970s.[8]

ARPAC Planning Committees Broadened

The Agricultural Research Policy Advisory Committee founded in 1969 took the lead in the next decade in coordinating the burgeoning array of planning activities. By 1974, ARPAC had broadened its membership to include representatives of the institutions receiving McIntire-Stennis forestry research funds and of the federally supported research stations in the 1890 land-grant colleges. In the same year it began implementing an ambitious planning structure designed to involve USDA and state agricultural researchers on a regional level in the formulation of priorities for the future.

The "Regional and National Agricultural Research Planning System" embodied a National Planning Committee as an ARPAC subcommittee charged with devising a five-year program of research priorities.

To compile this forecast and to make annual adjustments in the plan, four Regional Planning Committees were set up to represent state experiment stations and federal agencies administrators.

Each Regional Planning Committee could charter up to seven Research Program Groups made up of scientists and managers in broad subject areas (natural resources, forests, crops, animals, people/communities, competition/ trade, and general resources), and each of these Program Groups might have as many as fifteen Research Program Task Forces of scientists to identify priorities by specific commodities or problem areas.

The planning system did not develop along the exact hierarchical lines that were proposed but its National and Regional Planning Committees were created to solicit the opinions of the research community. The Southern, Western, and Northeastern Regions impaneled over eighty subject-matter study groups between them in the mid-1970s. The North Central Region employed nineteen preexisting advisory committees in its effort, having found the one new task force it tried a redundancy. The regional groupings brought in the regional differences in agriculture and its site-specific requirements to the planning and priority setting processes. The national dimension provided a country-wide perception that was sensitive to location differences while identifying common denominators of research needs across states and regions.[9]

With a system for more coordinated planning among agricultural research institutions in place, ARPAC undertook an effort to more fully involve the users of research in establishing priorities for the future. In the early 1970s, there arose a rather sudden concern over the future availability of food. This concern was prompted by world shortages of some commodities, rising domestic food costs, and unstable farm prices caused by disastrous weather globally and a massive Soviet grain purchase that depleted domestic supplies. While the economic disturbance was short-lived, the uneasiness that lingered presented the research establishment with an opportunity to present its case for increased support to a newly receptive audience.

In 1975, ARPAC convened a Conference on United States and World Food Needs in Kansas City, Missouri, to identify priorities for research to ensure continued food abundance over the next ten to fifteen years. More than 380 consumers and performers of agricultural research participated in the Kansas City Conference, breaking into sixteen working groups to rank a formidable list of specific research problems submitted by nearly 700 scientists and extension specialists.

The Conference representatives identified 1,011 problems that affected the capacity of the nation to improve food supplies, ranking them under three broad categories. Under organization of resources to provide food were the subcategories of human resources, social institutions, public policy, international development, and production and marketing systems. Human needs for food included nutrient requirements and composition, and food technology and safety. Management of resources to provide food, consisting of natural resources and barriers to increased commodity production, was a third category.

The conferees considered neither approaches to the solution of these problems nor the levels of funding that would be necessary to attack them and many of their highest priority areas related to national policy considerations out of the purview of researchers.[10] As a practical guide to future investigations the Conference report had a limited impact, but it did stand as evidence of the public research system's dedication to identifying and addressing issues of global importance.

While ARPAC was developing ways to identify new research needs on their behalf, the state agricultural experiment stations were developing new strategies to secure the federal support necessary to expand their investigations into these areas. Concluding that Hatch formula funds were not likely to be increased to a level that would allow significant departures from traditional program thrusts, research administrators reluctantly sought funding through legislation that earmarked new money for specific items included in the New Agenda.

Sociological Research and the Rural Development Act of 1972

Chief among the areas identified by the numerous priority reports for increased attention was rural development, that process by which rural residents were helped to identify their common needs and to marshal effectively their resources to better their lives materially and socially. Investigations into this process had been encouraged in the Purnell Act of 1925 and were specifically called for again in the Research and Marketing Act of 1946. A relative handful of rural sociologists (sixty-three by 1949) were employed in the state experiment stations as a result.

In the early years, these social scientists generally focused on how rural social values might be preserved as the countryside confronted rapid change. By mid-century, they were more likely to be pursuing studies which more closely complemented the station programs in production agriculture, identifying the characteristics of early adopters and finding ways to speed the acceptance of technological innovation. As it became apparent in the mid-1960s that increased production efficiency on the part of farmers did not translate automatically into a higher standard of living for all rural residents and that it could actually be culturally and environmentally disruptive, there was something of a reversion to the earlier concept of rural development, minus the moralistic overtones of the earlier studies.[11]

As the field of rural sociology developed a disciplinary focus, its practitioners began urging new legislation to support their work. A proposal emerged in 1969 to establish a national network of Rural Research Institutes in connection with each land-grant university to conduct research and extension activities to improve rural life. The state agricultural experiment stations resisted the idea of wholly new administrative units but welcomed the prospect of additional money to support the work of their existing corps of rural sociologists who were housed either in separate departments or affiliated with agricultural economics divisions within the stations.

The Rural Research Institutes proposal died in the absence of the stations' endorsement but interest in rural development investigations remained strong enough among the directors for them to cooperate with their extension service counterparts to form an Advisory Committee on Rural Development in 1970. Support in the Department of Agriculture was equally strong. Its proposed Special Grants budget request for the next fiscal year included $150,000 for each of four regional "centers of excellence" for rural development. Congress, averse to sanctioning such sums for new programs which it had not originated, eventually granted $75,000 for each of the four centers, then "recommended" that the state experiment stations devote $3,000,000 of their Hatch appropriations for 1971 to "Community Improvement Research."

The Regional Rural Development Centers served to identify rural problems, then encouraged and coordinated research and extension efforts to solve them. Their objectives were as ambitious as the goals of rural development: increase employment opportunities, improve the quality and availability of rural community services, upgrade rural housing, improve the environment, and build the problem-solving capacity of community residents. This agenda spanned a wide array of investigations already underway at the stations, so the

Regional Centers operated mainly to provide linkages between the projects and to coordinate regional approaches to common concerns.

In 1971, the North Central Regional Center for Rural Development was established in association with the Iowa station. The Northeast Center operated out of the New York station at Cornell University from its founding in 1972 until its transfer to Pennsylvania State University in 1986. Oregon State University housed the Western Center beginning in 1972, while Mississippi State University provided a home for the Southern Regional Center two years later.[12]

Further encouragement to rural development research at the state experiment stations was included in the Rural Development Act of 1972, a measure whose main intent was to consolidate federal loan, industrial assistance, health facilities, and waste management programs aimed at upgrading services in rural areas. Title V of the legislation was added at the insistence of the land-grant institutions to enable them to lend their expertise to the effort of making rural areas more attractive to residents and businesses.

The "Rural Development and Small Farm Research and Education" title of the 1972 Act authorized $10,000,000 for 1974, $15,000,000 for 1975, and $20,000,000 for 1976 to be paid to the states on a basis similar to the Hatch formula, with 10 percent reserved for interstate projects. To foster the integration of extension and research, each state's program was to be coordinated by the land-grant university administrative head of agriculture as the chairman of a citizens advisory council which would decide upon program thrusts.

After passing legislation to stimulate the economic and social revitalization of the countryside, Congress and the Richard M. Nixon administration seemed to lose interest when it came to actually funding the effort. Only $3,000,000 was forwarded to the states in each of the first three years of the program and this was split between extension and research. When divided between the fifty states and Puerto Rico these levels provided meager support for new research initiatives.

Cooperation between station social scientists and their extension counterparts, however, was enhanced by the administrative structure decreed in the Act and projects undertaken by them were impressive enough for Congress to resist efforts by successive presidential administrations to terminate the program as a distinct budget item. Annual funding thus was continued at $3,000,000 ($1,500,000 for research) for another four years after the initial authorization period expired in 1977. Still, the failure to support rural development research at the promised levels dissipated much of the hope that the disciplines involved would become more powerful components in the programs of the state agricultural experiment stations.[13]

Increased Support for the 1890 Institutions

Even while the Rural Development Act was in operation, the Special Grants program continued to be the primary federal funding source for the operation of the Regional Rural Development Centers. The centers were only one of a number of specific areas that were earmarked by Congress for support under Special Grants which became an increasingly significant alternative to Hatch and McIntire-Stennis formula allocations. Between 1971 and 1977, Special Grants for congressionally identified programs rose from $3,000,000 to $19,662,000 annually. Two-thirds of the Special Grants funds in the latter year were reserved for the support of the programs at the historically black 1890 land-grant institutions in a continuing effort to integrate them more fully into the public agricultural research system.

Significant increases in federal research dollars to the 1890 colleges began in 1972 when the institutions' presidents convinced the state experiment directors and the USDA to endorse a proposal that would tie future support to a goal of 15 percent of regular Hatch appropriations. Convinced by arguments that the 1890 institutions could better focus investigations on the problems of limited resource farmers and rural residents, Congress concurred in the request, providing $8,883,000 to the 1890 colleges' research programs for fiscal year 1972. Tuskegee Institute in Alabama, which had been a leader in research and extension since the days of George Washington Carver, was also made eligible for funds which continued to be divided according to the formula first agreed upon in 1967.

With these additional dollars, the sixteen 1890 institutions and Tuskegee Institute began to augment their capabilities over a range of disciplines that reflected local client needs and research opportunities. While continued financial support was often justified on their presumed ability to address the special problems of the disadvantaged, the actual research undertaken at the historically black institutions differed little from that of the elder stations. Investigations spanned the continuum from basic, to applied, to developmental just as they did in the state agricultural experiment stations where interest and expertise of individual scientists had a strong influence on program thrusts. With more limited operating expenses and facilities, however, the 1890 colleges and Tuskegee Institute had to be more selective in their activities, often finding opportunities in less traditional areas than the problems of major farm commodities producers.[14]

In addition to furnishing significantly greater amounts of support for the 1890 institutions, Special Grants continued to provide Congress with the opportunity to target money to its members' specific interests and gave the experiment stations an innovative mechanism for cooperating with federal agencies in addressing selected issues of national concern. In 1971, for instance, the state stations were voted supplemental funds under Special Grants authority to deal with an outbreak of Southern corn leaf blight that threatened a variety of corn that made up most of the crop in the United States. A crash program that tapped the skills of a number of scientists in the state experiment stations and the Agricultural Research Service quickly developed a new type of corn with resistance to the fungus that prompted the emergency and a new category of Special Grants was continued to focus on genetic vulnerability in crops.[15]

The Special Grants program also allowed the state stations to lend their expertise to addressing problems with implications beyond agriculture. The "energy crisis" of the early and mid-1970s prompted a national search for ways to lessen America's dependence on petroleum-derived fuels.

Energy Research

Food production consumed only a small portion of the nation's fossil fuel supplies (about 2.6 percent in 1975), so the main effort at decreasing oil consumption was directed outside agriculture in other federal agencies. Yet, modern agriculture was such an energy intensive enterprise that any rise in the price of fuel had a potentially enormous impact on the already-thin profit margins of farmers. Thus, when federal funds were made available for energy research, the state experiment stations with the assistance of the USDA lobbied successfully to secure a part of the money through Special Grants.

In 1974, the National Science Foundation forwarded $1,000,000 in "pass-through" grants to the Department's Agricultural Research Service for investigations into solar energy applications in agriculture and the state experiment stations received a portion through specific cooperative agreements. The next year, a new Energy Research and Development Administration became the granting agency with the Cooperative State Research Service acting to forward station project proposals related to the use of solar energy in crop drying, greenhouse-

and rural residence-heating, and food processing. This arrangement was continued in 1977 when a cabinet-level Department of Energy was created.[16]

Environmental Protection Research

During this same period Special Grants authority provided pass-through funds to the state agricultural experiment stations, again through CSRS, to assist the Environmental Protection Agency (EPA) in rehabilitating land devastated by strip mining of coal. Over $3,500,000 was forwarded in this manner to the experiment stations from 1975 through 1978 to develop reclamation technology and assess environmental effects of coal mining.

The state stations also were involved with the EPA in the continuing evaluation of pesticides for minor agricultural uses by providing the agency with the benefit-risk analyses used in its registration process. IR-4, the interregional project partially funded by Special Grants since the mid-1960s, was broadened in the 1970s to address a range of problems related to pesticide use.

In 1976, a National Pesticide Impact Assessment Program was launched incorporating and expanding the IR-4 effort to include all chemicals deemed critical to agriculture and forestry. As part of the program, Special Grants were allocated to each experiment station on the basis of its commitment of scientist-years to pesticide research and the state's proportion of farm income and expenditures for pesticides. Four stations, New York, Florida, Michigan, and California, became the sites for regional leader laboratories for the compilation of data while the national organizational headquarters remained in the New Jersey station at Rutgers University.

By the end of the decade IR-4 was also functioning to coordinate the state experiment stations' activities in integrated pest management which sought to discover effective mixes of chemical and biological controls, pest-resistant varieties, and cultural techniques to limit the adverse economic impacts of pests and pathogens on a range of farm crops.[17]

International Development Assistance

Special Grants pass-through funds also stimulated greater state experiment station involvement in international agricultural development programs. The land-grant institutions had long been active in educating foreign students in agricultural science and a number of state experiment stations since the 1960s had either conducted international assistance programs with foundation grants or contributed the services of individual scientists to such programs. This effort had grown to such importance by the mid-1970s that at least ten of the state agricultural experiment stations employed directors or coordinators for international development and one station (Florida) had a Department of International Programs.

Beginning in 1976, the United States Agency for International Development sought to formally tap the growing expertise of the stations by soliciting research proposals from them through CSRS. In the first year, $125,000 was made available through Special Grants for research into nitrogen-fixation mechanisms of crops grown in lesser developed countries. Edible legumes research under USAID sponsorship continued for the remaining years of the decade, averaging about $500,000 annually.[18]

International technology assistance, pesticide assessment and pest management, and alternative energy source development research were not new to the experiment stations when Special Grants were made available to encourage investigations into each of these areas. Attention to these problems was a natural addition to the programs of the state stations as they continually broadened their research concerns beyond the farm gate.

Special Grants were important as an indication of Congress' intent to direct funds to specific items on the New Agenda on a competitive basis and for providing a way for the stations to become involved in federal programs outside the USDA. The sums available as pass-through grants were not large enough to have a major impact on station research thrusts unless they did so as seed money to attract funds from regular Hatch and state appropriations. As new programs were added under Special Grants, that category of funds did steadily increase: from $1,717,000 in 1970 to $6,310,000 in 1977 excluding the money reserved to the 1890 institutions. Still, in the latter year, Special Grants comprised less than 5 percent of the federal funds administered by the Cooperative State Research Service.

In addition, more institutions were vying for a portion of these dollars by the mid-1970s. Land-grant status was conferred on colleges in Guam and the Virgin Islands in 1972 and on the University of the District of Columbia in 1974, making each of them eligible for all federal research-support allocations. And, although Special Grants had been available in theory to research institutions outside the state experiment station system since the inception of the program in 1965, it was not until 1973 that grants actually were awarded to such institutions.[19]

New Funding Strategies

Concerned that their portions of research dollars were diminishing as more grantees were made eligible for federal disbursements and encouraged by the apparent willingness of Congress to target appropriation increases to specific areas, two groups within the agricultural science community attempted to secure new legislation to reserve funding for their disciplines. Animal health researchers hoped to duplicate the feat of foresters a decade earlier when they framed a bill in 1972 that would subsidize veterinary research in the states on the basis of the livestock industry's contributions to agricultural income. The bill, with Experiment Station Committee on Organization and Policy support, passed both houses of Congress in 1974 but was vetoed by President Gerald R. Ford who objected to its cost. Congress failed to override the veto, choosing instead to add $750,000 under Special Grants for beef and pork production investigations in the 1975 fiscal year budget.[20]

An effort on the part of home economists to produce legislation for funding was no more successful. Nutritionists had tried in vain as early as 1941 to have funds set aside for their research interest but had to be content with a Research and Marketing Act call for more attention to human nutrition. Another attempt was made in 1961 to secure federal aid for home economics investigations, again without success in the absence of Kennedy administration backing.

Renewed interest in human health and consumer safety issues prompted home economists to try again in the early 1970s. Initiatives to address these concerns were discussed in Congress and the American Home Economics Association fastened on a plan to apportion research money through CSRS to the states on the basis of population with 25 percent of any allocation reserved for regional projects.

Unable to agree upon a list of priorities or criteria for limiting eligibility to a small enough number of institutions to make formula funding effective, the effort was abandoned soon after the animal health bill was vetoed. Like the animal researchers, home economists had to settle for Special Grants funding in 1975 when $750,000 was awarded to the food and nutrition part of their agenda.[21]

Despite all the activity revolving around Special Grants and other earmarking proposals, Hatch formula allocations continued to make up the bulk of federal funds to the state agricultural experiment stations. The total amount of funds distributed to the stations through CSRS increased from $82,948,000 in 1972 to $129,022,000 in 1977, an average gain of about 11 percent for each of the five years. Hatch funds contributed 78 percent of these dollars in 1972 and 76 percent in 1977 as McIntire-Stennis and Special Grants including 1890 institution grants registered slightly greater increases (from 5.6 to 6.4 percent and 15.0 to 15.2 percent, respectively). The pace of increases in state appropriations was roughly equal for the same period, with allocations rising from $247,691,000 to $393,353,000 for an average yearly gain of 12 percent. The ravages of inflation offset real gains by about 7 percent annually, so additional money for increased attention to human resources, energy, environmental, and nutrition issues demanded by New Agenda proponents was slight.

Confronted with slowing real increases in regular federal and state appropriations and ever greater demands for attention to new problems, the state agricultural experiment stations courted additional support outside the traditional appropriation channels. The National Science Foundation, the Environmental Protection Agency, the National Institutes of Health, the Agency for International Development, and other federal agencies contributed $27,299,000 in grants to individual state station scientists and programs in 1972. In 1977, $51,759,000 was received from these grantor agencies, an increase of nearly 90 percent in those five years.

Private foundations, industries, and commodity groups also were more effectively tapped for research money. In 1972, $16,021,000 came to the state stations from private donors; by 1977, the figure had nearly doubled to $31,819,000. While federal non-USDA money and private grants were a relatively small portion of the total funds available to the state agricultural experiment stations (8.5 percent and 5 percent, respectively, in 1977), their growing importance held profound implications for many stations. Because these dollars generally were directed by grantors to specific areas in their interest, state stations directors had more limited discretion in allocating them than they had with state appropriations and Hatch funds.

Directors integrated grant-driven investigations into existing research programs to avoid disrupting balances worked out over many years among the array of scientific disciplines represented in their experiment stations. The effort required greater administrative skills from the directors and greater entrepreneurial skills from the researchers to make grant programs effective. To acquire these funds, an increased sensitivity to the shifting interests of the various constituencies whom the grantors represented was necessary. Combined with the growing influence of the New Agenda advocates on the thinking of those who appropriated public money to research, this development promised less support for the more traditional long-term research programs to sustain and enhance agricultural productivity.[22]

High Returns on Public Investments Cited

Even as the state agricultural experiment stations moved to adjust their research thrusts to the new realities that determined continued support, they rallied in defense of their traditional programs. After all, they maintained, the public agricultural research network had developed a system of locally directed experimentation that, in aggregate, provided the foundation for enormous productivity gains among farmers that ultimately translated into reduced costs of food and fiber to all Americans. The most obvious manifestation of the magnitude of agricultural productivity advances was the fact that by the end of the 1970s, one farmer provided the needs of another seventy-eight people, compared with only enough for himself and six others at the turn of the century.

Numerous studies indicated that agricultural research played a significant role in contributing to the increased abundance of food and fiber. One of the most extensive of these analyses that measured costs of public investments in agricultural research and benefits in productivity gains accruing from the effort found an annual rate of return from all agricultural research of 65 percent between 1868 and 1926. The annual return rate on investments was estimated at between 95 and 110 percent for the years 1927 to 1950, and between 45 percent (for science-oriented investigations) and 130 percent (for technology-oriented work in the South) for the years 1950 to 1971. While these estimates were greater than some of the previous economic analyses of returns to public expenditures, none disputed the conclusion "that agricultural research has produced added productivity or output per unit of sufficient magnitude to yield extraordinarily high rates of return on investment."[23]

Continuing Responses to Challenges

While defending their historical role by reference to the high economic payoffs delivered by agricultural research, the state experiment stations increasingly were made aware in the 1970s that their responsibilities went beyond maintaining and enhancing productivity. For a growing number of Americans concerned with the direction of agricultural research, the overriding issue was no longer how much value was produced but rather how this value was distributed.[24] The stations were not deaf to these appeals and they, along with their federal partner, did respond with more attention to social-oriented investigations.

Some measure of the degree of this change was indicated in a comparison of the percentages of scientist-years assigned in 1965 and 1977 to the goals of agricultural research articulated in the 1966 Long-Range Study. Production efficiency and protection of farm and forest products remained the chief areas of concern over the entire period, with 51 percent of the effort in 1965 and 50 percent in 1977. The manpower investment in activities most closely connected to agribusiness did decline, however. Post-harvest investigations related to product development and quality dropped from 17 percent to 11 percent of the research effort over the twelve-year period. All of the goals that came to be associated with the New Agenda received increased attention. Research aimed at elevating level-of-living standards of rural people rose from 2 percent to 3 percent; advancing human health and nutrition increased from 4 percent to 7 percent; and improving rural community services and the environment went from 5 percent to 11 percent of the scientist-years expended by the public agricultural research system.

The total number of scientist-years available to the state experiment stations expanded only slightly between the mid-1960s and the late 1970s, forcing station directors to face some hard choices in continuing to serve the needs of their traditional clientele while addressing the concerns of increasingly vocal new constituencies.[25] The various critical reviews and advisory councils could help to identify and even assist in determining the relative importance of items which should be on the agricultural research agenda, but the individual stations were left with the task of actually translating these suggestions into research projects that could be undertaken with the financial and scientific resources available to them.

Notes

[1] Sylvan H. Wittwer, "Change, Choices, and Challenges," in *1985 Accomplishments for Research, Extension, and Higher Education: A Report to the Secretary of Agriculture*, Joint Council on Food and Agricultural Sciences (Washington: n.p., 1985), p. 3; USDA, Science and Education, *Paradox of Success*, pp. I-1 - 3.

[2] Lawrence Busch and William B. Lacy, *Science, Agriculture, and the Politics of Research* (Boulder, Colorado: Westview Press, 1983), pp. 35, 50-54, 58; Frederick H. Buttel, "The Land-Grant System: A Sociological Perspective on Value Conflicts and Ethical Issues," *Agriculture and Human Values* 2 (Spring 1985): 94; Ruttan, *Agricultural Research Policy*, p. 81.

[3] Jim Hightower, *Hard Tomatoes, Hard Times* (Washington: Agribusiness Accountability Project, 1972); Jerry Carlson, "More Research and Extension for Small Farmers," *Farm Journal* (August 1972), pp. 24-27; ESCOP, "Minutes, November 12, 1972."

[4] National Academy of Sciences, *Report on the Committee on Research Advisory to the U.S. Department of Agriculture* (Washington: NAS Division of Biology and Agriculture, National Research Council, 1972); *Des Moines (Iowa) Sunday Register*, January 28, 1973; Nicholas Wade, "Agriculture: NAS Panel Charges Inept Management, Poor Research," *Science* 179 (January 5, 1973): 45-57.

[5] USDA and NASULGC, *Agricultural and Food Research Issues and Priorities* ([Washington: USDA], 1978), pp. vi-ix.

[6] "USDA Press Release, January 17, 1973"; interview with T.S. Ronningen, February 28, 1985.

[7] United States General Accounting Office, *Agricultural Research—Its Organization and Management* (Washington: GAO, 1976), pp. 32-33; Wynne Thorne, *Report of a Study of Federal-State Relationships in Agricultural Research for the Cooperative State Research Service, United States Department of Agriculture* (N.p.: Utah A.E.S., 1975), pp. 1-6; "CSRS-Station Letter-2664(1), October 6, 1977"; interview with D.W. Barton, June 18, 1986.

[8] Moore, *Agricultural Research Service*, pp. 213-214; T.S. Ronningen and Hugo O. Graumann, "Incentives and Disincentives Important to Research Management and Administration," in *Assessment of the Agricultural Research System*, vol. 2, pt. A, *Commissioned Papers*, ed. U.S. Congress, Office of Technology Assessment, pp. 11-12; interview with Orville G. Bentley, Assistant Secretary of Science and Education, USDA, Washington, D.C., May 23, 1986.

[9] "CSRS-Station Letter-2663, January 25, 1974"; "CSRS-Station Letter-2705, October 20, 1975"; U.S. General Accounting Office, *Agricultural Research*, pp. 61-64.

[10] ARPAC, *Research to Meet U.S. and World Food Needs*; U.S. Congress, House Committee on Science and Technology, Subcommittee on Science, Research, and Technology and Subcommittee on Domestic and International Scientific Planning and Analysis, *Agricultural Research and Development: Special Oversight Hearings*, pt. 2 (94th Cong., 1st sess., September and October 1975), pp. 156-161.

[11] Bonney Youngblood, "Status of Rural Sociological Research in the State Agricultural Experiment Stations," *Rural Sociology* 14 (June 1949): 111; Buttel, "Land-Grant System," pp. 82-83.

[12] ESCOP, "Minutes, November 9, 1969" and "Interim Subcommittee Minutes, March 3-4, 1970"; "CSRS-Station Letter-2558(7i), January 5, 1970; U.S. Congress, House Committee on Appropriations, *Agriculture Appropriations for 1974: Hearings*, pt. 3, pp. 569-570; U.S. Congress, Senate Committee on Agriculture, Nutrition, and Forestry, *Rural Research in USDA: Hearings Before the Subcommittee on Agricultural Research and General Legislation* (95th Cong., 2nd sess., May 1978), pp. 4, 7.

[13] Rural Development Act, 86 Stat. 657 (1972); National Rural Center and Pennsylvania State University, *Rural Development and the Land-Grant Universities: An Evaluation of Title V of the Rural Development Act of 1972* (University Park: Pennsylvania State University, 1977), pp. 8-9, 19-22, 59, 138, 197.

[14] B.D. Mayberry, ed., *Development of Research*, p. 52; interview with B.D. Mayberry, April 15, 1986; interview with Mortimer H. Neufville, Dean, School of Agricultural Science, University of Maryland-Eastern Shore, Princess Anne, Maryland, June 13, 1986.

[15] ESCOP, "Legislative Subcommittee Minutes, February 1, 1971"; "CSRS-Station Letter-2492(4), November 23, 1971"; USDA, CSRS, "A Situation Statement on the Southern Corn Leaf Blight: Report by a Joint State-Federal Task Force, February 1971."

[16] Joseph B. Edmond, *Magnificent Charter: Origin and Role of the Morrill Land-Grant Colleges and Universities* (Hicksville, New York: Exposition Press, 1978), p. 191; "CSRS-Station Letters-2681 (October 29, 1974), 2681a (April 30, 1975), 2701a-c (August 22, September 12, and December 10, 1975)"; "Science and Education Administration-Cooperative Research-Station Letter-2803, June 8, 1979."

[17] ESCOP, "Minutes, November 9, 1975 and April 27-28, 1977"; "CSRS-Station Letters-2721a-e (April 12, 1976, June 24, 1977, and June 16, 1978) and 2743(2), June 13, 1977"; U.S. Congress, House Committee on Appropriations, Subcommittee on Agriculture, Rural Development, and Related Agencies, *Agriculture, Rural Development, and Related Agencies Appropriations for 1987: Hearings*, pt. 4 (99th Cong., 2nd sess., March 1986), pp. 737-738.

[18] Interview with W. Keith Kennedy, Provost Emeritus, Cornell University, Ithaca, New York, June 18, 1986; "CSRS-Station Letters-2719(1-3), April 4, 1975, December 6, 1976, August 15, 1977, and April 25, 1979."

[19] Science and Education Administration-Cooperative Research, *Hatch Administrative Manual*, pp. A2, A8; ESCOP, "Interim Subcommittee Minutes, February 8, 1973"; CSRS, *Funds for Research: 1974*, p. 31.

[20] ESCOP, "Minutes, April 26-27, 1972, April 24-25 and November 17, 1974"; "CSRS-Station letter-2492(7), January 28, 1975."

[21] ESCOP, "Minutes, November 5-12, 1941, April 27-28, 1961, April 24-25 and November 17, 1974"; "CSRS-Station Letter-2492(7), January 28, 1975."

[22] CSRS, "Appropriation History"; Joseph Havlicek, Jr. and Daniel Otto, "Historical Analysis of Investment in Food and Agricultural Research in the United States," in *Assessment of the Agricultural Research System*, vol. 2, pt. C, *Commissioned Papers*, ed. U.S. Congress, Office of Technology Assessment, p. 123.

[23] NASULGC, *The Leading Object . . .* (Washington: NASULGC, 1980), p. 6; Robert E. Evenson, "Agricultural Productivity and Public and Private Research Institutions," in *Research Perspectives: Proceedings of the Symposium on the Research Agenda for the State Agricultural Experiment Stations*, eds. ESCOP and CSRS (College Station: Texas Agricultural Experiment Station, 1985), pp. 69-72 (quotation on p. 72). See also R.E. Evenson, P.E. Waggoner, and V.W. Ruttan, "Economic Benefits from Research: An Example from Agriculture," *Science* 205 (September 14, 1979): 1101-1107.

[24] William W. Wood, Jr. "Discussion: Assessing and Projecting the Effects of Agricultural Research, Extension, and Technology," *American Journal of Agricultural Economics* 60 (December 1978): 983-984.

[25] Ruttan, *Agricultural Research Policy*, pp. 80-82.

CHAPTER VI
The New Agenda Institutionalized: 1977-1981

While the state agricultural experiment stations strove to amass the necessary array of scientific expertise and support facilities that would allow them to continue pursuing research relevant to the needs of diverse constituencies, they did not do so quickly enough to satisfy some national policymakers and many others who wanted to influence agricultural research policy. Nearly two decades of persistent demands for more socially responsive and politically acceptable planning directed toward national goals on the one hand and for more attention to basic scientific investigations on the other culminated in two related developments in the late 1970s. New legislation and a new presidential administration gave New Agenda critics access to the public agricultural research priority-setting processes to a greater extent than ever before.

Food and Agriculture Act of 1977

All those concerned with agricultural research policy, whether reformers who wanted the system reoriented or defenders who wanted its mission reaffirmed, were convinced that new legislation was necessary to guide the national effort into the future. Congress sought to reconcile the clashing perceptions of the contending parties in a bill that included agricultural research in an overall food and agriculture policy statement.

The result of this congressional action was Title XIV of the Food and Agriculture Act of 1977, a title whose eleven subtitles and seventy sections included a little of everything for everyone. To the questions of what problems deserved priority attention and who in the scientific community might best address them, Congress seemed to answer that all were important and every scientist could contribute to their solutions.[1]

The opening section of the National Agricultural Research, Extension, and Teaching Policy Act of 1977, in which Congress justified the need for new legislation, indicated the conflicting strains from which the Act emerged. The lawmakers applauded the wisdom of their predecessors who had founded and subsequently supported a research and extension partnership that had "significantly contributed to the development of the Nation's agricultural system," and pledged themselves to build upon that foundation. However, Title XIV went on to say, "further strengthening" was now necessary because the partners' work was "not fully coordinated" and, thus, "they have only been partially successful in responding to the needs of all persons affected by their research."

The need for strengthening was particularly acute if rising world demands for food and fiber were to be met, marketing system inadequacies overcome, and the fundamental core of scientific knowledge replenished. Toward these ends, then, Congress designated the United States Department of Agriculture as the "lead agency in the Federal Government for the food and agricultural sciences," established mechanisms for more effective planning among research performers and consumers, and initiated a new program of grants for "high-priority agricultural research to be awarded on the basis of competition among scientific research workers and all colleges and universities." Moreover, special money for a handful of specific problem areas was authorized as was increased support through traditional funding channels.[2]

New Initiatives and Advisory Groups

Title XIV included a list of fifteen broad areas in which new research initiatives were needed. Beginning with investigations to discover technologies which were less fossil-fuel dependent and ending with research into the efficient application of organic wastes to improve soil fertility, the items identified for increased attention represented many of the suggestions of the New Agenda proponents. Their continued input into the priority-setting process was meant to be insured in two advisory groups mandated in the 1977 Act, one for "doers" and another for "users" of agricultural research, extension, and teaching.

Of course, the Agricultural Research Policy Advisory Committee already existed to represent the federal and state research institutions but the absence of a continuing support staff and lack of official congressional sanction limited its potential. While USDA and state agricultural experiment station administrators would have preferred Congress to simply extend these services to ARPAC, the lawmakers decided a new policy group was needed that would include not only a broader segment of researchers but representatives of extension and higher education as well.[3]

A Joint Council on Food and Agricultural Sciences was called into being with the Secretary of Agriculture invested with the power to name members from his Department, the Office of Science and Technology Policy, the land-grant universities, the state agricultural experiment stations and cooperative extension services, and "other public and private institutions, producers, and representatives of the public who are interested in . . . the formulation of national policy in the food and agricultural sciences."

The Joint Council's mandated responsibilities were as broad as its potential membership. These included promoting coordination in the entire public agricultural research, extension, and teaching complex by providing a forum for communication, evaluating environmental and socioeconomic impacts of agricultural science and education activities, and identifying high priority areas for research. Two reports were to be annually compiled for the Secretary of Agriculture, one recommending program directions for the coming year and the other summarizing achievements of the past year. All of this was to be completed by a small, legislatively authorized staff group and through quarterly Council meetings, one of which would be held jointly with another new advisory group.

The National Agricultural Research and Extension Users Advisory Board members, like their counterparts on the Joint Council, were to be selected by the Secretary of Agriculture but their number and affiliations were determined by Congress. Designed to furnish "independent advisory opinions on the food and agricultural sciences," the Users Board was to be comprised of twenty-one delegates selected to represent the entire range of groups affected by agricultural research and education programs. Four members would represent agricultural commodity producers and another four would stand for "consumer interests." Farm suppliers and food processors, food marketers, environmentalists, and human nutritionists would be represented by two board members for each field. Finally, one member for each of the areas of rural development, animal health, farm labor, commodities transportation, and privately supported international development was to be included.

The Users Board's reporting responsibilities were more sharply drawn than those of the Joint Council. Annual recommendations on program directions, including suggestions for funding levels, were to be forwarded to the Secretary, while the President and Congress were to receive yearly appraisals of the chief executive's proposed budget in support of the agricultural sciences. Reviews of the policies and plans of the national research and extension system were also expected of the Users Board and it could impanel fact-finding groups to assist it in its deliberations. Ideally, then, the Users Board would provide broad-based outside opinion on how well the performers of research and extension were meeting the goals of Congress as embodied in the 1977 legislation.

Competitive Research Grants Authorized

The second entirely new feature introduced by Title XIV was an additional category of funding for agricultural research. To address the high-priority research areas that were to be identified with the help of the new advisory groups, the Secretary was to award research grants on a competitive basis to "State agricultural experiment stations, all colleges and universities, other research organizations, Federal agencies, private organizations or corporations, and individuals."

The categories of potential recipients were not new; the wording of Title XIV simply repeated that of the 1965 Specific Grants legislation in that regard, although in practice few outside the experiment stations had actually secured funds under the former law. What was new in the 1977 Act was that the new money was to be available to projects on the frontiers of science competing in a marketplace for expertise and imagination.[4] Also new were specific funding authorizations for the Competitive Grants program with $25,000,000 for 1978, $30,000,000 for 1979, $35,000,000 for 1980, $40,000,000 for 1981, and $50,000,000 for 1982 proposed.

In addition to legislating a new Competitive Grants program which had long been advocated in a succession of policy studies as a way to open up the agricultural research system to a broader spectrum of the scientific community, Congress reauthorized its two-decades-old forerunner. The Special Grants program of discretionary project grants to state experiment stations and other university-associated research institutions was continued with no specific funding levels directed. The Secretary of Agriculture retained the power to allocate whatever money became available, limited only by the stricture that the supported projects exploit promising scientific breakthroughs or expand state-federal research efforts. Either category was broad enough to insure that Special Grants would continue to be used as a means for Congress to direct attention at especially favored areas and for the state stations to work cooperatively on national and regional problems.

New Funds for Specific Programs

While Competitive and Special Grants programs provided funding mechanisms for investigations into problems that might emerge in the future, other new grant programs included in Title XIV indicated the concern of Congress for problems of the immediate present.

The nation's dependence on petroleum-derived products was still a major issue in the late 1970s, prompting the lawmakers to specify grant programs to discover and promote alternative energy sources. Agricultural and forest products held some promise as substitutes for farm and industry use and Congress sought to encourage the development of appropriate technology in this area by authorizing a maximum of $24,000,000 in project grants to university researchers over the five years beginning with 1978. Solar energy research and development competitive grants were also called for, although no funding levels were proposed.

As part of an effort to revitalize livestock and poultry research, Title XIV included a subtitle which resembled the vetoed animal health and disease research bill of 1974. Each state was to receive its portion of the $25,000,000 annually authorized according to its proportion of the nation's total income received from livestock and poultry production and according to its veterinary research capacity. Any amount over $100,000 was to be matched with state funds.

An institution's research capacity was to be determined by the Secretary with the assistance of an Animal Health Science Research Advisory Board, an eleven-member body representative of federal research agencies, veterinary colleges, state experiment stations, and national livestock organizations. The committee also was to suggest research priorities, including those of regional importance for which an additional $15,000,000 was to be provided annually for cooperative interstate projects.

Existing federally supported programs also were strengthened by new funding authorizations and amendments. Under the category of Hatch formula funds, $120,000,000 was called for in 1978 with $25,000,000 increases suggested for each of the following four years until the total reached $220,000,000 in 1982.

Marketing Set Aside Dropped

The state agricultural experiment stations were given greater discretion in the use of the money because the proviso first introduced in the Research and Marketing Act and continued in the Amended Hatch Act earmarking 20 percent for marketing studies was dropped in the 1977 legislation. The marketing economics studies that the original requirement had sought to encourage had been gradually superseded in the recent past by marketing technology investigations. Although significant descriptive and analytical research was carried out with the marketing set-aside, the lack of a perceived impact on marketing processes and policies gradually reduced the enthusiasm for the program among directors. While the state stations had had little difficulty in meeting the minimum requirement as the definition of marketing expanded to include processing and other food service research, the accounting procedures necessary to detail their compliance were a continuing administrative burden. Sensitive to the stations' dissatisfaction with the set-aside requirement and sharing widespread misgivings over a law that seemed to encourage research into an area that many felt was more appropriate to private industry, Congress withdrew the section.[5]

Evans-Allen Funds to 1890 Colleges

Although Title XIV did not directly increase the amount of money to support the agricultural research conducted in the 1890 land-grant universities and Tuskegee Institute, it did give more visibility to their programs by taking them out of the Special Grants category to stand alone. Special Grants had been the only authorization available to the USDA when support was initiated in 1967, and proponents took the earliest opportunity to place the program on a more stable funding basis. Aside from recognizing the importance of the decade-old subsidy to the historically black institutions, the change meant that the schools could no longer spend their funds over a five-year period but must do so in the year in which the money was received.

The informal agreement made in 1972 to fund this research at a level equal to 15 percent of the Hatch appropriations was written into law as was the allocation formula that had been followed since 1967. Thenceforth, dollars made available for research under this program were called "Evans-Allen funds" in recognition of the two men who had championed their cause in Congress throughout the 1970s,

Representative Frank E. Evans of Colorado and Senator James B. Allen of Alabama. In a further effort to incorporate their scientific expertise into the public agricultural research system, Title XIV made the 1890 institutions eligible for facilities grants when the original 1963 program was revived.

Secretary of Agriculture as New Agenda Spokesman

The National Agricultural Research, Extension, and Teaching Policy Act of 1977 contained a number of other initiatives that only indirectly affected the state agricultural experiment stations. The Secretary of Agriculture was directed to increase his Department's research and extension efforts in human nutrition, small farm technology, and international development and to undertake studies on water allocation problems and organic farming. With these additions, Title XIV touched upon almost every issue surrounding the direction of agricultural research, but it did not succeed in mediating between those who would control that direction. That task would be attempted by a new administration in Washington who would strive to implement the will of Congress as expressed in the ambiguities of the 1977 Act.

President Jimmy Carter brought with him to Washington a set of advisers who shared his populist desire to make the federal bureaucracy more responsive to the public. Bob Bergland, a Minnesota farmer-politician, was named as the Secretary of Agriculture and used that forum to bring a number of issues related to agriculture to public attention. To many of those in the agricultural research establishment, Secretary Bergland's championing of small farms, farm laborers, and organic farming seemed to represent the triumph of the New Agenda.

Chief among the Secretary's concerns were issues revolving around the structure of agriculture. The structure question included a number of complex components including the number and sizes of farms, the ownership and management of productive resources, barriers to entry into farming, the extent of commodity specialization and the technology employed.[6] But the central ingredient was a widespread concern that the "family farm," with all the values that concept stood for, was disappearing in the face of modernization.

Income stabilization, production control, and tax policies of the federal government were all assumed to be factors in the continuing trend toward fewer, larger, and more specialized farms, and agricultural research was assigned a prominent role since it led to biological and technological breakthroughs that afforded economies of scale to larger farms in many commodity enterprises.

Congress had expressed its concern for the family farm in the Food and Agriculture Act, stating that no federal farm payments program "be administered in a manner that will place the family farm at an unfair economic disadvantage" and, in Title XIV, amending the Rural Development Act of 1972 to include money for extension and research activities aimed directly toward serving small farmers with gross sales of less than $20,000 annually.

Two years later, Secretary Bergland began conducting a series of public meetings across the United States to highlight structure issues while convening a Structure of Agriculture Task Group within the Department to study the problem. Among the recommendations of the report which resulted from these activities was that the public agricultural research system must henceforth consider the potential structural impacts of scientific discovery and technology adoption in its research planning and must specifically address the unique problems of smaller and medium-sized farms.

Reflecting a similar viewpoint, a Senate committee in 1980 recommended that one-quarter of the federal agricultural science-support budget be earmarked for small farm programs. The suggestion was not enacted into law but, clearly, the research system's traditional insistence that its investigations were size-neutral would no longer serve as an effective defense for business as usual.[7]

The Bergland administration also challenged the public research establishment on the related issues of farm mechanization, chemical-intensive farming, and market enhancement investigations. Declaring that "we will not put federal money into research where . . . the major effect . . . will be the replacing of an adequate and willing work force with machines," the Secretary created an Agricultural Mechanization Task Force to recommend ways to evaluate the economic, social, environmental, and labor-displacement impacts of farm machinery research projects.

Similarly, a USDA Coordination Team for Organic Farming was assembled to evaluate the present research effort and indicate directions for the future to develop alternatives to chemical fertilizers and pesticides and farm management systems to use them efficiently. Following the lead of Congress, who had dropped the marketing requirement from the formula funding legislation partly because it encouraged product promotion research, the USDA under Bergland proposed to reduce its budget requests for state research support accordingly, despite the shared conclusions of state, federal, and agribusiness studies that indicated private industry would not likely fill the void if public post-harvest research was abandoned.[8]

If these initiatives from the USDA Secretary's office suggested to the state experiment stations that their traditional emphasis on the problems of production agriculture had little support in the upper echelons of federal administration, a general policy pronouncement from the office of Assistant Secretary of Conservation, Research, and Education confirmed their opinion.

In an October 1977 address to senior administrators of the Agricultural Research Service, the Deputy Assistant Secretary proclaimed that the priorities for federal expenditures of funds for agricultural science were human nutrition; energy conservation; land and water conservation and management; pest management; environmental protection; service to disadvantaged groups like minorities and women; and, conspicuously last, production and production efficiency. While the speech was delivered to the federal partner in the public agricultural research system, it forewarned the experiment stations that their traditional ally in Washington had been won over to the New Agenda.[9]

The state agricultural experiment stations had been adjusting their programs to better address social and environmental issues for some time and they would continue to do so under the new federal administration. What was new and troubling in the new situation was a series of organizational changes that, in the view of the state stations, reduced their input into the agricultural research policy process.

SEA Intensifies State-Federal Tensions

Following President Carter's pledge to improve management through administrative consolidation, a new Science and Education Administration (SEA) was interposed between the federal agricultural science agencies and the Assistant Secretary of Conservation, Research, and Education in 1978. A director was named to head the superagency which included the renamed Cooperative State Research Service (Cooperative Research), Agricultural Research Service (Agricultural Research), Extension Division (Extension), and National Agricultural Library (Technical Information Systems).

In the next year, the Science and Education Administration began reporting directly to the Secretary of Agriculture when the Assistant Secretary of Conservation, Research, and Education was transformed into the Assistant Secretary of Natural Resources and Environment, a position more suitable to the interests of its incumbent who was a former official of the National Wildlife Federation.[10]

Walter I. Thomas came to the deputy director's post of the Cooperative Research/Science and Education Administration in 1979 from the Pennsylvania Station and subsequently served as administrator of the Cooperative State Research Service until 1983. *(USDA photo)*

While this last move was welcomed by the state experiment stations as a gesture of confidence in the agricultural science components in the Department, it failed to halt the deterioration of relations between the state and federal research partners. Frustrations encountered in the process of reorganization prompted R.J. Aldrich, who had continued as the head of Cooperative Research under the title of Deputy Director, to resign in September of 1978 and return to the Missouri experiment station. Not until May of the following year was a successor found when Walter I. Thomas, the Associate Director of the Pennsylvania station, agreed to fill the vacancy. He met the same problems as his predecessor in representing the state stations' viewpoints within Department counsels.

SEA operated upon the laudable assumption that if the programs and needs of the partners in the public agricultural research and extension complex could be articulated as a united agenda to the budgetary decision makers in the USDA, the Office of Management and Budget, and Congress, the entire system would benefit by increased support. The plan had merit in theory, but in practice the system was so pluralistic that all efforts to promote greater coordination from Washington raised the specter of federal usurpation of authority in the states. To many in the effected USDA divisions as well as in the state experiment stations, the new arrangement was a "shotgun marriage" carried out for no other reason than to fulfill President Carter's commitment to reduce, on paper, the number of federal bureaus. Intra-agency restructuring within SEA did nothing to alter this conclusion.

A centralized Joint Planning and Evaluation Staff was formed to consolidate administrative activities related to planning, program reviews, and budget formulation for all the divisions within the Science and Education Administration. While Cooperative Research carried out the various project and program reviews as it had in the past, and even contributed staff scientists to the new management group, its traditional role as the main focus of state station concerns diminished. The shift of general oversight responsibilities for the national pesticide impact assessment program to a new USDA Office of Environmental Quality was another blow to morale within the Cooperative Research office.[11]

The new national planning organizations contributed another source of tension between the state and federal agricultural research allies. Just when the extensive ARPAC system was evolving into a useful forum for policy planning, the Joint Council arose to replace it. Simply because the Council included extension and teaching representatives as equal members, the voice of agricultural researchers within the planning structure was diluted. National committees for each of the three historic thrusts within the overall land-grant mission followed, as did counterparts on the regional level. Each of these committees brought in members from outside the traditional state-federal agricultural science and education complex, further reducing the influence of experiment station spokesmen.

So great was the confusion sown by so many new planning organizations imposed on top of remnants of the existing structure that the North Central Region Association of Directors declared in the summer of 1980 its intention to suspend cooperative planning activities. While the other three regional directors associations did not go so far as to secede from Joint Council efforts, they generally shared their colleagues' opinion that the state stations were not being given a voice in policy formulation commensurate to their importance. The widespread dissatisfaction with the national planning system and with the inordinate amount of attention given to these activities by the Science and Education Administration prompted a former CSRS Administrator to report to Congress that "the university half of the partnership concept is in disarray."[12]

State Stations Develop Proactive Stance

Convinced by changes in USDA administrative arrangements and planning activities that their contributions were undervalued, the state agricultural experiment stations began developing a proactive stance designed to evidence their historic importance and their continuing relevance to agriculture in the United States. As it had so often in the past, the Experiment Station Committee on Organization and Policy took the lead in the effort by commissioning a series of "white papers" in 1979 to address issues of national concern involving agricultural research.

One such study focused on scientist training, a major continuing contribution of the state experiment stations that often went unrecognized. The array of scientific disciplines represented in each of the stations, as well as the graduate stipends that research funds provided, afforded a system of graduate education which could not have been supported by academic interests and budgets alone.

A similar case was made for the stations' role in international development assistance through the training of foreign agricultural scientists in land-grant colleges and through scientific teams dispatched to developing countries to attack indigenous problems.

The farm structure debate was the topic of another ESCOP report that sought to furnish scientific data to enlighten the controversy over the role of research discoveries in consolidating farm ownership and management. The study results did little to resolve the conflict, supporting both the stations' contention that the vast majority of their research was size-neutral and the critics' assertion that whatever knowledge was produced was more valuable to larger farms because of economies-of-scale considerations. Still, the ESCOP effort stood as evidence that the state agricultural experiment stations increasingly were willing to invest their time and talents in assessing the social consequences of their programs.[13]

In addition to single-issue studies of topics of intense public concern, the state stations in 1978 launched a new interregional project to evaluate the historical value of their efforts and to enhance that value in the future. Designated IR-6, the National and Regional Analysis, Evaluation, Planning, and Financing of Agricultural Research project provided regional research funds for continuing cooperative investigations into the areas identified in the title.

Individual analyses conducted under IR-6 provided information of immediate use to the various planning committees and for budget formulation in ESCOP and SEA. Potentially more important in the long run, IR-6 stimulated the search for better ways to measure the economic and distributional impacts of agricultural research so that the public could better evaluate the usefulness of its investment in agricultural research. Without such analyses, the connection between scientific investigation and availability of inexpensive, nutritious food, for example, was obscured because benefits to consumers were in such small increments.[14]

All of these initiatives were designed to showcase the state experiment stations' contributions to improving agriculture and their capacity to address emerging problems. Toward this same end of communicating their dynamic and distinctive character, a number of state station leaders revived efforts to place an individual in Washington to give more visibility to the programs of the stations. The idea of creating a position for an "executive director" or "liaison officer" for ESCOP was a recurring one beginning in the mid-1960s when the Directors-At-Large were constituted.

By the early 1970s, sentiment among members of ESCOP's extension and resident instruction counterpart organizations also favored the proposal, prompting the National Association of State Universities and Land-Grant Colleges to name a Director of Governmental Relations for its Division of Agriculture. While this individual functioned to keep an eye on legislative developments of interest to the three science and education sections that comprised the Division, many station administrators maintained that their unique needs deserved full-time attention.

The flurry of activity related to formulation of the 1977 farm bill and the anticipated reorganization of the USDA under Secretary Bergland lent support to a renewed effort on behalf of a Washington-based spokesman to serve as "Executive Vice-Chairman of ESCOP." Despite the endorsement of three of the four regional directors associations in 1977, the proposed ultimately failed. Many station directors feared that the incumbent might become enmeshed in the very bureaucracy he was intended to monitor, while others hesitated to give the appearance of breaking ranks with their extension and teaching allies within the land-grant complex. The four regional Directors-At-Large, then, remained as the principal points of contact on the national level, with the Director-At-Large from the ESCOP chairman's region functioning as the group's leader. The arrangement retained a strong presence in Washington and was symbolic of the pluralism inherent in the state side of the public agricultural research partnership.[15]

Local Priorities Remain Imperative

The state directors' reluctance to name a single individual as spokesman for their cause underlined the distinctive nature of the agricultural experiment station system. They decried the changes in administrative and policy planning arrangements in Washington not because of their effect on the actual conduct of investigations at the state level but because they seemed to disregard the basic premise that a network of locally directed research institutions could best address, in aggregate, the needs of agriculture for the whole United States. Notwithstanding their concern over national developments, the experiment station directors still were overwhelmingly oriented toward the special needs of their particular states.

As integral units within the state land-grant universities receiving an average of nearly 70 percent of their support from non-federal sources, the agricultural experiment stations naturally owed their first allegiance to local priorities. State legislators, who provided about 80 percent of the non-federal funds out of tax revenues, were most interested in increasing the incomes of those in the food- and fiber-related sectors of the economy, so it was incumbent upon the stations to direct their main research thrusts toward this end. Only by successfully demonstrating their capacity to contribute to the health of the agricultural production, processing, and marketing economy could the state stations garner the support necessary to drive the social and environmental investigations demanded of them by less traditional constituencies.

The state experiment stations continued to develop a variety of mechanisms to remain responsive to the desires of their clients and to communicate their success in fulfilling those needs. Closer contacts with the extension service agents spread over the state was one way of keeping in touch with agricultural opinion, periodic station field days or open houses were another. More formally, nearly every station had one or more advisory councils in operation by the late 1970s. Varying in size from fifteen to 130 members representing organizations of farmers, cooperatives, food processors, conservationists, and consumers, the advisory groups served as templates where research opportunities identified by laymen could be matched to the research capabilities of station scientists.[16]

Budget Trends

Judged by increases in state appropriations and other non-federal funds made available to them between 1977 and 1981, the agricultural experiment stations had some success in courting local support. Total state appropriations to the stations went from $334,168,000 in 1977 to $490,987,000 in 1981, a rate of increase averaging nearly 12 percent annually.

Funds provided from other non-federal sources mounted even more rapidly. Industry contracts and grants rose from $31,819,000 to $50,729,000 in those four years. Private donations and proceeds from general and specific commodity check-off programs, by which producers assessed themselves through a transaction tax to support research in their areas, increased from $52,262,000 in 1977 to $86,793,000 in 1981. Sales of station products returned another $38,675,000 to the state research programs in 1977 and $58,530,000 in 1981. In aggregate, non-federal dollars grew nearly 50 percent over the four years, reinforcing the agricultural experiment stations' ties to local constituencies.[17]

Federal funds to the state agricultural experiment stations rose at a similarly impressive rate between 1977 and 1981 (nearly 57 percent) but, significantly, most of the gain was in categories outside the traditional Hatch formula. In 1977, Hatch money amounted to $97,973,000, or 76 percent of the money allocated through the Cooperative State Research Service; in 1981, Hatch equalled $128,615,000, or 64 percent of Cooperative Research-administered dollars.

Large increases in the Special Grants category and the new program authorizations in the 1977 Title XIV legislation that were funded beginning in 1979 accounted for a growing share of the federal support. By 1981, Special Grants amounted to $17,076,000, nearly $10,000,000 more than in 1977. Animal Health and Disease formula grants equalled $6,500,000 and the Alcohol Fuels research grants totaled $500,000. Beginning in 1980, $650,000 was also made available annually for grants to support investigations into extracting latex from the native guayule plant under a program authorized in 1978 legislation.

Each of these initiatives was funded far below the amounts called for in Title XIV: Congress had proposed $195,000,000 for Hatch and $40,000,000 for Animal Health research in 1981, for example.[18] The reluctance of lawmakers to actually provide appropriations to agricultural research at anywhere near the levels suggested in authorizing legislation was not new. However, it was particularly disappointing during this period when every review of the public research system, including those by the planning bodies created by Congress to offer advice on the subject, repeatedly called for substantial increases in support.

Competitive Grants Program Operation

The manner in which the Carter administration went about seeking additional dollars under Title XIV authority added further to the frustration of the state experiment stations. Wholly accepting the contention that national priorities in agricultural research could best be addressed through project grants open to all scientists, the executive budget requests during the Carter years directed all substantial increases in the category of Competitive Grants. While many of the state experiment station directors harbored some misgivings toward competitive grants because of the time necessary to formulate proposals and the lack of flexibility they afforded in local allocation, they had come to support the concept as a complement to traditional institutional formula funding. Thus, when $15,000,000 in Competitive Grants first became available in 1978 along with increases of $14,000,000 in the traditional categories, the experiment stations were satisfied with the result.

They were considerably less pleased when the following year's budget proposal, the first entirely developed by the Carter administration, was presented to Congress. The 1979 fiscal year agricultural research-support request asked that the Competitive Grants allocation be doubled to $30,000,000 and that the traditional formula and Special Grants funds be reduced by nearly $15,000,000. However much the USDA administrators who defended the proposal before the House agricultural appropriations subcommittee protested that the increase in Competitive Grants and the decrease in traditional sources were unrelated, Congress was understandably skeptical. Ultimately, formula funds were restored and Competitive Grants reduced to their 1978 levels.

Special Grants, the perenially favored way for Congress to direct research money to specific areas, benefited from an $8,500,000 increase for 1979. Subsequent executive branch budget requests did not again make the mistake of proposing cuts in formula grants although they did consistently ask for substantial increases in Competitive Grants, usually at the expense of Special Grants and the other specific funding programs in animal health and alcohol fuels. Just as consistently, Congress restored the proposed cuts with modest yearly increases across the board, including Competitive Grants which were raised to $16,000,000 in 1980 and 1981.[19]

The ill will resulting from the 1979 budget fiasco did not prevent the state agricultural experiment stations from pursuing, and winning, the majority of competitively awarded grants. Congressional appropriators, guided by the suggestions of a number of advisory opinions from the scientific community, designated four high-priority basic research areas in plant science as eligible for $10,000,000 in grant funding and reserved the remaining $5,000,000 for supporting fundamental human nutrition investigations. With their years of research into the congressionally favored areas of nitrogen fixation, biological stress, photosynthesis, and genetic improvement, the state experiment stations had a natural advantage in the competition for funds, even though administration of the grants program was modeled upon a review structure more familiar to National Science Foundation and National Institutes of Health grantees than to most state station scientists.

The office established by the USDA to manage the Competitive Grants program was placed under the Cooperative Research agency (except for a brief period in 1978 when it reported directly to SEA) but its staff was drawn primarily from federal grant organizations outside the traditional agricultural research complex. Scientists on temporary two-year appointments were chosen as managers for the five program areas to convene ad hoc peer review panels that recommended funding action on project proposals.

In the first year, only 17 percent of the 1,109 project requests were funded and then only at about one-half the level requested. With so little chance of securing adequate support, project submissions dropped to 861 in 1979, and to 600 in 1980. Peer review panels deemed more than half of the proposals worthy of funding but only 22 percent of 1979 and 34 percent of 1980 requests could be met with available money. Despite the relatively low levels of support in the initial years of the Competitive Grants operation, the new program was a significant step toward reinvigorating fundamental research and opening up the federal agricultural research treasury to the entire scientific community.[20]

The implications of the philosophy behind the enactment of the Competitive Grants were not lost upon the state agricultural experiment stations. Clearly, despite the opposition of powerful House appropriation members to the new program, they could expect little support among national policymakers for substantial increases in formula funds reserved for use at their discretion.

Like many provisions of the National Agricultural Research, Extension, and Teaching Policy Act of 1977, the Competitive Grants program evidenced the intention of Congress to assume a greater role in directing research. The activities of the Department of Agriculture in implementing the will of Congress were viewed by the state stations as an attempt to assert federal control over federal dollars, enormously straining relations between the traditional research partners in the late 1970s.

Intended to better coordinate the public agricultural research system, Title XIV paradoxically alienated the major component in the complex. Still, the legislation's renewed commitment to agricultural science was a hopeful sign for the future, prompting the state stations to work for increased recognition of their special value and continued relevance in addressing the problems of modern agriculture.

Notes

[1] Dale L. Stansbury, "Context and Implications of the National Agricultural Research, Extension, and Teaching Policy Act of 1977," unpublished manuscript, [ca. 1985].

[2] Title XVI: National Agricultural Research, Extension, and Teaching Policy Act, 91 Stat. 981 (1977).

[3] U.S. Congress, House Committee on Agriculture, *Agricultural Act of 1977: Report* (95th Cong., 1st sess., Report No. 95-348, May 1977), p. 163; interview with R.D. Rouse, April 16, 1986.

[4] Maury E. Bredahl, W. Keith Bryant, and V.W. Ruttan, "Behavior and Productivity Implications of Institutional and Project Funding of Research," *American Journal of Agricultural Economics* 62 (August 1980): 378.

[5] E.M. Babb, *Impacts of Federal Funding Requirements on Marketing Research*, pp. 4, 32; U.S. Congress, House Committee on Agriculture, *National Agricultural Research Policy Act of 1976: Report* (94th Cong., 2nd sess., Report No. 94-1172, May 1976), p. 18.

[6] W.D. Rasmussen, "The Structure of Farming and American History," in *Farm Structure: A Historical Perspective on Changes in the Number and Size of Farms*, ed. U.S. Congress, Senate Committee on Agriculture, Nutrition, and Forestry (96th Cong., 2nd sess., April 1980), p. 3.

[7] USDA, *A Time to Choose: Summary Report on the Structure of Agriculture* (Washington: USDA, 1981), pp. 7-9, 152; U.S. Congress, Senate Select Committee on Small Business, *Agricultural Research Policy: Report* (96th Cong., 2nd sess., April 1980), p. 2.

[8]Bergland quote in Busch and Lacy, *Science, Agriculture, and Politics of Research*, p. 150; USDA, "Secretary's Memorandum No. 2017, June 27, 1980"; "Science and Education Administration/Cooperative Research-Station Letter-2814, September 10, 1979"; Denis J. Prager and Gilbert S. Omenn, "Federal Support of Food and Agricultural Science: The Quid Pro Quo," in *Federal Funding Philosophies, Policies, and Procedures: Impact on Research in the Food and Agricultural Sciences*, ed. Western Association of Agricultural Experiment Station Directors ([Berkeley, California]: n.p., 1980), p. 22; Wiser and Bowers, *Marketing Research*, pp. 100-105.

[9]Don F. Hadwiger, *The Politics of Agricultural Research* (Lincoln: University of Nebraska Press, 1982), pp. 188-189.

[10]USDA, Science and Education Administration, *USDA's Science and Education Administration: What It Is—What It Does* (Washington: USDA, 1980), pp. 2-3; USDA, "Secretary's Memorandum No. 1993, July 23, 1979"; Hadwiger, *Politics of Agricultural Research*, p. 188; interview with T.S. Ronningen, November 17, 1985.

[11]Interview with O.G. Bentley, May 23, 1986; interview with R.L. Lovvorn, April 22, 1986; interview with D.W. Barton, June 18, 1986; U.S. Congress, House Committee on Appropriations, Surveys and Investigations Staff, "A Report on the Scientific Research Programs of the Department of Agriculture" in *Agriculture, Rural Development, and Related Agencies Appropriations for 1981: Hearings*, pt. 4, U.S. Congress, House Committee on Appropriations (96th Cong., 2nd sess., March 1980) pp. 791, 817 (quotation); ESCOP, "Interim Subcommittee Minutes, August 16-17 and November 28, 1979"; ESCOP, "Minutes, October 31-November 1, 1979."

[12]John P. Mahlstede, "Roles of the Joint Council on Food and Agricultural Sciences and the National Agricultural Research and Extension Users Advisory Board in Coordinating Research and Determining Research Priorities," in *Assessment of the Agricultural Research System*, vol. 2, pt. B, *Commissioned Papers*, ed. U.S. Congress, Office of Technology Assessment, pp. 3-4; Ron Knutson, Don Paarlberg, and Alex McCalla, "Forces Affecting Food and Agricultural Research Decisions," in *ibid.*, vol. 2, pt. A, *Commissioned Papers*, p. 12; Emery N. Castle, "Agricultural Education and Research: Academic Crown Jewels or Country Cousin?," Kellogg Foundation Lecture, NASULGC, November 18, 1980, p. 12n; R.L. Lovvorn, "Effect of Organization, Policy, and Procedures on Research Management," in *Assessment of the Agricultural Research System*, vol. 2, pt. A, *Commissioned Papers*, ed. U.S. Congress, Office of Technology Assessment, p. 14 (quotation).

[13]ESCOP, "Minutes, April 28-29, 1980" and "Interim Subcommittee Minutes, February 8-9, 1984"; Glenn L. Johnson and Sylvan H. Wittwer, *Agricultural Technology Until 2030: Prospects, Priorities, and Policies* (East Lansing: Michigan State University A.E.S. Special Report 12, 1984), pp. 51-52; ESCOP, *Research and the Family Farm* (Ithaca, New York: Cornell University, 1981), p. 7.

[14]ESCOP, "Minutes, October 31- November 1, 1979 and April 28-29, 1980"; Bobby R.Eddleman, "National and Regional Analysis, Evaluation, Planning, and Financing of Agricultural Research, IR-6," in *Research Perspectives*, eds. ESCOP and CSRS, p. 27.

[15]ESCOP, "Minutes, April 28-29 and November 18, 1970, November 12, 1972, October 12-13, 1976, and April 27-28, 1977" and "Interim Subcommittee Minutes, September 28, 1969, May 3-4, 1970, and July 14-15, 1971"; interview with Durward F. Bateman, Director, North Carolina Agricultural Research Service, Raleigh, N.C., April 22, 1986; interview with R.D. Rouse, April 16, 1986; interview with T.S. Ronningen, February 28, 1985.

[16]Interview with T.S. Ronningen, February 10, 1986; correspondence with J.E. Halpin, December 16, 1985; K.A. Huston, "Priority Setting Processes," pp. 18, 31-33.

[17]CSRS, *Inventories of Agricultural Research: FY 1977-FY 1981* (Washington: USDA, CSRS, 1978-1982), table IV.

[18] Ibid.; CSRS, "Appropriation History"; ESCOP, "Minutes, October 10-11, 1977."

[19] U.S. Congress, House Committee on Appropriations, Subcommittee on Agriculture, Rural Development, and Related Agencies, *Agriculture, Rural Development, and Related Agencies Appropriations for 1979: Hearings*, pt. 7 (95th Cong., 2nd sess., March 1978), pp. 533-535; D.L. Stansbury, "Context and Implications of the Act of 1977," p. 11; "SEA/CR-Station Letters-2617 (September 21, 1978), 2797 (January 22, 1979), 2802 (June 1, 1979), 2809 (July 20, 1979), 2819 (November 13, 1979), 2820 (January 28, 1980), 2839 (June 18, 1980), and 2846a (December 3, 1980)."

[20] USDA, CSRS, *First Two Years of Operation of the Competitive Research Grants Office* (Washington: USDA, CSRS, 1982), pp. 4-5, 16, 67; David W. Krogmann and Joe Key, "The Agriculture Grants Program," *Science* 213 (July 10, 1981): 179-181.

CHAPTER VII
Restoration and Rededication: 1981-1987

The acrimony that characterized relations between the state experiment stations and federal agricultural research administrators in the late 1970s was tempered in the 1980s by two developments. Legislative adjustments to the National Agricultural Research, Extension, and Teaching Policy Act made the initiatives embodied in the 1977 bill more palatable to the state stations while a new administration in the USDA overturned the most repugnant features of the Science and Education Administration organizational structure. Together, these events restored the state component in the national science and education complex to a position of leadership befitting its traditional importance and encouraged the state stations to work with renewed dedication within the nationally coordinated agricultural research system.

Title XIV Amendments at 1981
Reaffirm the Partnership

Title XIV was amended in 1981 as part of the scheduled reauthorization of the general farm bill of that year. The new version of the National Agricultural Research, Extension, and Teaching Policy Act did not repudiate the initiatives of 1977 which had opened research planning and funding opportunities to a broader spectrum of interests, but its clarifying amendments did go further in recognizing the role and mission of the traditional elements.

To the introductory section, wording was added to reaffirm the importance of the state-federal agricultural science partnership, hailed by Congress as having been "eminently successful" in providing "the most productive and efficient food and agricultural system in the world" which served as "the basis of our national affluence." Although the amended legislation stopped short of specifically recognizing state priorities as equal in importance to regional and national ones, it did allude to "the varied, dispersed, and in many cases, site-specific needs of American agriculture" as the feature that made the "unique partnership arrangement" so necessary for success. Evidence of renewed respect in Congress for the state agricultural experiment stations' traditional program thrusts was also found in a Title XIV amendment that ranked productivity maintenance and enhancement at the top of a list of "major needs and challenges" for the future. Another addition defined research on the basic, applied, and developmental continuum characteristic of the programs in the state stations. A further indication of the lawmakers' commitment to science and education as a priority concern was the inclusion of a section directing the USDA to add an assistant secretary-level position to administer the provisions of Title XIV.[1]

The main purpose of the 1981 amendments to the National Agricultural Research, Extension, and Teaching Policy Act was simply to renew the programs of 1977 for another four years. Yet even in this, the state experiment stations secured some significant changes in wording. Hatch formula funds were authorized to go from $220,000,000 in 1982 to $250,000,000 in 1985. While these figures were far below those suggested by the state stations (who proposed $430,000,000 for 1985), the experiment stations were heartened by a new proviso that guaranteed Hatch dollars at a minimum of 25 percent of USDA expenditures in cooperative research programs and another that prohibited the substitution of federal money in lieu of continued state support. Thus, Congress promised not to replace traditional formula allocations with specific competitively awarded grant programs and reaffirmed the idea that these dollars were meant to stimulate increased state aid, not supplant it.[2]

The 1981 amendments to Title XIV continued all the special programs initiated in the 1977 original with, in most cases, little change. The section reauthorizing research facilities grants was extended even though no funds had actually materialized in the intervening years. Alcohol fuels and guayule grant programs were also continued through 1985. So were the animal health formula allocations, but, to make the relatively small sums more effective in generating useful investigations, only accredited colleges of veterinary medicine and state experiment stations were to be recipients. Previously, any institution with a department of veterinary science or animal pathology had been eligible for support.

Competitive Grants remained open to all scientists. In addition to extending the programs through 1985 at the annually authorized level of $50,000,000, Congress defined high priority research to include basic investigations into scientific principles and techniques; research on biological nitrogen fixation, photosynthesis, and other productivity enhancing processes; basic and applied investigations related to animal health, human nutrition, and soil and water; and research to develop "new promising crops" like guayule and jojoba.

Within this broad framework, the Joint Council and Users Advisory Board were to continue to suggest more specific areas for emphasis. Both advisory panels, however, were restructured as Congress responded to the dissatisfaction of the state experiment stations which had culminated in the withdrawal of the North Central Region directors from national planning activities. Whereas the original Title XIV had left the composition of the Joint Council on Food and Agricultural Sciences to the discretion of the Secretary of Agriculture, the 1981 version set the number of members at a minimum of twenty-five, at least half of which were to come from the land-grant universities or experiment stations. The change gave the Joint Council a more corporate basis of representation closer to the proportional allocation of the public investment in research, extension, and teaching.

In a further effort to regain the trust of the state side of the science and education partnership, Congress directed the Joint Council to utilize existing regional research, extension, and teaching organizations to provide regional inputs into the national planning processes. The reconstituted Joint Council was also to compile and submit by July of 1983 a five-year plan for the agricultural sciences programs, with updated reports to follow every two years thereafter. The annual priorities and accomplishments summaries were to be continued as well.

The National Agricultural Research and Extension Users Advisory Board's membership was also adjusted at the insistence of the experiment stations who agreed with incumbent farmer representatives on the Board that this traditional constituency deserved a greater voice. Expanded from twenty-one to twenty-five members, the Users Advisory Board thenceforth included eight (instead of four) commodity producer delegates chosen to reflect regional differences.[3]

New Funding Authorizations

While these amendments to the National Agricultural Research, Extension, and Teaching Policy Act had the effect of expanding the traditional research interests' leadership role, other changes in the original legislation continued the trend of emphasizing new areas in need of attention. Although willing to give greater voice to the state agricultural experiment stations in research planning, the national lawmakers were still determined to indicate, and fund, specific program directions. Two fields of agricultural production were slated to receive greater emphasis through special matching grants support.

Despite the lack of support from the Experiment Station Committee on Organization and Policy, who believed the program's intent could be met through the Hatch process, a new subtitle was added to authorize $10,000,000 annually for rangeland and permanent pasture research. A Rangeland Research Advisory Board representing the USDA, state agricultural experiment stations, and national livestock organizations was called for to suggest priority areas for investigations into forage quality improvement, range watershed management, and rangeland revegetation.

An aquaculture research and extension program was launched by another new subtitle. It, too, created an advisory board to propose priorities related to enhancing the production of aquatic food species and authorized matching grants (of $7,500,000 yearly) to support fisheries science at the land-grant universities, experiment stations, and other capable research institutions.[4]

By focusing on a production enterprise of enormous potential for providing the protein needs of peoples in developing countries, the aquaculture research and extension grants program at least indirectly was related to a major new thrust of the Title XIV amendments, international development assistance. Toward this end, the Secretary of Agriculture was directed to lend support to Agency for International Development efforts in developing nations and to draw upon the talents of the land-grant institutions in meeting this charge.

The potential of the state experiment station system to contribute knowledge of value to foreign agriculture was strengthened through other sections of the 1981 legislation. American Somoa and Micronesia were made eligible to receive Hatch and other formula disbursements for the first time, thus expanding research on tropical agriculture within the public research complex. An intensified program in dairy goat research, another production area with international implications, was legislated as well when Congress set aside 1 percent of the annual Evans-Allen funds to support a Dairy Goat Research Center at one of the 1890 institutions.

All of the historically black land-grant colleges were to benefit from another amendment to Title XIV. Although they had been made eligible for the state agricultural experiment stations facilities grants

by the terms of the 1977 Act, the absence of subsequent appropriations in this category prompted efforts to reserve a separate budget
authorization in 1981. The lawmakers complied by directing that
$10,000,000 be forwarded annually through 1986 to the 1890 colleges
and Tuskegee University for the acquisition and improvement of
research facilities. The institutions had already worked out an allocation plan based on each station's perception of needs, so no legislated
formula accompanied the grants.[5]

Taken together, the 1981 amendments to the National Agricultural
Research, Extension, and Teaching Policy Act somewhat clarified
congressional expectations as to the role of the agricultural research
partners. While it gave greater recognition to the value of the state
agricultural experiment stations, Congress did not abandon attempts
to shape more specifically the national research program. Although it
ranked productivity enhancement at the top of its list of "major needs
and challenges," the remaining entries, significantly, were closer to
New Agenda concerns: new food, fiber, and energy resources;
agricultural energy use; natural resources conservation and management; human health and welfare; human nutrition; and international
agricultural development. Expanded special research and extension
programs in solar energy, small farms technology, and human
nutrition were also included in amendments. Clearly, Congress was
not prepared to return entirely the setting of agricultural science
priorities to the traditional USDA-state land-grant universities
establishment.

Orville G. Bentley, former director of
the North Dakota and the Illinois
Stations, became the USDA's first
Assistant Secretary of Science and
Education in 1982. *(USDA photo)*

Assistant Secretary of Science and Education Named

The revisions in Title XIV were welcomed by the state agricultural experiment stations and reorganizations in the Department of Agriculture agencies concerned with agricultural science were equally promising. Spokesmen for the experiment stations had for many years urged Congress to compel the USDA to create an assistant secretary-level position to concentrate entirely on science and education activities. The lawmakers had been on the verge of complying in the original 1977 Title XIV but had relented when the executive branch took issue with the idea of letting Congress mandate the titles of its departmental officers through legislation. In 1981, a compromise was agreed upon: the amended Title XIV authorized the naming of an additional assistant secretary to carry out its provisions and the USDA retained the right to enumerate the exact duties of the position.

In the fall of 1982, new Secretary of Agriculture John R. Block selected Orville G. Bentley as the Department's first Assistant Secretary of Science and Education. Dr. Bentley was a popular choice among the station directors because of his impeccable scientific credentials in biochemistry and his long experience in state experiment station administration. Having served over the preceding quarter-century as dean of agriculture in the land-grant universities of North Dakota, then Illinois, and as co-chairman of the Agricultural Research Policy Advisory Committee in the mid-1970s, he was intimately familiar with the unique role of the state experiment stations and skilled in the task of articulating that role in national counsels. With this background, Bentley was admirably suited to the position that the experiment stations hoped would elevate their visibility in budget preparation sessions within the Ronald Reagan administration and more knowledgeably defend their programs in hearings before Congress.[6]

Even before an Assistant Secretary of Science and Education was appointed, the "shotgun marriage" of USDA agencies that were placed under him was dissolved. In June of 1981, the Cooperative State Research Service, Agricultural Research Service, Extension Service, and National Agricultural Library reassumed their former titles and independent statuses. Walter Thomas continued as head of CSRS, serving as Administrator until he resigned because of failing health in 1983. His successor was the energetic former director of the

Colorado station and a past chairman of ESCOP, John Patrick Jordan. Under his stewardship, CSRS embarked on the arduous tasks of restoring intra-agency morale and state station confidence in the wake of the SEA interregnum.

CSRS Acts to Restore Confidence

To accomplish these purposes, the agency set about refining its specific goals and overall mission. The process was begun soon after the Science and Education Administration was dismantled when a panel of nine representatives of state experiment stations, schools of veterinary medicine, 1890 colleges, and non-land grant institutions was invited by the agency in early 1982 to review the role of CSRS in the public agricultural research system. Insisting that the agency must be more than a bookkeeping office through which federal funds flowed, the group recommended that CSRS be given the administrative authority and professional support necessary to enhance its position as "the connecting link between the [research] efforts of the states and those of the federal government."[7]

The appointment of a sympathetic Assistant Secretary and the restoration of autonomy elevated the status of CSRS in the eyes of the stations, but a 1982 reductions-in-force order and subsequent personnel ceilings limited its ability to expand its review functions. Forced to

John P. Jordan, administrator of the Cooperative State Research Service since 1983, had previously been director of the Colorado Station. *(USDA photo)*

operate in reduced circumstances, Administrator Jordan concentrated on building an atmosphere of collegiality among his scientific staff and improving the agency's credibility in the agricultural research community. Professionals in CSRS were encouraged to view themselves as a "faculty" with special expertise in promoting research excellence at the state stations.

With the opportunity for increased numbers of on-site program reviews constrained by financial and staff considerations, Jordan continued his predecessors' emphasis on quality rather than quantity. While reviews still were unofficially scheduled to be performed for each station program once every five years, routine evaluations were discouraged in favor of ones that would coincide with station self-studies and major changes in program staffs. Scientists outside the agency increasingly were relied upon to serve as peer reviewers on CSRS-led visiting teams in a continuing effort to place the best talent in the scientific community at the disposal of each state experiment station.

Toward the same end of improving the quality of research undertaken in the system, CSRS began to more closely scrutinize the investigations carried out under authority of the non-competitive portion of Special Grants. The majority of funds in this category went to strengthen nationally coordinated activities like the Integrated Pest Management program, but the handful that originated from individual congressmen responding to the entreaties of powerful producer groups within their districts often could make no such claim. Although willing to concede the inevitability of such programs as a trade-off for continued congressional support for the entire system, CSRS with the backing of the state stations insisted on rigorous evaluations of the scientific merit of these projects and sought ways to broaden their coverage to at least a regional scope.[8]

To build the agency's administrative procedures upon a firm philosophical base, Administrator Jordan enlisted the CSRS faculty in developing a unified "Strategic Plan" to guide its activities into the future. Over the course of 1985 and 1986, CSRS scientists met in a series of staff meetings to articulate an organizational mission and goals and to develop an intra-agency system to continuously address identified objectives. The resulting mission statement recognized the broad responsibility of CSRS "to advance science and technology in support of agriculture, forestry, people and communities: in partnership with the state agricultural experiment station system, colleges, universities and other research organizations, and in concert with the Secretary of Agriculture and the intent of Congress."

To fulfill the mission, three goals were identified: obtaining federal resources for the acquisition of new knowledge, promoting excellence in the research system, and improving cooperation between the various research partners. To insure the agency's responsiveness to issues related to these goals, CSRS professionals were to serve voluntarily on standing committees concerned with resource acquisition, partner relationships, information services, research management, new dimensions in science, and quality assurance. A seventh panel made up of the chairmen of the other committees would coordinate planning among them.

Consistent with the philosophy of Assistant Secretary Bentley and Administrator Jordan in both its statement of mission and structure for implementation, the 1986 Strategic Plan was a significant departure from the immediate past. As recently as 1982, a CSRS mission statement had emphasized the agency's role as the representative of the Secretary of Agriculture rather than as the servant of science and the SEA management plan of the late 1970s had hardly been conducive to the participatory decision-making processes embodied in the scientist-controlled committee system introduced in the new Strategic Plan. Like the state agricultural experiment stations with which it so closely worked, the Cooperative State Research Service was determined to reassert its role in the public agricultural research partnership.[9]

Accountability Demands Continue

The agency was wise in describing its mission in terms of its commitment to agricultural science rather than on the narrower basis of serving the USDA and state stations because national policymakers continued their efforts to open the system to new interests. The Reagan administration's Office of Science and Technology Policy (OSTP) favored competitive grants for fundamental investigations as the primary target for increased support of agricultural research, a position endorsed by a blue-ribbon conference of science administrators impaneled by the OSTP and the Rockefeller Foundation in the summer of 1982. The Winrock Conference findings, further echoing the conclusions of the Pound Report of a decade earlier, questioned the efficacy of traditional formula funding and planning mechanisms to address national priorities. Despite the reaffirmation of the historical partnership evidenced in the language of the amended version of Title XIV, some members of Congress shared the skepticism, particularly after the lawmakers' own Office of Technology Assessment came to similar conclusions after a 1981 study.[10]

On two occasions in the early 1980s, Congress moved to express its continuing concern for expanding research directions and opportunities through new legislation. Convinced that investigations into non-chemical farming systems had not increased to the degree called for in either version of Title XIV, twenty-two House members sponsored an organic farming support bill in 1982. The proposal would have financed for five years a system of regional centers for research and extension efforts in organic agriculture in association with land-grant universities. Ultimately accepting the agricultural research establishment's contention that farming could not be divided into categories of conventional versus organic and that its existing programs could furnish the desired information through regular channels, Congress did not pass the measure.[11]

Congressional proponents of a bill to reserve a portion of federal research appropriations for small private firms was more successful. The Small Business Innovation Development Act of 1982 set aside annually an increasing fraction (0.2 percent in 1983, rising to 1.25 percent in 1986 and thereafter) of all federal funds to stimulate innovative technological research in the private sector, particularly by "small and disadvantaged firms." The set-aside applied to funds administered through CSRS, earmarking money for projects that ranged from six months to two years in areas already addressed by public institutions: air, water, and soil; plant and animal production and protection; food science and nutrition; forestry and related resources; and rural and community development.[12]

Title XIV Amendments of 1985
Revive Productivity

Responding to the growing perception that the rate of commodity-yield gains was stagnating and that the core of knowledge upon which future increases depended was eroding,[13] Congress had identified productivity enhancement as a priority concern in the amended Title XIV of 1981. When that title came up for renewal as part of the 1985 general farm bill, this traditional program emphasis received even greater attention. Indicative of the renewed interest in assisting agriculture in providing plentiful domestic supplies of comestibles was the official designation given the new farm bill: The Food Security Act of 1985.

Included among the amendments related to the support of science and education, a major new subtitle was appended to promote research to enhance agricultural productivity while conserving natural resources. Research under the new sections was to be integrated with extension efforts in a program that employed operating farms in field experiments of between five- and fifteen-years duration. Special emphasis was placed upon projects involving "legume-crop rotation, the use of green manure, animal manures, and municipal wastes . . . , and biological methods of weed, disease, and insect control," reflecting the continuing attractiveness of organic farming practices to lawmakers.[14]

Hesitant to authorize new spending programs in an era of burgeoning budget deficits, Congress legislated no specific amounts to fund the productivity enhancement program. Consistent with this action, authorizations for specific program thrusts embodied in the 1977 and 1981 versions of the National Agricultural Research, Extension, and Teaching Policy Act remained level when the animal health, aquaculture, and rangeland research grants were extended through 1990. The alcohol fuels program was shifted to support from Competitive Grants.

Hatch formula funds were slated for increases but at a miserly rate of less than 4 percent annually, with $270,000,000 authorized for 1986 and $310,000,000 for 1990. Only Competitive Grants were to receive substantially increased funds when the approved annual ceiling jumped from $50,000,000 in 1985 to $70,000,000 in 1986 and subsequent years.

Much of the support for the competitively awarded grants program derived from congressional interest in the potentials of biotechnology, a collection of techniques to manipulate the genetic material of living organisms at the cellular or molecular level. Since 1972, when a group of Stanford University researchers successfully implanted the gene of one organism into another, biological engineering through DNA recombination had seized the imagination of a growing number of scientists who saw enormous possibilities. The interest was especially acute in agriculture where the limits of significant productivity advances were generally accepted as having been reached by traditional methods of plant and animal breeding and chemical and mechanical technologies. The promise of superior plant strains that could fix their own nitrogen, resist disease, and overcome adverse growing conditions, for example, was attractive to producers and consumers alike since fewer costly, environmentally damaging inputs would be needed to produce more abundant crops. Presented in this way, the opportunities inherent in molecular genetics research were irresistible to lawmakers concerned with encouraging new technology in the public interest.[15]

While the addition of $20,000,000 in annually authorized funds for Competitive Grants implicitly promoted investigations to develop biotechnological expertise in the public research sector, other amendments to Title XIV in 1985 illustrated fears among congressmen over the ramifications of the anticipated revolution on the ecology and the structure of agriculture. Reflecting concerns over the accidental release of laboratory-engineered life forms into the environment, Congress appended to the section on "major needs and challenges" a call for the better coordination of biotechnology regulations at the federal level, including the standardization of risk assessment procedures.

Another new section directed the Secretary of Agriculture to give special attention to "the unique problems of small- and medium-sized farms in gaining information" about biotechnological breakthroughs. Clearly, the legislators' enthusiasm for the new technology was tempered by the realization that the uncontrolled application of these techniques could greatly accelerate the trend toward farm consolidation.

To many observers in and out of Congress in the first half of the 1980s, the family farm seemed on the verge of extinction because of unfavorable economic conditions engendered, at least in part, by the farmers' very success in producing an abundance of food and fiber. Mounting surpluses of many staples depressed prices received by farmers while international markets, which had expanded rapidly enough in the 1970s to bring unaccustomed prosperity to the farm sector, stagnated in the next decade.

The Food Security Act of 1985 was framed in the midst of this latest farm crisis and its provisions, including many of those relating to science and education, sought to save the family farm by restoring the competitive advantage of the American farmer in domestic and world markets. Thus, not only was biotechnology research to be conducted in light of its applicability to small- and medium-sized farms, so were all other federally subsidized investigations, according to another section of the amended Title XIV. Furthermore, Congress "encouraged" the Secretary of Agriculture to name "at least one State cooperating institution" to pursue inter-disciplinary research into the effects of socioeconomic and technological developments on the structure of agriculture. Research to develop the commercial potential of specialty crops which could supplement or substitute for traditional money crops for which demand had fallen was ordered in another amendment.

Ironically, eight years after the original National Agricultural Research, Extension, and Teaching Policy Act had dropped the 20 percent marketing requirement in the use of formula funds, the newest version of the Act directed the Secretary to make available a minimum of $10,000,000 annually to research institutions to develop quality-enhancing post-harvest technology to expand agricultural markets. Yet another provision mandated grants to establish International Trade Development Centers at land-grant universities that had valuable expertise and a willingness to match federal dollars.

Topicality aside, the National Agricultural Research, Extension, and Teaching Policy Act Amendments of 1985 made only a few changes in the legislation that governed relations in the public agricultural research partnership. The USDA, for the first time, was allowed to award money on a competitive basis to state experiment stations to build and upgrade research facilities. Previously, USDA facilities funds had gone to ARS to build and operate such laboratories on its own, resulting in a surfeit of congressionally mandated installations which often could not be adequately staffed.[16]

Advisory Boards Strengthened

Additionally, the membership of the Joint Council on Food and Agricultural Sciences was altered to include a representative for food technologists on the board. The change indicated the revived interest in Congress for research promoting product quality improvement to stimulate market acceptance of agricultural commodities. Both the Joint Council and the National Agricultural Research and Extension Users Advisory Board were rechartered through 1990. The significance of the 1985 version of Title XIV, however, lay not in these minor procedural adjustments but rather in its illustration of the continuing desire of Congress to shape the research agenda.

The two national advisory boards on research, extension, and teaching directions remained as the congressionally mandated forums for the consolidation of opinion on priorities. After its rather troubled start, the Joint Council had developed an increasingly effective structure for building a consensus on future directions for science and education activities, especially after the 1981 amendments to Title XIV prompted it to abandon attempts to impose an overly complex hierarchical structure upon existing regional planning relationships. The three national committees for research, extension, and teaching were retained thereafter, but the four regions were left to themselves in fashioning more local priority setting arrangements. With this concession to regional variation, the Joint Council was better able to gain the trust of the state stations while Assistant Secretary Bentley could more fully involve the federal component.

The Users Advisory Board was similarly successful in overcoming the initial suspicions among station directors that it was anti-agriculture. According to participating USDA delegates on the committee, even its first report "amazed almost everyone in its relevance and degree of consensus." That report had been compiled following a series of hearings held across the country to sample public opinion. Subsequent activities involved advocates and critics of the agricultural establishment in meetings to hammer out objectives. In most every case, the resulting recommendations mirrored those of the Joint Council.

Together, the national advisory panels went far toward the goal of providing national policymakers with an agenda arrived at by a consensus of public institutions, private industry, and consumers and expressed in understandable terms of problems and opportunities. With so much time and energy expended in the annual process of presenting a united front, participants in the planning efforts were understandably discouraged when prevailing economic conditions prevented substantial increases in financial support.[17]

ESCOP Planning and Program Initiatives

Frustrated by the Joint Council's inability to translate its efforts into more dollars and desiring to put forward the distinctiveness of the state experiment stations in the agricultural research system, ESCOP launched its own Research Planning Subcommittee in 1984. While the National Agricultural Research Committee functioned as an auxiliary to the Joint Council, consolidating and forwarding research priorities to that body, station directors felt that their recommendations lost their state and regional focus in the process. By the time those priority suggestions emerged from Joint Council deliberations, they were further diluted. The new subcommittee, comprised of the Directors-At-Large and two other representatives from each of the regions, would seek to supplement in more detail the information provided to the Joint Council in an effort to maintain a higher profile for the stations' programs.

To encourage the better coordination of the activities of the various planning agencies, ESCOP at the same time declared its intention to designate the same individuals as state station representatives to the four Regional Research Committees, two Regional Research, Extension, and Teaching Councils, the National Agricultural Research Committee, and the Joint Council. Under this arrangement, not only would fewer resources be diverted to the time consuming planning processes, but the state stations could better advance a consistent position on research needs and opportunities.[18]

In addition to making these adjustments to participate more effectively in planning, ESCOP intensified its activities designed to stress the relevance of state agricultural experiment station programs to public policy. In 1984, a year-old ad hoc Special Initiatives Subcommittee was made permanent and given the task of identifying new problem areas and recommending ways that these might be addressed through research. Emphasizing emerging issues not as problems but as opportunities, the subcommittee sponsored reports on international and domestic marketing, computer applications in agriculture, ground water quality, and remote sensing technology.

More ambitious than these single-issue white papers was a series of reports, authored by groups of cooperating station and CSRS administrators, on the current status and future direction of the state agricultural experiment station system. The first of these, *Research 1984*, described institutional arrangements, the place of scientific investigation in the context of societal needs, and planning processes used to identify priorities. A second joint publication, entitled *Research Perspectives*, collected the proceedings of a four-day symposium held in Washington, D.C. in 1985. There, representatives of state stations, the USDA, the Executive Office, Congress, and industry presented and discussed papers on institutional relationships, research implications of emerging trends, and new research opportunities.

This last topic was the subject of a subsequent workshop in Atlanta, Georgia, held in the summer of 1985 that resulted in a report released as *Research Initiatives* in the next year. Fifty-two scientists and administrators from the public research system reached consensus on twenty-one major new high priority initiatives and ninety-nine specific objectives defined as steps to achieve the initiatives. Furthermore, the workshop participants estimated the amount of resources that would be required to undertake the initiatives, assigning levels of support to each area based on a projected 20 percent increase in funds over the next five years. While the workshop came up with many of the same priorities identified in earlier exercises of this kind, it was novel in applying more systematic assessment strategies and in attaching a realistic price tag to its recommendations. Although the report did not specify what funding mechanisms should be tapped to subsidize the new initiatives, the panelists' stated assumption that one-half of the start-up costs would be furnished from state sources implied that increases should come through formula funding.

The sponsors of the Atlanta conference certainly believed that base programs of the stations were capable of shifting resources into the new priority areas. The fact that they historically had successfully done so was the subject of a fourth study commissioned by ESCOP and CSRS in 1986 to highlight the dynamism of the system in responding to changing needs and opportunities of the past.[19]

Inter-regional projects, funded through a combination of the regional research portion of Hatch dollars and annual Special Grants, continued as the primary method of cooperatively addressing national initiatives. Evaluation and planning projects at the state stations continued to revolve around IR-6, while IR-4 provided a focus for pesticide (and, beginning in 1982, animal drug) related research activities.

As part of the latter project, state agricultural experiment stations contributed members to a National Integrated Pest Management Coordinating Committee established in 1982 to identify program thrusts in this area. During the same period, pesticide assessment efforts were strengthened when the Indiana station at Purdue

John D. Axtell, a crop scientist at the Indiana Station, developed high-lysine grain sorghum through biochemical genetics, improving the nutritional value and digestibility of this human food and livestock-fodder crop, particularly important in lesser developed countries. (Indiana A.E.S. photo)

University contracted through CSRS to develop and maintain a standard database acceptable to industry, scientists, and regulators concerned with the effects of pesticides.

A North Central Region project initiated in 1977 provided the model for another national cooperative project related to environmental deterioration. Designated as IR-7 in 1982, the expanded project involved the state stations, the Environmental Protection Agency, the Forest Service, and the Bureau of Land Management in a National Atmospheric Deposition Program Monitoring Network to measure and assess the consequences of acid precipitation on agricultural productivity and the general ecology. The Colorado State University experiment station coordinated the state stations' activities under IR-7.[20]

Biotechnology Initiatives

While inter-regional projects were an effective method for approaching some of the more pressing issues confronting agriculture, regional research funds, even with supplementary Special Grants, were not sufficient to launch the kind of effort envisioned in biotechnology. Many of the state agricultural experiment stations had been involved in fundamental genetic investigations related to that broad field for many years but, in general, their efforts lagged behind those of private industry which foresaw enormous profit potential in the application of the new technologies. Sensitive to reviving charges that their public programs served private commercial interests, the state stations were initially reluctant to commit substantial resources to the exploitation of biotechnological techniques. Threatened by the loss of many of the institutions' leading scientists to biotechnology firms and realizing that their full participation in the emerging field was necessary if the public interest was to be served, the stations began a concerted effort in the 1980s to infuse new support into their basic biology programs.

Frustrated by the outcome of previous attempts to garner substantial funding for new programs through traditional appropriation channels, a group of influential state directors pushed a biotechnology initiative as a separate budget item beginning in 1981. ESCOP, NASULGC, and Assistant Secretary Bentley threw their support behind the measure over the following two years. The united force of their argument convinced Congress to add an additional $20,000,000 in the Competitive Grants category expressly for biotechnology in the

1985 fiscal year. Although that sum was far short of the $70,000,000 proposed by the station directors, it was a significant victory for them given the prevailing economic and political climate. The space given biotechnology in the language of the 1985 amendments to Title XIV seemed to ensure that the support in Congress would continue.[21]

In successfully promoting the biotechnology initiative, the state experiment stations stressed their potential as contributors to the regulatory development process. Since the earliest advances in recombinant DNA investigations had occurred in medicine, the National Institutes of Health emerged in the 1970s as the federal leader in the development of control regulations, but as the techniques of genetic manipulation spread to other disciplines, the Environmental Protection Agency, the Food and Drug Administration, and the USDA all began to confront fears that undesirable mutant organisms might be released into the environment, find a niche, and adversely affect the ecology.

To address these issues on a broad front, the state experiment stations in 1984 proposed through the NASULGC Division of Agriculture that a National Biological Impact Assessment Board of federal, state, and private sector experts be created to construct guidelines for the development and release of recombinant DNA organisms. Citing the state stations' proven ability in monitoring new plant cultivar releases over many decades and their more recent efforts in pesticide impact assessment, the proposal suggested that the existing station system offered a ready-made structure for compiling the kinds of data necessary to regulate biotechnology as it moved beyond the laboratory stage. With nearly every station engaged in some aspect of biotechnological investigation by the mid-1980s, they were rapidly developing the special competence that was needed as well.

Public alarm over the proposed release of genetically engineered organisms into the environment prompted the formation of a Biological Sciences Coordinating Committee on the national level in 1986 with the various federal agencies retaining the power to detail regulatory procedures in their areas of oversight. As the Department of Agriculture set to the task of refining its own role, the state agricultural experiment stations stood ready to contribute their considerable expertise.[22]

The funding of the biotechnology initiative through Competitive Grants had the strong backing of the state experiment stations because of their need for core support for this expensive field of research. The furor that had arisen over the implementation of the first Competitive Grants program was avoided when the President proposed and Congress passed modest increases in traditional formula funds to accompany the expanded grant allocations.

Funding Trends

Between 1981 and 1986, Hatch appropriations rose from $128,615,000, to $155,545,000, an increase of ,21 percent. Nearly one-half of the five-year gain came in the 1982 fiscal year, fueling hopes among the station directors that the confidence in the public research partnership expressed in Title XIV amendments of 1981 was to be backed by expanded financial support in the category of federal discretionary funds to the states. Another increase of nearly 6 percent followed for 1983, but thereafter the rate of increase slowed to less than 3 percent for each of the two following years.

Then, for 1986, the amount of Hatch formula disbursements was actually decreased for the first time in the one hundred-year history of the Hatch Act. While the 0.6 percent decline in Hatch dollars was less than that for either Special Grants or Competitive Grants (which fell by 10.6 percent and 3.8 percent, respectively), the Hatch proportion of CSRS-administered funds had dwindled to 53 percent in 1986, down from 64 percent just five years earlier. Despite the state experiment stations' success in amending the National Agricultural Research, Extension, and Teaching Policy Act to reaffirm their traditional importance, the trend toward making them compete with the rest of the scientific community for additional federal dollars continued unabated.[23]

Competitive Grants, which rose from $16,000,000 in 1981 to $44,233,000 in 1986 (plus $6,799,000 for competitive forestry research), made up an increasing portion of funds which flowed through the USDA. In 1981, they equaled 8 percent of CSRS-managed dollars and in 1986, amounted to 15 percent of the total.

Special Grants, many of which were awarded competitively as well, increased from $17,076,000 to $28,632,000 between 1981 and 1986. By the latter year, Special Grants comprised 10 percent of the money available through CSRS compared to 8.5 percent five years earlier.

Other specifically mandated research categories, taken together, remained essentially level. Animal Health and Disease grants fell slightly from $6,500,000 in 1981 to $5,964,000 in 1986. Alcohol Fuels Disbursements ($500,000 in 1981) were moved to Competitive Grants in 1985, the same year that an equal amount was first appropriated for the Rangeland Research Grants program. Only Native Latex allocations rose significantly, going from $500,000 in 1981 to $702,000 in 1982 and each of the following years.[24]

Annual sums available for research at the agricultural experiment stations from non-federal sources throughout the period continued to be about three times greater than those passing through the CSRS allocations channel. State appropriations, as before, made up the vast majority of these funds, with sales, industry grants, and private donations adding up to less than 25 percent of the total non-federal money. Generally, state-legislated subsidies continued to come to the stations in annual lump sums for allocation according to opportunities as perceived by the individual directors. Yet, paralleling trends at the national level, the degree of support from state lawmakers likely was to be tied closely to the economic health of the state and the station director increasingly was obliged to consult a broader set of advisors in distributing research dollars.[25]

Stations Enhance Coordination and Cooperation

As the subject matter of research programs continued to broaden and sources of funding became more diverse, directors often found themselves less able to personally set agendas for their experiment stations. Demands and opportunities for new thrusts contended with the need to maintain and expand traditional investigations while the directors' available methods for influencing directions came to reside more and more in the power to employ faculty. Academic and, often, extension considerations affected the latitude of the directors' authority even in this area, so that administrative mechanisms for achieving consensus grew in importance.

The trend was not new. Vice presidents with oversight responsibilities for research all across campus, including that in agriculture, were an increasingly common feature of university administrations in the 1960s and '70s. Station councils of academic and research department heads in the colleges of agriculture often had existed for many years, broadening their memberships in the more recent past to include biological and physical science representatives outside the station who were eligible for agriculture-related grants. Citizen advisory groups of producers, processors, and consumers also were more prevalent, offering a wider source of opinion in shaping program directions.

As state legislators, like national lawmakers, more carefully scrutinized their own support for agricultural investigations, the state experiment stations had to call on all of these planning resources to evidence their current relevance and project their future value in addressing the economic and social issues revolving around agriculture. Between 1982 and 1985 alone, these efforts resulted in the publication of long-range plans for agricultural research (often including extension and teaching priorities) by at least fourteen state agricultural experiment stations.[26]

Centers of Excellence

These special priority identifying activities, along with less formal but similar activities carried out at many other stations, illustrated the dynamic response of the system to emerging problems in the ever widening fields of agricultural science. So, too, did new administrative arrangements designed to better exploit research opportunities. Unique geoclimatic and socioeconomic conditions had long prompted individual stations to devote special attention to commodities of overriding importance to area farmers, a development that, on the intra-state level, hastened the creation of outlying branches concentrating on specific types of farm enterprises.

As overall funding trends in the 1970s and '80s showed a proportionate decline in discretionary money for general programs and a corresponding rise in grant dollars for specific areas, many stations moved toward a "centers of excellence" approach to research on a regional and national plane. While station directors doubtless would have preferred to advance each of their programs at an equally rapid pace to retain the backing of all segments of their traditional clientele while garnering the support of new constituencies, the competition for available dollars was becoming too intense to afford the luxury. Often their only recourse was to maintain core programs with formula and state appropriations while aggressively pursuing federal agency, foundation, and industry grants to build the facilities and professional staffs necessary to excel in specific areas.

Sometimes this meant cooperating informally with neighboring state stations to divide responsibilities for regional concerns according to traditional strengths. Washington's station, for example, phased out its sheep research program to concentrate more on swine while Idaho's station did the reverse. New York's and Pennsylvania's stations briefly agreed to have the former assume regional leadership for grape investigations, but the arrangement dissolved when Pennsylvania grape growers successfully pushed for new state funds earmarked for viticulture research at their own experiment station. Political considerations throughout the system limited the more widespread adoption of trade-off agreements between stations that might have cooperated to use research money more effectively. More usual were individual stations operating as de facto centers of excellence in particular commodity areas, as North Carolina did in tobacco, Louisiana did in sugar cane, and Georgia did in poultry for the Southern Region.[27]

Beginning in the mid-1970s, an increasing number of stations formally established inter-disciplinary departments and institutes to coordinate work in fields linked not so much by commodity as by problem area or experimental method. In the decade after 1975, for example, the New Jersey station at Rutgers added departments of mosquito control research and of radiation science, and a center for urban food marketing investigations. The Idaho station created a Post Harvest Institute for Perishibles.

The Michigan station established a center for pesticide research and New York's Geneva experiment station added an integrated pest management department. The Indiana station housed a Laboratory for Applications of Remote Sensing and the Arizona station began one for computer applications in agriculture.

The Nebraska experiment station sponsored a center for meteorology and climate studies. The Oregon station became the site for a Nitrogen Fixation Laboratory while the California station helped found a Plant Gene Expression Center.

By 1985, the Maryland-Eastern Shore, Nebraska, and Virginia experiment stations had joined the Florida, Michigan, and West Virginia stations in including institutes for international development within their formal administrative structures. Virtually all of these new departments concerned with relatively new areas of agricultural investigation were founded to promote trans-campus cooperation between scientists in research programs that transcended traditional subject-matter lines.[28]

The Mission Remains

The search for better ways to organize administration within the state agricultural experiment stations to stimulate the more effective pursuit of knowledge continued as the system approached the end of its first century of service to agriculture. Realizing that the days of unquestioned budget authority and unilateral agenda setting were long past, each station incorporated an ever broader range of research concerns and a wider array of scientific talent to fulfill its mission of discovering the knowledge necessary for the abundant production of food and fiber while protecting and enhancing natural and human resources. Although efforts in these directions had never stopped at the individual state stations during the late 1970s, they often were carried out in an atmosphere of suspicion toward their traditional partners in the USDA. Legislation and departmental reorganizations at the national level during the 1980s did much to restore the participants' confidence in the system as a whole, allowing them to approach continuing challenges with renewed dedication.

Notes

[1] National Agricultural Research, Extension, and Teaching Policy Act Amendments of 1981, 95 Stat 1294 (1981); ESCOP, "Minutes, September 29-30, 1980."

[2] ESCOP, "Minutes, September 29-30, 1980 and August 13-14, 1981."

[3] ESCOP, "Minutes, September 29-30, 1980."

[4] ESCOP, "Minutes, October 31-November 1, 1979 and April 28-29, 1981" and "Interim Subcommittee Minutes, November 28, 1979."

[5] Association of Research Directors and CSRS, *Progress and Productivity Through Research and Service: Agricultural Research at the 1890 Institutions* (N.p.: n.p., 1986), p. 20; interview with B.D. Mayberry, April 15, 1986; interview with M.H. Neufville, June 13, 1986.

[6] NASULGC and USDA, *National Program of Research for Agriculture*, p. 15; U.S. Congress, House Committee on Agriculture, *Agricultural Act of 1977: Report*, p. 47; interview with T.S. Ronningen, February 10, 1986.

[7] Special Panel, "Meeting the Expanding Need for Agricultural Research: Review of the Cooperative State Research Service, February 8-12, 1982 by the Special Panel," unpublished manuscript in author's possession, pp. 2-5 (quotation on p. 5); interview with R.D. Rouse, April 16, 1986.

[8] Interview with John Patrick Jordan, Administrator, Cooperative State Research Service, USDA, Washington, D.C., May 28, 1986; interview with O.G. Bentley, May 23, 1986; Keith A. Huston, Director-At-Large, North Central Region, to author, January 28, 1986.

[9] CSRS, "Strategic Plan of the Cooperative State Research Service of the United States Department of Agriculture," 3 pts., CSRS Internal Working Paper, May 1986, pt. 1, "Direction of Future Activities," pp. 1-4 (quotation on p. 4) and pt. 2, "Implementing Future Activities," p. 3; CSRS, *Mission of the Cooperative State Research Service* [Washington: USDA, CSRS, 1982], p. 1.

[10] USDA, Science and Education, *Paradox of Success*, p. VI-9; F.H. Buttel, Martin Kenney, Jack Kloppenburg, Jr., and J. Tadlock Cowan, "Problems and Prospects in Agricultural Research: The Winrock Report," *Rural Sociologist* 3 (March 1983): 67-69; George E. Brown, Jr., "Agricultural Policy, Agricultural Research, and the Future," address to the Organization of Professional Employees of the Department of Agriculture, Beltsville, Maryland, April 15, 1983; U.S. Congress, Office of Technology Assessment, *An Assessment of the United States Food and Agricultural Research System* (Washington: OTA, 1981). The OTA final report admitted that it "reaches somewhat different conclusions" than those of the papers commissioned by its authors as part of the study, most of which applauded the existing decentralized system for its flexibility and responsiveness.

[11] U.S. Congress, House Committee on Agriculture, Subcommittee on Forests, Family Farms, and Energy, *Organic Farming Act of 1982: Hearings* (97th Cong., 2nd sess., June 1982), pp. 4-6, 10-19, 75.

[12] USDA, Science and Education Office of Grants and Program Systems, *Food and Agriculture Competitively Awarded Research and Education Grants: Fiscal Year 1984* (Washington: USDA, 1984), pp. 75-81; "CSRS-Station Letter-2899a, April 27, 1983."

[13] Knutson, Paarlberg, and McCalla, "Forces Affecting Food and Agricultural Research Decisions," p. 3.

[14] National Agricultural Research, Extension, and Teaching Policy Act Amendments of 1985, Public Law 99-198 (1985); Lewrene K. Glaser, *Provisions of the Food Security Act of 1985* (Washington: USDA, Economic Research Service Agriculture Information Bulletin No. 498, 1986), p. 63.

[15] F.H. Buttel, J. Kloppenburg, Jr., M. Kenney, and J.T. Cowan, "Genetic Engineering and the Restructuring of Agricultural Research," *Rural Sociologist* 3 (May 1983): 133; Congressional Quarterly, *Farm Policy: The Politics of Soil, Surpluses, and Subsidies* (Washington: Congressional Quarterly Inc., 1984), p. 52.

[16] Interview with O.G. Bentley, May 23, 1986.

[17] Ibid.; interview with T.S. Ronningen, February 10, 1986; ESCOP, "Minutes, April 28-29, 1981"; Huston, "Priority Setting Processes," p. 85; James Nielson and John M. Brazzel, "Evaluation As an Aid to Decisionmaking in the Food and Agricultural Sciences," in *Federal Funding Philosophies*, ed. Western Association of A.E.S. Directors, p. 66 (quotation).

[18] ESCOP, "Minutes, September 25-27 and November 14, 1984."

[19] ESCOP and CSRS, *Research 1984: The State Agricultural Experiment Stations* [N.p.: n.p., 1984]; ESCOP and CSRS, *Research Perspectives*; ESCOP and CSRS, *Research Initiatives: A Research Agenda for the State Agricultural Experiment Stations* (College Station: Texas A.E.S., 1986); interview with Billy R. Baumgardt, Director, Indiana Agricultural Experiment Station, West Lafayette, Indiana, July 22, 1986.

[20] U.S. Congress, House Committee on Appropriations, *Agriculture Appropriations for 1987: Hearings*, p. 679; ESCOP. "Minutes, September 28-30, 1982"; interview with B.R. Baumgardt, July 22, 1986; "Chemistry of Atmospheric Deposition - Effects on Agriculture, Forestry, Surface Waters, and Materials" file in Regional Research Office, CSRS.

[21] Buttel et al., "Genetic Engineering," pp. 136-139; interview with D.F. Bateman, April 22, 1986; interview with O.G. Bentley, May 23, 1986; ESCOP, "Minutes, February 8-9, 1984."

[22] Stephen D. Jellinek, "Regulatory Trends in the Environmental Protection Agency," in *Research Perspectives*, eds. ESCOP and CSRS, pp. 101-102; U.S. General Accounting Office, *Biotechnology: The U.S. Department of Agriculture's Biotechnology Research Efforts, Briefing Report* (Washington: GAO, 1985), p. 12; NASULGC, Division of Agriculture Committee on Biotechnology, *Emerging Biotechnologies in Agriculture: Issues and Policies, A National Biological Impact Assessment Program, March 1985 Update*, Chapter 7 [Washington: NASULGC, 1985], pp. 3-6; *Washington Post*, May 21, 1986.

[23] Interview with O.G. Bentley, May 23, 1986; CSRS, "Appropriation History."

[24] CSRS, "Appropriation History,"; U.S. Congress, Senate Committee on Appropriations, *Agriculture, Rural Development, and Related Agencies Appropriation Bill, 1986* (99th Cong., 1st sess., Report 99-137, September 1985), p. 28.

[25] CSRS, *Inventories of Agricultural Research: FY 1981-FY 1984*, table IV; Thomas S. Ronningen to author, December 12, 1985; interview with B.R. Baumgardt, July 22, 1986.

[26] Joint Council on Food and Agricultural Sciences, *1985 Accomplishments*, pp. 46-48.

[27] Washington State University College of Agriculture and Home Economics Research Center, *Report to the Legislature on Agricultural Research* ([Pullman: Washington State University], 1986), pp. 9-10; interview with T.C. Byerly, April 10, 1986; interview with D.W. Barton, June 18, 1986; interview with D.F. Bateman, April 22, 1986.

[28] CSRS, *1984-85 Director of Professional Workers in State Agricultural Experiment Stations and Other Cooperating State Institutions* (Washington: USDA Agriculture Handbook Number 305, 1984); USDA, Research and Education Committee, *1984 Annual Report on the Food and Agricultural Sciences from the Secretary of Agriculture to the President and Congress of the United States* ([Washington: USDA], 1985), p. iii.

CHAPTER VIII
Legacy from the Past . . . Promises for the Future

Noteworthy agricultural research has accrued in the United States over the past century in increasing amounts, intensity, quality, and sophistication. The continuing momentum of investigations dedicated to agricultural situations deserves attention beyond that given in the strictly chronological approach followed in the foregoing chapters.[1]

Science Wedded to Opportunity

While the structure of the experiment station system proved an effective method of harnessing the disparate activities of researchers to the goal of economic development in agriculture, the interests and skills of individual scientists determined the specific thrusts of investigations. Agricultural research has advanced through efforts of many scientists who transformed their inspirations into useful outcomes. The first successful prototypes of agricultural experiment stations were conceived and given life by scientists who understood that an array of disciplinary expertise with supporting personnel, facilities, and equipment was necessary for conversion of ideas into knowledge useful to agriculture. Subsequently, directors of state agricultural experiment stations built their institutions around well-trained scientists who could identify intersections between their varied disciplinary capabilities and research interests and important opportunities and needs in agriculture. As agriculture itself became more complex, willingness to cooperate with scientists from other departments and disciplines became a major adjunct to research potential in selecting new research recruits. Coincidently, the disciplinary mix of scientists widened as more kinds of disciplinary expertise were required. Thus, the capabilities of understanding and addressing agricultural questions deepened and became more sophisticated. Cross-disciplinary synergisms became inspirational as well as operational forces along with ideas from individual scientists stimulated by interactions with their peers.

As integral components of the state land-grant institutions whose mission was to produce and apply new knowledge to the problems of society, the state agricultural experiment stations connected the capabilities of scientists with opportunities in agriculture in the immensely varied geoclimatic regions of the nation. The decentralized nature of the system gave each state and region the capacity to address the site-specific needs of farming, lending scientific research in the stations a mission orientation whether basic, applied, or developmental.

Located near to the agricultural problems they were addressing, station scientists used feedback information to improve the usefulness of their investigations. When applied and developmental research failed to solve complex problems of immediate interest to farmers, investigators naturally delved deeper into fundamental areas. However pragmatic their purpose, many scientists embarked upon basic research which yielded new information of potential value in answering questions often unrelated to the original problem under study. Both agriculture and science advanced in the process.

Research-generated advances in agriculture depended on a number of precursor events and discoveries, many intended only to advance a scientific discipline. Individual scientists made connections between selected advances to bring their ideas to fruition. A National Science Foundation-sponsored study of ten major innovations and inventions, including hybrid corn and the "Green Revolution" wheats,

Carl B. Huffaker, California Station entomologist, contributed fundamental knowledge on host-parasite interaction systems and applied his findings to biological control of Klamath weed and a variety of insect and mite pests. *(University of California, Berkeley photo)*

illustrated the importance of individual scientific creativity and a constantly renewed base of knowledge in the discovery process. Of the twenty-one factors identified as essential to successful innovation, the investigators' recognition of scientific opportunity and need and their persistence in the face of obstacles consistently ranked high. For each innovation, the average time between first conception and final realization was nearly two decades with an average of fifty-three supporting discoveries before and after the first conception.

Creative, skilled, persistent research that exploited a vital core of scientific knowledge was a key to the innovation process in nearly every case. Research management was important, too, when it served to provide funds and foster inter-disciplinary approaches to accelerate the process, two areas in which the state experiment station system encouraged by its very nature.[2]

The experiment stations excelled, too, in diffusing innovations after the first realization of success, adapting discoveries to varying ecological niches in ways that gained sufficient confidence among farmers to risk their own resources to adopt new technologies. Positive correlations between the number of branch stations in a state and agricultural productivity gains illustrate the continuing need to link research laboratories with farms.[3]

Working in the state agricultural experiment stations, scientists successfully applied good science to agricultural problems and oppor-

Hector F. Deluca of the Wisconsin Station identified molecular mechanisms of action in vitamins, contributing to fundamental knowledge in biogenetics and the treatment of human diseases. *(University of Wisconsin-Madison photo)*

tunities in a wide range of disciplines. Selected examples of performance illuminate specific connections between research excellence and important outcomes. At the Connecticut station in New Haven, Donald F. Jones demonstrated the advantages of double-crossing corn to maintain hybrid vigor in 1917, then later helped discover a method of restoring fertility in male corn to make detasseling by a hand a thing of the past. In California, Carl B. Huffaker seized upon his knowledge of insect species to import a beetle parasitic to goat weed, which, once established, reduced the livestock-toxic plant to manageable levels and served as a forerunner to the current extensive efforts at biological weed control.

Hector F. DeLuca of the Wisconsin station pursued research that contributed to an understanding of the metabolism and molecular mechanism of action of physiologically active compounds like vitamin A and D and applied his findings to treatment of human diseases like vitamin D-resistant rickets. North Carolina station scientist Ellis B. Cowling's studies in the comparative biochemistry of wood decay led him to the discovery of the smallest known enzyme. Subsequently, he became one of the world's leading authorities on the emerging issue of the effects of acid rain upon plant life and structures.

Numerous other examples could be cited of the contributions of visionary individuals working within their disciplinary specialties on questions that intrigued their scientific curiosity. The state experiment station system furnished an effective arrangement for coordinat-

Ellis B. Cowling's studies at the North Carolina Station on the comparative biochemistry of wood decay contributed to his reputation as a widely recognized authority on the effects of acid rain. *(North Carolina State University photo)*

ing their activities and relating them to the needs of society, encouraging a synergism that advanced agriculture and the frontiers of knowledge.

Responding to a Century of Challenges: A Summary

The process that began one hundred years ago as the state agricultural experiment stations were established to fulfill the charge of the Hatch Act "to promote scientific investigation and experiment respecting the principles and applications of agricultural science," underwent enormous change over the century that followed. Initially defining their role in terms of increasing the productive capacity of farmers, the state stations steadily expanded their interests as the concept of agriculture itself broadened to include not only food and fiber production but the maintenance and enhancement of natural and human resources involved in and affected by that production. By its simple call for the continuous conduct of scientific research in agriculture by a decentralized complex of locally directed and nationally coordinated institutions, the Hatch Act imparted a legacy that encouraged the evolution of a federated system uniquely responsive to the changing needs of American society.

In 1887, the most obvious need was for immediate answers to questions farmers were encountering in expanding their agricultural enterprises in the West, adjusting to new markets furnished by a rapidly increasing urban population in the East, and overcoming problems associated with the production of traditional staple crops in the South.

Relying almost entirely upon federal funds in their earliest years, all of the state experiment stations struggled to supply information of immediate value to their local farmers to help them enhance productivity while building a core of scientific knowledge upon which future advances could be based. The twin strains of service to producers and the advance of science came to characterize the programs of the experiment stations as they courted financial support and aspired to legitimacy within the developing scientific disciplines. Steady accretions in state appropriations came as the allegiance of commercial farmers was earned through the application of discoveries made by station investigators. Additional federal support, reserved for "original researches," followed too, helping stations maintain the delicate balance between the applied and the fundamental.

All the while, the disciplines included in agricultural science grew more sophisticated and specialized, encouraging the development of administrative arrangements within the stations to effectively integrate the increasingly disparate activities of their scientists into flexible but unified overall research programs. The experiment stations grew in power and prestige within their university communities, supplying information necessary to support the other two elements in the land-grant triad, teaching and extension.

Working closely with leaders among the state experiment station directors, the USDA office with responsibility for the oversight of formula allocations evolved a set of accounting and project review procedures to link the state stations into a network that could address the needs of agriculture for the entire nation. The federal Office of Experiment Stations and its successors also mediated relations between the stations and the scientific bureaus within the Department of Agriculture as they expanded their own research role in the sometimes uneasy partnership.

Well into the twentieth century, the research conducted in the state agricultural experiment stations was devoted primarily to developing better yielding varieties of crops and livestock and overcoming natural constraints to increased productivity. The assumption that more efficient production of more abundant commodities would result in prosperity for the farm sector and, by extension, for the general rural economy underlay decisions on research directions throughout the public agricultural research system. Rising surpluses in many commodities, attendant falling prices received by farmers, and a widening gap in the socioeconomic status of rural and urban dwellers in the 1920s and '30s prompted the stations to reevaluate their focus. The larger problems of rural social welfare and the expansion of market opportunities began to receive increased attention in the stations, a development further encouraged by new federal funding measures that explicitly added these issues to the agricultural research agenda.

Discovering and developing biological and mechanical technologies to assist farmers in producing more with less remained the primary goal of agricultural researchers even as they broadened the scope of their studies to consider social welfare concerns. The capacity of the farm sector to successfully meet the revived and intensified demand for food and fiber supplies that came with America's entry into the Second World War attested to the value of technological innovations in agriculture and helped usher in a postwar "golden age" for science. For agricultural research, the result was growing financial support from both state and federal sources which allowed the stations to expand professional staffs and facilities to exploit new opportunities presented by advances in scientific methodology. If the tools of science became more sophisticated, so did the expectations of farmer clients whose operations became larger, more specialized, and more susceptible to economic fluctuations stemming from market changes and natural disasters. Agriculture became increasingly knowledge-intensive with yield maintenance and advance ever more dependent on the application of the discoveries of agricultural science.

The state agricultural experiment stations justifiably were credited for their important role in furnishing much of the knowledge that supported the enormous productivity gains that characterized a domestic "Green Revolution." As the revolution progressed to reveal unanticipated costs to traditional rural socioeconomic structure and environmental quality, the stations were also held accountable for their contributions to these consequences.

As the questioning of the stations' social relevance grew in the 1960s and '70s, the state research institutions embarked on a more intensive quest to assess the effects of technological innovation on society and the environment. Additional dollars from Congress increasingly came through channels outside of the traditional Hatch formula allocations as lawmakers influenced by demands for a socially conscious new agenda began to direct resources to specific program thrusts. New legislation earmarked research money for forestry, for rural development, and for a changing array of special problems of interest to Congress. Each new bill expanded the number of eligible recipients, forcing the state experiment stations to compete for increased support within the wider scientific community.

A similar process occurred on the state level where land-grant colleges were transforming into multipurpose universities with research components outside the traditional disciplines represented in agricultural science. Agricultural programs lost status in the process.

Experiencing an acute need for more money to address emerging issues while maintaining the excellence of their traditional program thrusts and realizing the futility of seeking substantial increases through discretionary funds, the state agricultural experiment stations accepted, albeit grudgingly, the new reality. Traditional regional and national planning activities were opened to research performers outside the station system. Research needs and opportunities identified by these groups were ranked by priority and a national research information system was constructed to chart how well the public agricultural research complex responded.

Funding outside of federal and state appropriations increasingly was pursued by the stations as they seized upon their accumulated scientific expertise to compete successfully for grants from agriculture-related industries, private and public foundations, and federal agencies outside of the USDA. New station administrative arrangements were introduced to broaden the coverage of research programs by tapping the talents of investigators outside the experiment stations. The Cooperative State Research Service assisted the stations' efforts, brokering grant funds from other federal agencies and incorporating a wider array of scientists in station review activities.

The growing inclination of Congress to limit the discretion of the state stations in expending federal funds according to their perceptions of priorities culminated in the National Agricultural Research, Extension, and Teaching Policy Act of 1977. While the legislation recognized the past contributions of the federated partnership, it implicitly questioned its current and future relevance.

A new competitive grants program promised a sorely needed infusion of new funds for high priority, mission-oriented basic research but the state station scientists were just one set among many individuals in the public and private scientific community who competed for those dollars. Nor were competitive grants, once won, particularly useful in conducting the long-term, site-specific types of investigations that had been the most important ingredient in the stations' successful research programs.

A new national advisory council that gave equal voice to agricultural science and education institutions with little regard to past accomplishments or potential future contributions was created to supersede the system painstakingly developed by the stations and the USDA. Another continuing advisory group of research consumers was mandated to assist national policymakers identify priorities worthy of funding. Congress gave both panels direction by listing a series of areas in need of increased attention and by earmarking new funds for animal disease, human nutrition, alcohol fuels, and native latex research.

Challenged by the implications of Title XIV, the state agricultural experiment stations responded by continuing to develop research programs that gave information of value to their broadening local constituencies and accelerated activities designed to show national policymakers that these programs, in aggregate, fulfilled national needs. Experiment station directors cooperated to sponsor studies that translated important public issues into station research opportunities, to expand inter-regional research projects into model programs for regulating pesticides and monitoring pollution, and to rally support behind a competitive grants program to increase the biotechnological research capacity in the station system.

Combined, these initiatives had some success in gaining more visibility for the stations. Amended versions of Title XIV in 1981 and 1985 included strong reaffirmations of the value of the state-federal agricultural research partnership as well as a pledge from Congress to rely upon this traditional strength in seeking to improve agriculture through science. Acceding to a request from the stations, Congress directed the Department of Agriculture to add an assistant secretary-level office to look after the interests of science and education. Adjustments in the memberships of the advisory councils gave greater representation to the state stations and their traditional producer clients. Finally, the amended legislation recognized that maintaining and enhancing productivity to insure continued abundance was a high priority for agricultural research just as it had been a century before.

These provisions helped restore the state agricultural experiment stations to a position of leadership in the public research system, but the system itself was no longer comprised only of the state stations and their federal USDA partner. One hundred years after the signing of the Hatch Act, virtually no one questioned the appropriateness of financing agricultural research with public money. Instead, the issue became how best to make use of the dollars so necessary to continue the effort effectively and fairly. Having responded successfully to a century of challenges arising out of changing expectations, the state agricultural experiment station system remained as the experienced-forged model for using public tax money to provide the knowledge necessary to meet the food and fiber demands of an expanding population while addressing the complex problems of economic and social welfare.

Notes

[1] Much of the following discussion is based upon an untitled paper written for the author by Thomas S. Ronningen in October 1986.

[2] Battelle Columbus Laboratories, *Science, Technology, and Innovation: Prepared for the National Science Foundation* (Columbus, Ohio: Battelle Columbus Laboratories, 1973), pp. 6-11.

[3] Evenson, Waggoner, and Ruttan, "Economic Benefits from Research," p. 1104.

Appendix

Basic Legislation Authorizing Establishment of
and Federal Grant Payments to
Agricultural Experiment Stations

Act of 1862 Donating Lands for Colleges of Agriculture and Mechanic Arts

[First Morrill Act]

AN ACT Donating public lands to the several States and Territories which may provide colleges for the benefit of agriculture and the mechanic arts

Be it enacted by the Senate and House of Representatives of the United States of America in Congress assembled, That there be granted to the several States, for the purposes hereinafter mentioned, an amount of public land, to be apportioned to each State a quantity equal to thirty thousand acres for each Senator and Representative in Congress to which the States are respectively entitled by the apportionment under the census of eighteen hundred and sixty; *Provided*, That no mineral lands shall be selected or purchased under the provisions of this act.

Sec. 2. *And be it further enacted*, That the land aforesaid, after being surveyed, shall be apportioned to the several States in sections or subdivisions of sections, not less than one-quarter of a section; and whenever there are public lands in a State subject to sale at private entry at one dollar and twenty-five cents per acre, the quantity to which said State shall be entitled shall be selected from such lands within the limits of such State, and the Secretary of the Interior is hereby directed to issue to each of the States in which there is not the quantity of public lands subject to sale at private entry at one dollar and twenty-five cents per acre, to which said State may be entitled under the provisions of this act, land scrip to the amount in acres for the deficiency of its distributive share; said scrip to be sold by said States and the proceeds thereof applied to the uses and purposes prescribed in this act, and for no other use or purpose whatsoever; *Provided*, That in no case shall any State to which land scrip may thus be issued be allowed to locate the same within the limits of any other State, or of any Territory of the United

States, but their assignees may thus locate said land scrip upon any of the unappropriated lands of the United States subject to sale at private entry at one dollar and twenty-five cents, or less, per acre; *And provided, further*, That not more than one million acres shall be located by such assignees in any one of the States; *And provided, further*, That no such location shall be made before one year from the passage of this act.

Sec. 3. *And be it further enacted*, That all expenses of management, superintendence, and taxes from date of selection of said lands, previous to their sales, and all expenses incurred in the management and disbursement of the moneys which may be received therefrom, shall be paid by the States to which they may belong, out of the treasury of said States, so that the entire proceeds of the sale of said lands shall be applied without any diminution whatever to the purposes hereinafter mentioned.

Sec. 4 [original]. *And be it further enacted*, That all moneys derived from the sale of the lands aforesaid by the States to which the lands are apportioned, and from the sales of land scrip hereinbefore provided for, shall be invested in stocks of the United States, or of the States, or some other safe stocks, yielding not less than five per centum upon the par value of said stocks; and that the moneys so invested shall constitute a perpetual fund, the capital of which shall remain forever undiminished, (except so far as may be provided in section fifth of this act,) and the interest of which shall be inviolably appropriated, by each State which may take and claim the benefit of this act, to the endowment, support, and maintenance of at least one college where the leading object shall be, without excluding other scientific and classical studies, and including military tactics, to teach such branches of learning as are related to agriculture and the mechanic arts, in such manner as the legislatures of the States may respectively prescribe, in order to promote the liberal and practical education of the industrial classes in the several pursuits and professions in life.

Sec. 4 [as amended March 3, 1883]. That all moneys derived from the sale of lands aforesaid by the States to which lands are apportioned, and from the sales of lands scrip hereinbefore provided for, shall be invested in stocks of the United States or of the States, or some other safe stocks; or the same may be invested by the States having no State stocks, in any other manner after the legislatures of such States shall have assented thereto, and engaged that such funds shall yield not less than five per centum upon the amount so invested and that the principal thereof shall forever remain unimpaired; *Provided*, That the moneys so invested or loaned shall constitute a perpetual fund, the capital of which shall remain forever undiminished (except so far as may be provided in section five of this act), and the interest of which shall be inviolably appropriated, by each State which may take and claim the benefit of this act, to the endowment, support, and maintenance of at least one college where the leading objects shall be, without excluding other scientific and classical studies, and including military tactics, to teach such branches of learning as are related to agriculture and the mechanic arts, in such manner as the legislatures of the States may respectively prescribe, in order to promote the liberal and practical education of the industrial classes in the several pursuits and professions in life.

Sec. 4 [as amended April 13, 1926]. That all moneys derived from the sale of lands aforesaid by the States to which lands are apportioned and from the sales of land scrip hereinbefore provided for shall be invested in bonds of the United States or of the States or some other safe bonds; or the same may be invested by the States having no State bonds in any manner after the legislatures of such States shall have assented thereto and engaged that such funds shall yield a fair and reasonable rate of return, to be fixed by the State legislatures, and that the principal thereof shall forever remain unimpaired: *Provided*, That the moneys so invested or loaned shall constitute a perpetual fund, the capital of which shall remain forever undiminished (except so far as may be provided in section 5 of this Act), and the interest of which shall be inviolably appropriated, by each State which may take and claim the benefit of this Act, to the endowment, support, and maintenance of at least one college where the leading object shall be, without excluding other scientific and classical studies and including military tactics, to teach such branches of learning as are related to agriculture and the mechanic arts, in such manner as the legislatures of the States may respectively prescribe, in order to promote the liberal and practical education of the industrial classes in the several pursuits and professions in life.

Sec. 5. *And be it further enacted.* That the grant of land and land scrip hereby authorized shall be made on the following conditions, to which, as well as to the provisions hereinbefore contained, the previous assent of the several States shall be signified by legislative acts:

First. If any portion of the fund invested, as provided by the foregoing section, or any portion of the interest thereon, shall, by any action or contingency, be diminished or lost, it shall be replaced by the State to which it belongs, so that the capital of the fund shall remain forever undiminished; and the annual interest shall be regularly applied without diminution to the purposes mentioned in the fourth section of this act, except that a sum, not exceeding ten per centum upon the amount received by any State under the provisions of this act, may be expended for the purchase of lands for sites or experimental farms, whenever authorized by the respective legislatures of said States.

Second. No portion of said fund, nor the interest thereon, shall be applied, directly or indirectly, under any pretense whatever, to the purchase, erection, preservation, or repair of any building or buildings.

Third. Any State which may take and claim the benefit of the provisions of this act shall provide, within five years, at least not less than one college, as described in the fourth section of this act, or the grant to such State shall cease; and said State shall be bound to pay the United States the amount received of any lands previously sold, and that the title to purchasers under the State shall be valid.

Fourth. An annual report shall be made regarding the progress of each college, recording any improvements and experiments made, with their cost and results, and such other matters, including State industrial and economical statistics, as may be supposed useful; one copy of which shall be transmitted by mail free, by each, to all the other colleges which may be endowed under the provisions of this act, and also one copy to the Secretary of the Interior.

Fifth. When lands shall be selected from those which have been raised to double the minimum price, in consequence of railroad grants, they shall be computed to the States at the maximum price, and the number of acres proportionately diminished.

Sixth. No State while in a condition of rebellion or insurrection against the Government of the United States shall be entitled to the benefit of this act.

Seventh. No State shall be entitled to the benefits of this act unless it shall express its acceptance thereof by its legislature within two years from the date of its approval by the President.

Sec. 6. *And be it further enacted*, That land scrip issued under the provisions of this act shall not be subject to location until after the first day of January, one thousand eight hundred and sixty-three.

Sec. 7. *And be it further enacted*, That the land officers shall receive the same fees for locating land scrip issued under the provisions of this act as is now allowed for the location of military bounty land warrants under existing laws; *Provided*, That their maximum compensation shall not be thereby increased.

Sec. 8 *And be it further enacted*, That the governors of the several States to which scrip shall be issued under this act shall be required to report annually to Congress all sales made of such scrip until the whole shall be disposed of, the amount received for the same, and what appropriation has been made of the proceeds.

Approved July 2, 1862 (12 Stat. 503).

Act of 1887 Establishing Agricultural Experiment Stations

[Hatch Act]

AN ACT To establish agricultural experiment stations in connection with the colleges established in the several States under the provisions of an act approved July second, eighteen hundred and sixty-two, and of the acts supplementary thereto

Be it enacted by the Senate and House of Representatives of the United States of America in Congress assembled, That in order to aid in acquiring and diffusing among the people of the United States useful and practical information on subjects connected with agriculture, and to promote scientific investigation and experiment respecting the principles and applications of agricultural science, there shall be established, under direction of the college or colleges or agricultural department of colleges in each State or Territory established, or which may hereafter be established, in accordance with the provisions of an act approved July second, eighteen hundred and sixty-two, entitled "An act donating public lands to the several States and Territories which may provide colleges for the benefit of agriculture and the mechanic arts," or any of the supplements to said act, a department to be known and designed as an "agricultural experiment station": *Provided*, That in any State or Territory in which two such colleges have been or may be so established the appropriation hereinafter made to such State or Territory shall be equally divided between such colleges, unless the legislature of such State or Territory shall otherwise direct.

Sec. 2. That it shall be the object and duty of said experiment stations to conduct original researches or verify experiments on the physiology of plants and animals; the diseases to which they are severally subject, with the remedies for the same; the chemical composition of useful plants at their different stages of growth; the comparative advantages of rotative cropping as pursued under a varying series of crops; the capacity of new plants or trees for acclimation; the analysis of soils and water; the chemical composition of manures, natural or artificial, with experiments designed to test their comparative effects on crops of different kinds; the adaptation and value of grasses and forage plants; the composition and digestibility of the different kinds of food for domestic animals; the scientific and economic questions involved in the production of butter and cheese; and such other researches or experiments bearing directly on the agricultural industry of the United States as may in each case be deemed advisable, having due regard to the varying conditions and needs of the respective States or Territories.

Sec. 3. That in order to secure, as far as practicable, uniformity of methods and results in the work of said stations, it shall be the duty of the United States Commissioner [now Secretary] of Agriculture to furnish forms, as far as practicable, for the tabulation of results of investigation or experiments; to indicate from time to time such lines of inquiry as to him shall seem most important, and, in general, to furnish such advice and assistance as will best promote the purpose of this act. It shall be the duty of each of said stations annually, on or before the first day of February, to make to the governor of the State or Territory in which it is located a full and detailed report of its operations, including a statement of receipts and expenditures, a copy of which report shall be sent to each of said stations, to the said Commissioner [now Secretary] or Agriculture, and to the Secretary of the Treasury of the United States.

Sec. 4. That bulletins or reports of progress shall be published at said stations at least once in three months, one copy of which shall be sent to each newspaper in the States or Territories in which they are respectively located, and to such individuals actually engaged in farming as may request the same, and as far as the means of the station will permit. Such bulletins or reports and the annual reports of said stations shall be transmitted in the mails of the United States free of charge for postage, under such regulations as the

Postmaster General may from time to time prescribe.

Sec. 5. That for the purpose of paying the necessary expenses of conducting investigations and experiments and printing and distributing the results as hereinbefore prescribed, the sum of fifteen thousand dollars per annum is hereby appropriated to each State, to be specially provided for by Congress in the appropriations from year to year, and to each Territory entitled under the provisions of section eight of this act, out of any money in the Treasury proceeding from the sales of public lands, to be paid in equal quarterly payments on the first day of January, April, July, and October in each year, to the treasurer or other officer duly appointed by the governing boards of said colleges to receive the same, the first payment to be made on the first day of October, eighteen hundred and eighty-seven; *Provided, however,* That out of the first annual appropriation so received by any station an amount not exceeding one-fifth may be expended in the erection, enlargement, or repair of a building or buildings necessary for carrying on the work of such station; and thereafter an amount not exceeding five per centum of such annual appropriation may be so expended.

Sec. 6. That whenever it shall appear to the Secretary of the Treasury from the annual statement of receipts and expenditures of any of said stations that a portion of the preceding annual appropriations remains unexpended, such amount shall be deducted from the next succeeding annual appropriation to such station, in order that the amount of money appropriated to any station shall not exceed the amount actually and necessarily required for its maintenance and support.

Sec. 7. That nothing in this act shall be construed to impair or modify the legal relation existing between any of the said colleges and the government of the States or Territories in which they are respectively located.

Sec. 8. That in States having colleges entitled under this section to the benefits of this act and having also agricultural experiment stations established by law separate from said colleges, such States shall be authorized to apply such benefits to experiments at stations so established by such States; and in case any State shall have established under the provisions of said act of July second aforesaid, an agricultural department or experiment station, in connection with any university, college, or institution not distinctively an agricultural college or school, and such State shall have established or shall hereafter establish a separate agricultural college or school, which, shall have connected therewith an experimental farm or station, the legislature of such State may apply in whole or in part the appropriation by this act made, to such separate agricultural college, or school, and no legislature shall by contract, express or implied, disable itself from so doing.

Sec. 9. That the grants of moneys authorized by this act are made subject to the legislative assent of the several States and Territories to the purposes of said grants; *Provided,* That payment of such installments of the appropriation herein made as shall become due to any State before the adjournment of the regular session of its legislature meeting next after the passage of this act shall be made upon the assent of the governor thereof duly certified to the

Secretary of the Treasury.

Sec. 10. Nothing in this act shall be held or construed as binding the United States to continue any payments from the Treasury to any or all the States or institutions mentioned in this act, but Congress may at any time amend, suspend, or repeal any or all the provisions of this act.

Approved March 2, 1887 (24 Stat. 440).

Act of 1890 Providing for the Further Endowment and Support of Colleges of Agriculture and Mechanic Arts

[Second Morrill Act]

AN ACT To apply a portion of the proceeds of the public lands to the more complete endowment and support of the colleges for the benefit of agriculture and the mechanic arts established under the provisions of an act of Congress approved July second, eighteen hundred and sixty-two

Be it enacted by the Senate and House of Representatives of the United States of America in Congress assembled, That there shall be, and hereby is, annually appropriated, out of any money in the Treasury not otherwise approved, to each State and Territory for the more complete endowment and maintenance of colleges for the benefit of agriculture and the mechanic arts now established, or which may be hereafter established, in accordance with an act of Congress approved July second, eighteen hundred and sixty two, the sum of fifteen thousand dollars for the year ending June thirtieth, eighteen hundred and ninety, and an annual increase of the amount of such appropriation thereafter for ten years by an additional sum of one thousand dollars over the preceding year, and the annual amount of be paid thereafter to each State and Territory shall be twenty-five thousand dollars to be applied only to instruction in agriculture, the mechanic arts, the English language and the various branches of mathematical, physical, natural, and economic science, with special reference to their applications in the industries of life, and to facilities for such instruction: *Provided,* That no money shall be paid out under this act to any State or Territory for the support and maintenance of a college where a distinction of race or color is made in the admission of students, but the establishment and maintenance of such colleges separately for white and colored students shall be held to be a compliance with the provisions of this act if the funds received in such State or Territory be equitably divided as hereinafter set forth: *Provided,* That in any State in which there has been one college established in pursuance of the act of July second, eighteen hundred and sixty-two, and also in which an educational institution of like character has been established, or may be hereafter established, and is now aided by such a state from its own revenue, for the education of colored students in agriculture and the mechanic arts, however named or styled, or whether or not it has received money heretofore under the act to which this act is an amendment, the legislature of such a State may propose and report to the Secretary of the Interior a just and equitable division of the fund to be received under this act between one college for white students and one institution for colored students established as aforesaid, which shall be divided into two parts and paid accordingly, and thereupon such institution for colored students shall be entitled to the benefits of this act and subject to its provisions, as much as it would have been if it had been included under the act of eighteen hundred and sixty-two, and the fulfillment of the foregoing provisions shall be taken as a compliance with the provision in reference to separate colleges for white and colored students.

Sec. 2. That the sums hereby appropriated to the States and Territories for the further endowment and support of colleges shall be annually paid on or before the thirty-first of July of each year, by the Secretary of the Treasury, upon the warrant of the Secretary of the Interior, out of the Treasury of the United States, to the State or Territorial treasurer, or to such officer as shall be designated by the laws of such State or Territory to receive the same, who shall, upon the order of the trustees of the college, or the institution for the colored students, immediately pay over said sums to the treasurers of the respective colleges or other institutions entitled to receive the same, and such treasurers shall be required to report to the Secretary of Agriculture and to the Secretary of the Interior, on or before the first day of September of each year, a detailed statement of the amount so received and of its disbursement. The grants of moneys authorized by this act are made subject to the legislative assent of the several States and Territories to the purpose of said grants: *Provided,* That payments of such installments of the apportion herein made as shall become due to any State before the adjournment of the regular session of legislature meeting next after the passage of this act shall be made upon the assent of the governor thereof, duly certified to the Secretary of the Treasury.

Sec. 3. That if any portion of the moneys received by the designated officer of the State or Territory for the further and more complete endowment, support, and maintenance of colleges, or of institutions for colored students, as provided in this act, shall, by any action or contingency, be diminished or lost, or be misapplied, it shall be replaced by the State or Territory to which it belongs, and until so replaced no subsequent appropriation shall be apportioned or paid to such State or Territory; and no portion of said moneys shall be applied, directly or indirectly, under any pretense whatever, to the purchase, erection, preservation, or repair of any building or buildings. An annual report by the president of each of said colleges shall be made to the Secretary of Agriculture, as well as to the Secretary of the Interior, regarding the condition and progress of each college, including statistical information in relation to its receipts and expenditures, its library, the number of its students and professors, and also as to any improvements and experiments made under the direction of any experiment stations attached to said colleges, with their cost and results, and such other industrial and economical statistics as may be regarded as useful, one copy of which shall be transmitted by mail free to all other colleges further endowed under this act.

Sec. 4. That on or before the first day of July in each year, after the passage of this act, the Secretary of the Interior shall ascertain and certify to the Secretary of the Treasury as to each State and Territory whether it is entitled to receive its share of the annual appropriation for colleges, or of institutions for colored students, under this act, and the amount which thereupon each is entitled, respectively, to receive. If the Secretary of the Interior shall withhold a certificate from any State or Territory of its appropriation the facts and reasons therefor shall be reported to the President, and the amount involved shall be kept separate in the Treasury until the close of the next Congress, in order that the State or Territory may, if it should so desire, appeal to Congress from the determination of the Secretary of the Interior. If the next Congress shall not direct such sum to be paid it shall be covered into the Treasury. And the Secretary of the Interior is hereby charged with the proper administration of this law.

Sec. 5. That the Secretary of the Interior shall annually report to Congress the disbursements which have been made in all the States and Territories, and also whether the appropriation of any State or Territory has been withheld, and if so, the reasons therefor.

Sec. 6. Congress may at any time amend, suspend, or repeal any or all of the provisions of this act.

Approved, August 30, 1890 (26 Stat. 417).

Act of 1906 for the Further Endowment of Agricultural Experiment Stations

[Adams Act]

AN ACT To provide for an increased annual appropriation for agricultural experiment stations and regulating the expenditure thereof

Be it enacted by the Senate and House of Representatives of the United States of America in Congress assembled, That there shall be, and hereby is, annually appropriated, out of any money in the Treasury not otherwise appropriated, to be paid as hereinafter provided, to each State and Territory, for the more complete endowment and maintenance of agricultural experiment stations now established or which may hereafter be established in accordance with the act of Congress approved March second, eighteen hundred and eighty-seven, the sum of five thousand dollars in addition to the sum named in said act for the year ending June thirtieth, nineteen hundred and six, and an annual increase of the amount of such appropriation thereafter for five years by an additional sum of two thousand dollars over the preceding year, and the annual amount to be paid thereafter to each State and Territory shall be thirty thousand dollars, to be applied only to paying the necessary expenses of conducting original researches or experiments bearing directly on the agricultural industry of the United States, having due regard to the varying conditions and needs of the respective States or Territories.

Sec. 2. That the sums hereby appropriated to the States and Territories for the further endowment and support of agricultural experiment stations shall be annually paid in equal quarterly payments on the first day of January, April, July, and October of each year by the Secretary of the Treasury upon the warrant of the Secretary of Agriculture, out of the Treasury of the United States, to the treasurer or other officer duly appointed by the governing boards of said experiment stations to receive the same, and such officers shall be required to report to the Secretary of Agriculture on or before the first day of September of each year a detailed statement of the amount so received and of its disbursements, on schedules prescribed by the Secretary of Agriculture. The grants of money authorized by this act are made subject to legislative assent of the several States and Territories to the purpose of said grants: *Provided*, That payment of such installments of the appropriation herein made as shall become due to any State or Territory before the adjournment of the regular session of legislature meeting next after the passage of this act shall be made upon the assent of the governor thereof, duly certified by the Secretary of the Treasury.

Sec. 3. That if any portion of the moneys received by the designated officer of any State or Territory for the further and more complete endowment, support, and maintenance of agricultural experiment stations as provided in this act shall by any action or contingency be diminished or lost or be misapplied, it shall be replaced by said State or Territory to which it belongs, and until so replaced no subsequent appropriation shall be apportioned or paid to such State or Territory; and no portion of said moneys exceeding five per centum of each annual appropriation shall be applied, directly of indirectly, under any pretense whatever, to the purchase, erection, preservation, or repair of any building or buildings, or to the purchase or rental of land. It shall be the duty of each of said stations annually, on or before the first day of February, to make to the governor of the State or Territory in which it is located a full and detailed report of its operations, including a statement of receipts and expenditures, a copy of which report shall be sent to each of said stations to the Secretary of Agriculture, and to the Secretary of the Treasury of the United States.

Sec. 4. That on or before the first day of July in each year after the passage of this act the Secretary of Agriculture shall ascertain and certify to the Secretary of the Treasury as to each State and Territory whether it is complying with the provisions of this act and is entitled to receive its share of the annual appropriation for agricultural experiment stations under this act and the amount which thereupon each is entitled, respectively, to receive. If the Secretary of Agriculture shall withhold a certificate from any State or Territory of its appropriation, the facts and reasons therefore shall be reported to the President, and the amount involved shall be kept separate in the Treasury until the close of the next Congress, in order that the State or Territory may, if it shall so desire, appeal to Congress from the determination of the Secretary of Agriculture. If the next Congress shall not direct such sum to be paid, it shall be covered into the Treasury; and the Secretary of Agriculture is thereby charged with the proper administration of this law.

Sec. 5. That the Secretary of Agriculture shall make an annual report to Congress on the receipts and expenditures and work of the agricultural experiment stations in all of the States and Territories, and also whether the appropriation of any State or Territory has been withheld; and if so, the reason therefor.

Sec. 6. That Congress may at any time amend, suspend, or repeal any or all of the provisions of this act.

Approved March 16, 1906 (34 Stat. 63).

[Section 1 of the Adams Act was clarified and construed to limit the annual appropriation under the act to $15,000 for each State and Territory in the act making appropriations for the United States Department of Agriculture for the fiscal year ended June 30, 1907 (34 Stat. 669, 696).]

Act of 1925 for the More Complete Endowment of the Agricultural Experiment Stations

[Purnell Act]

AN ACT To authorize the more complete endowment of agricultural experiment stations, and for other purposes

Be it enacted by the Senate and House of Representatives of the United States of America in Congress assembled, That for the more complete endowment and maintenance of agricultural experiment stations now established, or which may hereafter be established, in accordance with the act of Congress approved March 2, 1887, there is hereby authorized to be appropriated, in addition to the amounts now received by such agricultural experiment stations, the sum of $20,000 for the fiscal year ending June 30, 1926; $30,000 for the fiscal year ending June 30, 1927; $40,000 for the fiscal year ending June 30, 1928; $50,000 for the fiscal year ending June 30, 1929; $60,000 for the fiscal year ending June 30, 1930; and $60,000 for each fiscal year thereafter, to be paid to each State and Territory; and the Secretary of Agriculture shall include the additional sums above authorized to be appropriated in the annual estimates of the Department of Agriculture, or in a separate estimate, as he may deem best. The funds appropriated pursuant to this act shall be applied only to paying the necessary expenses of conducting investigations or making experiments bearing directly on the production, manufacture, preparation, use, distribution, and marketing of agricultural products and including such scientific researches as have for their purpose the establishment and maintenance of a permanent and efficient agricultural industry, and such economic and sociological investigations as have for their purpose the development and improvement of the rural home and rural life, and for printing and disseminating the results of said researches.

Sec. 2. That the sums hereby authorized to be appropriated to the States and Territories for the further endowment and support of agricultural experiment stations shall be annually paid in equal quarterly payments on the 1st day of January, April, July, and October of each year by the Secretary of the Treasury upon a warrant of the Secretary of Agriculture out of the Treasury of the United States, to the treasurer or other officer duly appointed by the governing boards of such agricultural experiment stations to receive the same and such officers shall be required to report to the Secretary of Agriculture on or before the 1st day of September of each year a detailed statement of the amount so received and of its disbursement on schedules prescribed by the Secretary of Agriculture. The grants of money authorized by this act are made subject to legislative assent of the several States and Territories to the purpose of said grants: *Provided*, That payment of such installments of the appropriation herein authorized to be made as shall become due to any State or Territory before the adjournment of the regular session of the legislature meeting next after the passage of this act shall be made upon the assent of the governor thereof duly certified to the Secretary of the Treasury.

Sec. 3. That if any portion of the moneys received by the designated officer of any State or Territory for the further and more complete endowment, support, and maintenance of agricultural experiment stations as provided in this act shall by any action or contingency be diminished or lost or be misapplied, it shall be replaced by said State or Territory to which it belongs and until so replaced no subsequent appropriation shall be apportioned or paid to such State or Territory, and no portion of said moneys exceeding 10 per centum of each annual appropriation shall be applied directly or indirectly, under any pretense whatever, to the purchase, erection, preservation, or repair of any building or buildings or to the purchase or rental of land. It shall be the duty of each of the said stations annually, on or before the 1st day of February, to make to the governor of the State or Territory in which it is located a full and detailed report of its operations, including a statement of receipts and expenditures for the fiscal year next preceding, a copy of which report shall be sent to each of the said stations and the Secretary of Agriculture and to the Secretary of the Treasury of the United States.

Sec. 4. That on or before the 1st day of July in each year after the passage of this act the Secretary of Agriculture shall ascertain and certify to the Secretary of the Treasury as to each State and Territory whether it is complying with the provisions of this act and is entitled to receive its share of the annual appropriations for agricultural experiment stations under this act and the amount which thereupon each is entitled, respectively, to receive. If the Secretary of Agriculture shall withhold from any State or Territory a certificate of its appropriation, the facts and reasons therefor shall be reported to the President and the amount involved shall be kept separate in the Treasury until the close of the next Congress in order that the State or Territory may, if it shall so desire, appeal to Congress from the determination of the Secretary of Agriculture. If the next Congress shall not direct such sum to be paid, it shall be covered into the Treasury. The Secretary of Agriculture is hereby charged with the proper administration of this law.

Sec. 5. That the Secretary of Agriculture shall make an annual report to Congress on the receipts and expenditures and work of the agricultural experiment stations in all of the States and Territories, and also whether the appropriation of any State or Territory has been withheld; and if so, the reason therefor.

Sec. 6. That Congress may at any time amend, suspend, or repeal any and all of the provisions of this act.

Approved February 24, 1925 (43 Stat. 970).

Act of 1935 Providing for Agricultural Research and More Complete Endowment and Support of Land-Grant Colleges

[Bankhead-Jones Act]

AN ACT To provide for research into basic laws and principles relating to agriculture and to provide for the further development of cooperative agricultural extension work and the more complete endowment and support of land-grant colleges

Be it enacted by the Senate and House of Representatives of the United States of America in Congress assembled,

Title I

Sec. 1.[1] The Secretary of Agriculture is authorized and directed to conduct research into laws and principles underlying basic problems of agriculture in its broadest aspects; research relating to the improvement of the quality of, and the development of new and improved methods of production of, distribution of, and new and extended uses and markets for, agricultural commodities and byproducts and manufactures thereof; and research relating to the conservation, development, and use of land and water resources for agricultural purposes. Research authorized under this section shall be in addition to research provided for under existing law (but both activities shall be coordinated so far as practicable) and shall be

---

[1]Amended by Act of August 14, 1946.

conducted by such agencies of the Department of Agriculture as the Secretary may designate or establish.

Sec. 2. The Secretary is also authorized and directed to encourage research similar to that authorized under section 1 to be conducted by agricultural experiment stations established or which may hereafter be established in pursuance of the act of March 2, 1987, providing for experiment stations, as amended and supplemented, by the allotment and payment as provided in section 5 to Puerto Rico and the States and Territories for the use of such experiment stations of sums appropriated therefor pursuant to this title.

Sec. 3. For the purposes of this title there is authorized to be appropriated, out of any money in the Treasury not otherwise appropriated, the sum of $1,000,000 for the fiscal year beginning after the date of the enactment of this title, and for each of the four fiscal years thereafter $1,000,000 more than the amount authorized for the preceding fiscal year, and $5,000,000 for each fiscal year thereafter. Moneys appropriated in pursuance of this title shall also be available for the purchase and rental of land and the construction of buildings necessary for conducting research provided for in this title, for the equipment and maintenance of such buildings, and for printing and disseminating the results of research. Sums appropriated in pursuance of this title shall be in addition to, and not in substitution for, appropriations for research or other activities of the Department of Agriculture and sums appropriated or otherwise made available for agricultural experiment stations.

Sec. 4. Forty per centum of the sums appropriated for any fiscal year under section 3 shall be available for the purposes of section 1: *Provided*, That not to exceed 2 per centum of the sums appropriated may be used for the administration of section 5 of this title. The sums available for the purposes of section 1 shall be designated as the "Special research fund, Department of Agriculture," and no part of such special fund shall be used for the prosecution of research heretofore instituted or for the prosecution of any new research project except upon approval in writing by the Secretary. One-half of such special research fund shall be used by the Secretary for the establishment and maintenance of research laboratories and facilities in the major agricultural regions at places selected by him and for the prosecution, in accordance with section 1, of research at such laboratories.

Sec. 5.[2] (a) Sixty per centum of the sums appropriated for any fiscal year under section 3 shall be available for the purposes of section 2. The Secretary shall allot, for each fiscal year for which an appropriation is made, to Puerto Rico and each State and Territory an amount which bears the same ratio to the total amount to be allotted as the rural population of Puerto Rico or the State or Territory bears to the rural population of Puerto Rico and all the States and Territories as determined by the last preceding decennial census. No allotment and no payment under any allotment shall be made for any fiscal year in excess of the amount which Puerto Rico or the State or Territory makes

[2]Amended by Act of September 21, 1944.

available for such fiscal year out of its own funds for research and for the establishment and maintenance of necessary facilities for the prosecution of such research. If Puerto Rico or any State or Territory fails to make available for such purposes for any fiscal year a sum equal to the total amount to which it may be entitled for such year, the remainder of such amount shall be withheld by the Secretary. The total amount so withheld may be allotted by the Secretary of Agriculture to Puerto Rico and the States and Territories which make available for such year an amount equal to that part of the total amount withheld which may be allotted to them by the Secretary of Agriculture, but no such additional allotment to Puerto Rico or any State or Territory shall exceed the original allotment to Puerto Rico or such State or Territory for that year by more than 20 per centum thereof.

(b) The sums authorized to be allotted to Puerto Rico and the States and Territories shall be paid annually in quarterly payments on July 1, October 1, January 1, and April 1. Such sums shall be paid by the Secretary of the Treasury upon warrant of the Secretary of Agriculture in the same manner and subject to the same administrative procedure set forth in the act of March 2, 1887, as amended June 7, 1888.

Sec. 6. As used in this title the term "Territory" means Alaska and Hawaii.

Sec. 7. The Secretary of Agriculture is authorized and directed to prescribe such rules and regulations as may be necessary to carry out this act.

Sec. 8. The right to alter, amend, or repeal this act is hereby expressly reserved.

Sec. 22.[3] In order to provide for the more complete endowment and support of the colleges in the several States and the Territory of Hawaii entitled to the benefits of the act entitled "An act donating public lands to the several States and Territories which may provide colleges for the benefit of agriculture and the mechanic arts," approved July 2, 1862, as amended and supplemented (U.S.C., title 7, secs. 301-328; Supp. VII, sec. 304), there are hereby authorized to be appropriated annually, out of any money in the Treasury not otherwise appropriated, the following amounts:

(a) For the fiscal year beginning after the date of the enactment of this act, and for each fiscal year thereafter, $980,000; and

(b) For the fiscal year following the first fiscal year for which an appropriation is made in pursuance of paragraph (a) $500,000, and for each of the two fiscal years thereafter $500,000 more than the amount authorized to be appropriated for the preceding fiscal year, and for each fiscal year thereafter $1,500,000. The sums appropriated in pursuance of paragraph (a) shall be paid annually to the several States and the Territory of Hawaii in equal shares. The sums appropriated in pursuance of paragraph (b) shall be in addition to sums appropriated in pursuance of paragraph (a) and shall be allotted and paid annually to each of the several States and the Territory of Hawaii in the proportion which the total population of each such State and

---

[3]Amended by Act of June 12, 1952.

the Territory of Hawaii bears to the total population of all the States and the Territory of Hawaii, as determined by the last preceding decennial census. Sums appropriated in pursuance of this section shall be in addition to sums appropriated or authorized under such act of July 2, 1862, as amended and supplemented, and shall be applied only for the purposes of the colleges defined in such act, as amended and supplemented. The provisions of law applicable to the use and payment of such sums under the act entitled "An act to apply a portion of the proceeds of the public lands to the more complete endowment and support of the colleges for the benefit of agriculture and the mechanic arts established under the provisions of an act of Congress approved July second, eighteen hundred and sixty-two," approved August 30, 1890, as amended and supplemented, shall apply to the use and payment of sums appropriated in pursuance of this section.

Approved June 29, 1935 (49 Stat. 436).

Amendment of the Bankhead-Jones Act and the Agricultural Marketing Act of 1946

[Research and Marketing Act]

AN ACT To provide for further research into basic laws and principles relating to agriculture and to improve and facilitate the marketing and distribution of agricultural products

Be it enacted by the Senate and House of Representatives of the United States of America in Congress assembled,

Title I

Title I of the Act entitled "An Act to provide for research into basic laws and principles relating to agriculture and to provide for the further development of cooperative agricultural extension work and the more complete endowment and support of land-grant colleges", approved June 29, 1935 (the Bankhead-Jones Act), is amended as follows:

(1) By substituting for section 1, title I, the following section:

"**Sec. 1.** It is hereby declared to be the policy of the Congress to promote the efficient production and utilization of products of the soil as essential to the health and welfare of our people and to promote a sound and prosperous agricultural and rural life as indispensable to the maintenance of maximum employment and national prosperity. It is also the intent of Congress to assure agriculture a position in research equal to that of industry which will aid in maintaining an equitable balance between agriculture and other sections of our economy. For the attainment of these objectives, the Secretary of Agriculture is authorized and directed to conduct and to stimulate research into the laws and principles underlying the basic problems of agriculture in its broadest aspects, including but not limited to: Research relating to the improvement of the quality of, and the development of new and improved methods of the production, marketing, distribution, processing, and utilization of plant and animal commodities at all stages from the original producer through to the ultimate consumer; research into the problems of human nutrition and the nutritive value of agricultural commodities, with particular reference to their content of vitamins, minerals, amino and fatty acids, and all other constituents that may be found necessary for the health of the consumer and to the gains or losses in nutritive value that may take place at any stage in their production, distribution, processing, and preparation for use by the consumer; research relating to the development of present, new, and extended uses and markets for agricultural commodities and byproducts as food or in commerce, manufacture, or trade, both at home and abroad, with particular reference to those foods and fibers for which our capacity to produce exceeds or may exceed existing economic demand; research to encourage the discovery, introduction, and breeding of new and useful agricultural crops, plants, and animals, both foreign and native, particularly for those crops and plants which may be adapted to utilization in chemical and manufacturing industries; research relating to new and more profitable uses for our resources of agricultural manpower, soils, plants, animals, and equipment than those to which they are now, or may hereafter be, devoted; research relating to the conservation, development, and use of land, forest, and water resources for agricultural purposes; research relating to the design, development, and the more efficient and satisfactory use of farm buildings, farm homes, farm machinery, including the application of electricity and other forms of power; research relating to the diversification of farm enterprises, both as to the type of commodities produced, and as to the types of operations performed, on the individual farm; research relating to any other laws and principles that may contribute to the establishment and maintenance of a permanent and effective agricultural industry including such investigations as have for their purpose the development and improvement of the rural home and rural life, and the maximum contribution by agriculture to the welfare of the consumer and the maintenance of maximum employment and national prosperity; and such other researches or experiments bearing on the agricultural industry or on rural homes of the United States as may in each case be deemed advisable, having due regard to the varying conditions and needs of Puerto Rico, the respective States, and Territories. In effectuating the purposes of this section, maximum use shall be made of existing research facilities owned or controlled by the Federal Government or by State agricultural experiment stations and of the facilities of the Federal and State extension services. Research authorized under this section shall be in addition to research provided for under existing law (but both activities shall be coordinated so far as practicable)."

(2) By adding at the end thereof the following new sections:

"**Sec. 9.** (a) In order to carry out further the purposes of section 2 of this title, there is hereby authorized to be appropriated in addition to all other appropriations authorized by this title the following sums:

"(1) $2,500,000 for the fiscal year ending June 30, 1947, and each subsequent fiscal year.

"(2) An additional $2,500,000 for the fiscal year ending June 30, 1948, and each subsequent fiscal year.

"(3) An additional $5,000,000 for the fiscal year ending June 30, 1949, and each subsequent fiscal year.

"(4) An additional $5,000,000 for the fiscal year ending June 30, 1950, and each subsequent fiscal year.

"(5) An additional $5,000,000 for the fiscal year ending June 30, 1951, and each subsequent fiscal year.

"(6) In addition to the foregoing such additional funds beginning with the fiscal year ending June 30, 1952, and thereafter, as the Congress may deem necessary.

"The moneys appropriated in pursuance of this title shall also be available, for the purchase and rental of land and the construction or acquisition of buildings necessary for conducting research provided for in this title, for the equipment and maintenance of such buildings, and for printing and disseminating the results of research. Sums appropriated in pursuance of this title shall be in addition to, and not in substitution for, sums appropriated or otherwise made available for agricultural experiment stations. The said agricultural experiment stations are authorized to plan and conduct any research provided for under this title in cooperation with each other and such other appropriate agencies and individuals as may contribute to the solution of these problems and sums appropriated in pursuance of this title shall be available to meet the necessary expenses of such research.

"Unexpended balances of allotments to experiment stations from appropriations made under this section during the first five fiscal years may remain available for expenditure by the same experiment stations at which the unexpended balances occurred for the purposes specified in section 1 and for the following periods: Unexpended balances of the first year's allotments, five years; of the second fiscal year's allotments, four years; of the third fiscal year's allotments, three years; of the fourth fiscal year's allotments, two years; and of the fifth fiscal year's allotments, one year; and any unexpended balances of allotments to any experiment stations from appropriations made under this section of any subsequent fiscal year shall be deducted from the next succeeding annual allotments to such experiment stations.

"(b) Not less than 97 per centum of the sums appropriated for any fiscal year under this section shall be available for the purposes of section 2 to be allotted to Puerto Rico, each State and Territory as follows:

"(1) Twenty per centum of the sums appropriated for any fiscal year under this section shall be allotted equally to Puerto Rico, each State and Territory: *Provided*, That no allotment and no payment under any allotment shall be made for any fiscal year in excess of the amount which Puerto Rico or the State or Territory makes available for such fiscal year out of its own funds, for research and for the establishment and maintenance of necessary facilities for the prosecution of such research. If Puerto Rico or any State or Territory fails to make available for such purposes for any fiscal year a sum equal to the amount to which it may be entitled for such year, the remainder of such amount shall be withheld by the Secretary.

"(2) Not less than 52 per centum of the sums appropriated for any fiscal year under this section shall be allotted to Puerto Rico, each State and Territory as follows: One-half in an amount which bears the same ratio to the total amount to be allotted as the rural population of Puerto Rico or the State or Territory bears to the total rural population of Puerto Rico and all the States and Territories as determined by the last preceding decennial census; and one-half in an amount which bears the same ratio to the total amount to be allotted as the farm population of Puerto Rico or the State or Territory bears to the total farm population of Puerto Rico and all the States and Territories as determined by the last preceding decennial census: *Provided*, That no allotment and no payment under any allotment shall be made for any fiscal year in excess of the amount which Puerto Rico, or the State or Territory makes available for such fiscal year out of its own funds for research and for the establishment and maintenance of necessary facilities for the prosecution of such research. If Puerto Rico or any State or Territory fails to make available for such purposes for any fiscal year a sum equal to the amount to which it may be entitled for such year, the remainder of such amount shall be withheld by the Secretary.

"(3) Not more than 25 per centum of the sums appropriated for any fiscal year under this section shall be allotted to the States for cooperative research in which two or more State agricultural experiment stations are cooperating to solve problems that concern the agriculture of more than one State. The funds available for such purposes shall be designated as the 'Regional research fund, Office of Experiment Stations' and shall be used only for cooperative regional projects recommended by a committee of nine persons elected by and representing the directors of the State agricultural experiment stations and approved by the Secretary of Agriculture or his authorized representative. The necessary travel expense of said committee of nine in performance of their duties may be paid from the regional research fund, Office of Experiment Stations, provided for under this subsection.

"(c) Three per centum of the sums appropriated for any fiscal year under this section shall be available to the Office of Experiment Stations of the United States Department of Agriculture for administration of research under this section, including participation in planning and coordinating the cooperative regional research.

"**Sec. 10.** (a) In order to carry out further research on utilization and associated problems in connection with the development and application of present, new, and extended uses of agricultural commodities and products thereof authorized by section 1 of this title, and to disseminate information relative thereto, and in addition to all other appropriations authorized by this title, there is hereby authorized to be appropriated the following sums:

"(1) $3,000,000 for the fiscal year ending June 30, 1947, and each subsequent fiscal year.

"(2) An additional $3,000,000 for the fiscal year ending June 30, 1948, and each subsequent fiscal year.

"(3) An additional $3,000,000 for the fiscal year ending June 30, 1949, and each subsequent fiscal year.

"(4) An additional $3,000,000 for the fiscal year ending June 30, 1950, and each subsequent fiscal year.

"(5) An additional $3,000,000 for the fiscal year ending June 30, 1951, and each subsequent fiscal year.

"(6) In addition to the foregoing, such additional funds beginning with the fiscal year ending June 30, 1952, and thereafter, as the Congress may deem necessary.

"The Secretary of Agriculture, in accordance with such regulations as he deems necessary, and when in his judgment the work to be performed will be carried out more effectively, more rapidly, or at less cost than if performed by the Department of Agriculture, may enter into contracts with such public or private organizations or individuals as he may find qualified to carry on work under this section without regard to the provisions of section 3709, Revised Statutes, and with respect to such contracts he may make advance progress or other payments without regard to the provisions of section 3648, Revised Statutes. Contracts hereunder may be made for work to continue not more than four years from the date of any such contract. Notwithstanding the provisions of section 5 of the Act of June 20, 1874, as amended (31 U.S.C. 713), any unexpended balances of appropriations properly obligated by contracting with an organization as provided in this subsection may remain upon the books of the Treasury for not more than five fiscal years before being carried to the surplus fund and covered into the Treasury. Research authorized under this subsection shall be conducted so far as practicable at laboratories of the Department of Agriculture. Projects conducted under contract with public and private agencies shall be supplemental to and coordinated with research of these laboratories. Any contracts made pursuant to this authority shall contain requirements making the results of research and investigations available to the public through dedication, assignment to the Government, or such other means as the Secretary shall determine.

"(b) In order to carry out further the purposes of section 1, other than research on utilization of agricultural commodities and the products thereof, and in addition to all other appropriations authorized by this title, there is hereby authorized to be appropriated for cooperative research with the State agricultural experiment stations and such other appropriate agencies as may be mutually agreeable to the Department of Agriculture and the experiment stations concerned, the following sums:

"(1) $1,500,000 for the fiscal year ending June 30, 1947, and each subsequent fiscal year.

"(2) An additional $1,500,000 for the fiscal year ending June 30, 1948, and each subsequent fiscal year.

"(3) An additional $1,500,000 for the fiscal year ending June 30, 1949, and each subsequent fiscal year.

"(4) An additional $1,500,000 for the fiscal year ending June 30, 1950, and each subsequent fiscal year.

"(5) In addition to the foregoing such additional funds beginning with the fiscal year ending June 30, 1951, and thereafter, as the Congress may deem necessary.

"(c) The Secretary may incur necessary administrative expenses not to exceed 3 per centum of the amount appropriated in any fiscal year in carrying out this section, including the specific objects of expense enumerated in section 3 of this title.

"(d) The 'Special research fund, Department of Agriculture', provided by section 4 of this title, shall continue to be available solely for research into laws and principles underlying basic problems of agriculture in its broadest aspects; research relating to the improvement of the quality of, and the development of, new and improved methods of production of, distribution of, and new and extended uses and markets for, agricultural commodities and byproducts and manufactures thereof; and research relating to the conservation, development, and use of land and water resources for agricultural purposes. Such research shall be in addition to research provided for under other law (but both activities shall be coordinated so far as practicable) and shall be conducted by such agencies of the Department of Agriculture as the Secretary of Agriculture may designate or establish.

"Sec. 11.[4] Notwithstanding any other provision of this title, (1) not less than 20 percentum of the funds authorized to be appropriated under section 9 (a) shall be used by State agricultural experiment stations for conducting marketing research projects approved by the Department of Agriculture, and (2) cooperative research projects provided for under sections 9 (b) (3) and (10) (b) shall be carried out under cooperative agreements between the Secretary of Agriculture and the cooperating agencies and shall include appropriate provisions for preventing duplication or overlapping of work within the State or States cooperating. Should duplication or overlapping occur subsequent to approval of a cooperative research project, the Secretary of Agriculture is authorized and directed to withhold unexpended balances of such projects notwithstanding the prior approval thereof. The Secretary of Agriculture shall include in his annual report to Congress a complete statement of research work being performed under contracts or cooperative agreements under this title, showing the names of the agencies cooperating and the amounts expended thereon, segregated by Federal and non-Federal funds."

Title II

This title may be cited as the "Agricultural Marketing Act of 1946".

Sec. 202. The Congress hereby declares that a sound, efficient, and

---

[4]Amended by Act of July 31, 1947.

privately operated system for distributing and marketing agricultural products is essential to a prosperous agriculture and is indispensable to the maintenance of full employment and to the welfare, prosperity, and health of the Nation. It is further declared to be the policy of Congress to promote through research, study, experimentation, and through cooperation among Federal and State agencies, farm organizations, and private industry a scientific approach to the problems of marketing, transportation, and distribution of agricultural products similar to the scientific methods which have been utilized so successfully during the past eighty-four years in connection with the production of agricultural products so that such products capable of being produced in abundance may be marketed in an orderly manner and efficiently distributed. In order to attain these objectives, it is the intent of Congress to provide for (1) continuous research to improve the marketing, handling, storage, processing, transportation, and distribution of agricultural products; (2) cooperation among Federal and State agencies, producers, industry organizations, and others in the development and effectuation of research and marketing programs to improve the distribution processes; (3) an integrated administration of all laws enacted by Congress to aid the distribution of agricultural products through research, market aids and services, and regulatory activities, to the end that marketing methods and facilities may be improved, that distribution costs may be reduced and the price spread between the producer and consumer may be narrowed, that dietary and nutritional standards may be improved, that new and wider markets for American agricultural products may be developed, both in the United States and in other countries, with a view to making it possible for the full production of American farms to be disposed of usefully, economically, profitably, and in an orderly manner. In effectuating the purposes of this title, maximum use shall be made of existing research facilities owned or controlled by the Federal Government or by State agricultural experiment stations and of the facilities of the Federal and State extension services. To the maximum extent practicable marketing research work done hereunder in cooperation with the States shall be done in cooperation with the State agricultural experiment stations; marketing educational and demonstrational work done hereunder in cooperation with the States shall be done in cooperation with the State agricultural extension service; market information, inspection, regulatory work and other marketing service done hereunder in cooperation with the State agencies shall be done in cooperation with the State departments of agriculture, and State bureaus and departments of market.

Sec. 203. The Secretary of Agriculture is directed and authorized:

(a) To conduct, assist, and foster research, investigation, and experimentation to determine the best methods of processing, preparation for market, packaging, handling, transporting, storing, distributing, and marketing agricultural products: *Provided*, That the results of such research shall be made available to the public for the purpose of expanding the use of American agricultural products in such manner as the Secretary of Agriculture may determine.

(b) To determine costs of marketing agricultural products in their various forms and through the various channels and to foster and assist in the development and establishment of more efficient marketing methods (including analyses of methods and proposed methods), practices, and facilities, for the purpose of bringing about more efficient and orderly marketing, and reducing the price spread between the producer and the consumer.

(c) To develop and improve standards of quality, condition, quantity, grade, and packaging, and recommend and demonstrate such standards in order to encourage uniformity and consistency in commercial practices.

(d) To conduct, assist, foster, and direct studies and informational programs designed to eliminate artificial barriers to the free movement of agricultural products.

(e) To foster and assist in the development of new or expanded markets (domestic and foreign) and new and expanded uses and in the moving of larger quantities of agricultural products through the private marketing system to consumers in the United States and abroad.

(f) To conduct and cooperate in consumer education for the more effective utilization and greater consumption of agricultural products: *Provided*, That no money appropriated under the authority of this Act shall be used to pay for newspaper or periodical advertising space or radio time in carrying out the purposes of this section and section 203 (e).

(g) To collect and disseminate marketing information, including adequate outlook information on a market-area basis, for the purpose of anticipating and meeting consumer requirements, aiding in the maintenance of farm income, and bringing about a balance between production and utilization of agricultural products.

(h) To inspect, certify, and identify the class, quality, quantity, and condition of agricultural products when shipped or received in interstate commerce, under such rules and regulations as the Secretary of Agriculture may prescribe, including assessment and collection of such fees as will be reasonable and as nearly as may be to cover the cost of the service rendered, to the end that agricultural products may be marketed to the best advantage, that trading may be facilitated, and that consumers may be able to obtain the quality product which they desire, except that no person shall be required to use the service authorized by this subsection. Any official certificate issued under the authority of this subsection shall be received by all officers and all courts of the United States as prima facie evidence of the truth of the statements therein contained.

(i) To determine the needs and develop or assist in the development of plans for efficient facilities and methods of operating such facilities for the proper assembly, processing, transportation, storage, distribution, and handling of agricultural products.

(j) To assist in improving transportation services and facilities and in obtaining equitable and reasonable transportation rates and services and adequate transportation facilities for agricultural products and farm supplies by making complaint or petition to the Interstate Commerce Commission, the Maritime Commission, the Civil Aeronautics Board, or other Federal or State transportation regulatory body with respect to rates, charges, tariffs, practices, and services, or by working directly with individual carriers or groups of carriers.

(k) To collect, tabulate, and disseminate statistics on marketing agricultural products, including, but not restricted to statistics on market supplies, storage stocks, quantity, quality, and condition of such products in various positions in the marketing channel, utilization of such products, shipments and unloads thereof.

(l) To develop and promulgate, for the use and at the request of any Federal agency or State, procurement standards and specifications for agricultural products, and submit such standards and specifications to such agency or State for use or adoption for procurement purposes.

(m) To conduct, assist, encourage, and promote research, investigation, and experimentation to determine the most efficient and practical means, methods, and processes for the handling, storing, preserving, protecting, processing, and distributing of agricultural commodities to the end that such commodities may be marketed in an orderly manner and to the best interest of the producers thereof.

(n) To conduct such other research and services and to perform such other activities as will facilitate the marketing, distribution, processing, and utilization of agricultural products through commercial channels.

Sec. 204. (a) In order to conduct research and service work in connection with the preparation for market, processing, packaging, handling, storing, transporting, distributing, and marketing of agricultural products as authorized by this title, there is hereby authorized to be appropriated the following sums:

(1) $2,500,000 for the fiscal year ending June 30, 1947, and each subsequent fiscal year.

(2) An additional $2,500,000 for the fiscal year ending June 30, 1948, and each subsequent fiscal year.

(3) An additional $5,000,000 for the fiscal year ending June 30, 1949, and each subsequent fiscal year.

(4) An additional $5,000,000 for the fiscal year ending June 30, 1950, and each subsequent fiscal year.

(5) An additional $5,000,000 for the fiscal year ending June 30, 1951, and each subsequent fiscal year.

(6) In addition to the foregoing, such additional funds beginning with the fiscal year ending June 30, 1952, and thereafter as the Congress may deem necessary.

Such sums appropriated in pursuance of this title shall be in addition to, and not in substitution for, sums appropriated or otherwise made available to the Department of Agriculture.

(b) The Secretary of Agriculture is authorized to make available from such funds such sums as he may deem appropriate for allotment to State departments of agriculture, State bureaus and departments of markets, State agricultural experiment stations, and other appropriate State agencies for cooperative projects in marketing service and in marketing research to effectuate the purposes of title II of this Act: *Provided*, That no such allotment and no payment under any such allotment shall be made for any fiscal year to any State agency in excess of the amount which such State agency makes available out of its own funds for such research. The funds which State agencies are required to make available in order to qualify for such an allotment shall be in addition to any funds now available to such agencies for marketing services and for marketing research. The allotments authorized under this section shall be made to the ageny or agencies best equipped and qualified to conduct the specific project to be undertaken. Such allotments shall be covered by cooperative agreements between the Secretary of Agriculture and the cooperating agency and shall include appropriate provisions for preventing duplication or overlapping of work within the State or States cooperating. Should duplication or overlapping occur subsequent to approval of a cooperative project or allotment of funds, the Secretary of Agriculture is authorized and directed to withhold unexpended balances on such projects notwithstanding the prior approval thereof.

Sec. 205. (a) In carrying out the provisions of title II of this Act, the Secretary of Agriculture may cooperate with other branches of the Government, State agencies, private research organizations, purchasing and consuming organizations, boards of trade, chambers of commerce, other associations of business or trade organizations, transportation and storage agencies and organizations, or other persons or corporations engaged in the production, transportation, storing, processing, marketing, and distribution of agricultural products whether operating in one or more jurisdictions. The Secretary of Agriculture shall have authority to enter into contracts and agreements under the terms of regulations promulgated by him with States and agencies of States, private firms, institutions, and individuals for the purpose of conducting research and service work, making and compiling reports and surveys, and carrying out other functions relating thereto when in his judgment the services or functions to be performed will be carried out more effectively, more rapidly, or at less cost than if performed by the Deprtment of Agriculture. Contracts hereunder may be made for work to be performed within a period not more than four years from the date of any such contract, and advance, progress, or other payments may be made. The provisions of section 3648 (31 U.S.C., sec. 529) and section 3709 (41 U.S.C., sec. 5) of the Revised Statutes shall not be applicable to contracts or agreements made under the authority of this section. Any unexpended balances of appropriations obligated by contracts as authorized by this section may, notwithstanding the provisions of section 5 of the Act of June 20, 1874, as amended (31 U.S.C., sec. 713) remain upon the books of the Treasury for not more than five fiscal years before being carried to the surplus fund and covered into the Treasury. Any contract made pursuant to this section shall contain requirements making the result of such research and investigations available to the public by such means as the Secretary of Agriculture shall determine.

(b) The Secretary of Agriculture shall promulgate such orders, rules, and regulations as he deems necessary to carry out the provisions of this title. In his annual report to Congress, he shall include a complete statement of research work being performed under contracts or cooperative agreements under this title, showing the names of the agencies cooperating and the amounts expended thereon, segregated by Federal and non-Federal funds.

Sec. 206. In order to facilitate administration and to increase the effectiveness of the marketing research, service, and regulatory work of the Department of Agriculture to the fullest extent practicable, the Secretary of Agriculture is authorized, notwithstanding any other provisions of law, to transfer, group, coordinate, and consolidate the functions, powers, duties, and authorities of each and every agency, division, bureau, service, section, or other administrative unit in the Department of Agriculture primarily concerned with research, service, or regulatory activities in connection with the marketing, transportation, storage, processing, distribution of, or service or regulatory activities in connection with, the utilization of, agricultural products, into a single administrative agency. In making such changes as may be necessary to carry out effectively the purposes of this title, the records, property, personnel, and funds of such agencies, divisions, bureaus, services, sections, or other administrative units in the Department of Agriculture affected thereby are authorized to be transferred to and used by such administrative agency to which the transfer may be made, but such unexpended balances of appropriations so transferred shall be used only for the purposes for which such appropriations were made.

Sec. 207. When used in this title, the term "agricultural products" includes agricultural, horticultural, viticultural, and dairy products, livestock and poultry, bees, forest products, fish and shellfish, and any products thereof, including processed and manufactured products, and any and all products raised or produced on farms and any processed or manufactured product thereof.

Sec. 208. The Secretary of Agriculture shall have the power to appoint, remove, and fix, in accordance with existing law, the compensation of such officers and employees, and to make such expenditures as he deems necessary including expenditures for rent outside the District of Columbia, travel, supplies, books, equipment, and such other expenditures as may be necessary to the administration of this title: *Provided*, That the Secretary of Agriculture may appoint and fix the compensation of any technically qualified person, firm, or organization by contract or otherwise on a temporary basis and for a term not to exceed six months in any fiscal year to perform research, inspection, classification, technical, or other special services, without regard to the civil-service laws or the Classification Act of 1923, as amended.

Title III

Sec. 301. In order to aid in implementing the research and service work authorized under titles I and II of this Act, and to assist in obtaining the fullest cooperation among Federal and State agencies, producers, farm organizations, and private industry, in the development of and in effectuating such research and service programs, and in order to secure the greatest benefits from the expenditure of funds, the Secretary of Agriculture shall establish a national advisory committee. The functions of such advisory committee shall be to consult with the Secretary of Agriculture and other appropriate officials of the Department of Agriculture, to make recommendations relative to research and service work authorized by this Act, and to assist in obtaining the cooperation of producers, farm organizations, industry groups, and Federal and State agencies in the furtherance of such research and service programs. The chairman of the committee shall be the Secretary of Agriculture or such other official of the Department of Agriculture as he shall designate. The committee shall consist of eleven members, six of whom shall be representatives of producers or their organizations. The committee shall meet at least once each quarter and at such other times as are deemed necessary. Members of the committee may not appoint alternates to serve in their stead. Committee members other than the chairman shall not be deemed to be employees of the United States and are not entitled to compensation, but the Secretary of Agriculture is authorized to allow their traveling and subsistence expenses necessary in connection with their attendance at meetings called by him for the purposes of this section.

Sec. 302. In the furtherance of the research and service work authorized by this Act, the Secretary of Agriculture may, in addition to the national advisory committee, establish appropriate committees, including representatives of producers, industry, government, and science, to assist in effectuating specific research and service programs.

Approved August 14, 1946 (60 Stat. 1082).

Act of 1955 Consolidating the Hatch Act and Laws Supplementary Thereto

[Amended Hatch Act]

AN ACT To consolidate the Hatch Act of 1887 and laws supplementary thereto relating to the appropriation of Federal funds for the support of agricultural experiment stations in the States, Alaska, Hawaii, and Puerto Rico.

Be it enacted by the Senate and House of Representatives of the United States of America in Congress assembled, That the Hatch Act of March 2, 1887, relating to the appropriation of Federal funds for the support of State agricultural experiment stations, is hereby amended to read as follows:

"**Sec. 1.** It is the policy of Congress to continue the agricultural research as State agricultural experiment stations which has been encouraged and supported by the Hatch Act of 1887, the Adams Act of 1906, the Purnell Act of 1925, the Bankhead-Jones Act of 1935, and title I, section 9, of that Act as added by the Act of August 14, 1946, and Acts amendatory and supplementary thereto, and to promote the efficiency of such research by a codification and simplification of such laws. As used in this Act, the terms 'State' or 'States' are defined to include the several States, Alaska, Hawaii, and Puerto Rico. As used in this Act, the term 'State agricultural experiment station' means a department which shall have been established, under direction of the college or university or agricultural departments of the college or university in each State in accordance with an Act approved July 2, 1862 (12 Stat. 503), entitled 'An Act donating public lands to the several States and Territories which may provide colleges for the benefit of agriculture and the mechanic arts'; or such other substantially equivalent arrangements as any State shall determine.

"**Sec. 2.** It is further the policy of the Congress to promote the efficient production, marketing, distribution, and utilization of products of the farm as essential to the health and welfare of our peoples and to promote a sound and prosperous agriculture and rural life as indispensable to the maintenance of maximum employment and national prosperity and security. It is also the intent of Congress to assure agriculture a position in research equal to that of industry, which will aid in maintaining an equitable balance between agriculture and other segments of our economy. It shall be the object and duty of the State agricultural experiment stations through the expenditure of the appropriations hereinafter authorized to conduct original and other researches, investigations, and experiments bearing directly on and contributing to the establishment and maintenance of a permanent and effective agricultural industry of the United States, including researches basic to the problems of agriculture in its broadest aspects, and such investigations as have for their purpose the development and improvement of the rural home and rural life and the maximum contribution by agriculture to the welfare of the consumer, as may be deemed advisable, having due regard to the varying conditions and needs of the respective States.

"**Sec. 3.** (a) There are hereby authorized to be appropriated for the purposes of this Act such sums as Congress may from time to time determine to be necessary.

"(b) Out of such sums each State shall be entitled to receive annually a sum of money equal to and subject to the same requirement as to use for marketing research projects as the sums received from Federal appropriations for State agricultural experiment stations for the fiscal year 1955, except that amounts heretofore made available from the fund known as the 'Regional research fund, Office of Experiment Stations' shall continue to be available for the support of cooperative regional projects as defined in subsection 3 (c) (3), and the said fund shall be designated 'Regional research fund, State agricultural experiment stations', and the Secretary of Agriculture shall be entitled to receive annually for the administration of this Act, a sum not less than that available for this purpose for the fiscal year ending June 30, 1955: *Provided*, That if the appropriations hereunder available for distribution in any fiscal year are less than those for the fiscal year 1955 the allotment to each State and the amounts for Federal administration and the regional research fund shall be reduced in proportion to the amount of such reduction.

"(c) Any sums made available by the Congress in addition to those provided for in subsection (b) hereof for State agricultural experiment station work shall be distributed as follows:

"1. Twenty per centum shall be allotted equally to each State;

"2. Not less than 52 per centum of such sums shall be allotted to each State, as follows: One-half in an amount which bears the same ratio to the total amount to be allotted as the rural population of the State bears to the total rural population of all the States as determined by the last preceding decennial census current at the time each such additional sum is first appropriated; and one-half in an amount which bears the same ratio to the total amount to be allotted as the farm population of the State bears to the total farm population of all the States as determined by the last preceding decennial census current at the time such additional sum is first appropriated;

"3. Not more than 25 per centum shall be allotted to the States for cooperative research in which two or more State agricultural experiment stations are cooperating to solve problems that concern the agriculture of more than one State. The funds available for such purposes, together with funds available pursuant to subsection (b) hereof for like purpose shall be designated as the 'Regional research fund, State agricultural experiment stations', and shall be used only for such cooperative regional projects as are recommended by a committee of nine persons elected by and representing the directors of the State agricultural experiment stations, and approved by the Secretary of Agriculture. The necessary travel expenses of the committee of nine persons in performance of their duties may be paid from the fund established by this paragraph.

"4. Not less than 20 per centum of any sums appropriated pursuant to this subsection for distribution to States shall be used by State agricultural experiment stations for conducting marketing research projects approved by the Department of Agriculture.

"5. Three per centum shall be available to the Secretary of Agriculture for administration of this Act.

"(d) Of any amount in excess of $90,000 available under this Act for allotment to any State, exclusive of the regional research fund, State agricultural experiment stations, no allotment and no payments thereof shall be made in excess of the amount which the State makes available out of its own funds for research and for the establishment and maintenance of facilities necessary for the prosecution of such research: *And provided further*, That if any State fails to make available for such research purposes for any fiscal year a sum equal to the amount in excess of $90,000 to which it may be entitled for such year, the remainder of such amount shall be withheld by the Secretary of Agriculture.

"(e) 'Administration' as used in this section shall include participation in planning and coordinating cooperative regional research as defined in subsection 3 (c) 3.

"(f) In making payments to States, the Secretary of Agriculture is authorized to adjust any such payment to the nearest dollar.

"**Sec. 4.** Moneys appropriated pursuant to this Act shall also be available, in addition to meeting expenses for research and investigations conducted under authority of section 2, for printing and disseminating the results of such research, retirement of employees subject to the provisions of an Act approved March 4, 1940 (54 Stat. 39), administrative planning and direction, and for the purchase and rental of land and the construction, acquisition, alteration, or repair of buildings necessary for conducting research. The State agricultural experiment stations are authorized to plan and conduct any research authorized under section 2 of this Act in cooperation with each other and such other agencies and individuals as may contribute to the solution of the agricultural problems involved, and moneys appropriated pursuant to this Act shall be available for paying the necessary expenses of planning, coordinating, and conducting such cooperative research.

"**Sec. 5.** Sums available for allotment to the States under the terms of this Act, excluding the regional research fund authorized by subsection 3 (c) 3, shall be paid to each State agricultural experiment station in equal quarterly payments beginning on the first day of July of each fiscal year upon vouchers approved by the Secretary of Agriculture. Each such station authorized to receive allotted funds shall have a chief administrative officer known as a director, and a treasurer or other officer appointed by the governing board of the station. Such treasurer or other officer shall receive and account for all funds allotted to the State under the provisions of this Act and shall report, with the approval of the director, to the Secretary of Agriculture on or before the first day of September of each year a detailed statement of the amount received under provisions of this Act during the preceding fiscal year, and of its disbursement on schedules prescribed by the Secretary of Agriculture. If any portion of the allotted moneys received by the authorized receiving officer of any State agricultural experiment station shall by any action or contingency be diminished, lost, or misapplied, it shall be replaced by the State concerned and until so replaced no subsequent appropriation shall be allotted or paid to such State.

"**Sec. 6.** Bulletins, reports, periodicals, reprints of articles, and other publications necessary for the dissemination of results of the researches and experiments, including lists of publications available for distribution by the experiment stations, shall be transmitted in the mails of the United States under penalty indicia: *Provided, however,* That each publication shall bear such indicia as are prescribed by the Postmaster General and shall be mailed under such regulations as the Postmaster General may from time to time prescribe.

Such publications may be mailed from the principal place of business of the station or from an established subunit of said station.

"**Sec. 7.** The Secretary of Agriculture is hereby charged with the responsibility for the proper administration of this Act, and is authorized and directed to prescribe such rules and regulations as may be necessary to carry out its provisions. It shall be the duty of the Secretary to furnish such advice and assistance as will best promote the purposes of this Act, including participation in coordination of research initiated under this Act by the State agricultural experiment stations, from time to time to indicate such lines of inquiry as to him seem most important, and to encourage and assist in the establishment and maintenance of cooperation by and between the several State agricultural experiment stations, and between the stations and the United States Department of Agriculture.

"On or before the first day of July in each year after the passage of this Act, the Secretary of Agriculture shall ascertain as to each State whether it is entitled to receive its share of the annual appropriations for agricultural experiment stations under this Act and the amount which thereupon each is entitled, respectively, to receive.

"Whenever it shall appear to the Secretary of Agriculture from the annual statement of receipts and expenditures of funds by any State agricultural experiment station that any portion of the preceding annual appropriation allotted to that station under this Act remains unexpended, such amount shall be deducted from the next succeeding annual allotment to the State concerned.

"If the Secretary of Agriculture shall withhold from any State any portion of the appropriations available for allotment, the facts and reasons therefor shall be reported to the President and the amount involved shall be kept separate in the Treasury until the close of the next Congress. If the next Congress shall not direct such sum to be paid, it shall be carried to surplus.

"The Secretary of Agriculture shall make an annual report to the Congress during the first regular session of each year of the receipts and expenditures and work of the agricultural experiment stations in all the States under the provisions of this Act and also whether any portion of the appropriation available for allotment to any State has been withheld and if so the reasons therefor.

"**Sec. 8.** Nothing in this Act shall be construed to impair or modify the legal relation existing between any of the colleges or universities under whose direction State agricultural experiment stations have been established and the government of the States in which they are respectively located. States having agricultural experiment stations separate from such colleges or universities and established by law, shall be authorized to apply such benefits to research at stations so established by such States: *Provided,* That in any State in which more than one such college, university, or agricultural experiment station has been established the appropriations made pursuant to this Act for such State shall be divided between such institutions as the legislature of such State shall direct.

"**Sec. 9.** The Congress may at any time, amend, suspend, or repeal any or all of the provisions of this Act."

Sec. 2. The following listed sections or parts of sections of the Statutes at Large heretofore covering the provisions consolidated in this Act are hereby repealed: *Provided, however*, That any rights or liabilities existing under such repealed sections or parts of sections shall not be affected by their repeal:

Bankhead-Jones Act, title I, sections 2 to 8, June 29, 1935 (49 Stat. 436; 7 U.S.C. 427 a-g).

Section 9, and related provisions of section 11 of the Bankhead-Jones Act, title I, as added by title I of the Research and Marketing Act (60 Stat. 1082; 7 U.S.C. 427h, 427j).

Department of Agriculture Organic Act of 1944, title I, section 105, amending the Bankhead-Jones Act, title I, section 5, by adding subsection (c) (58 Stat. 735; 7 U.S.C. 427d).

Act approved June 7, 1888, amending the Hatch Act (25 Stat. 176; U.S.C. 372).

Adams Act approved March 16, 1906 (34 Stat. 63; 7 U.S.C. 369, 371, 373, 366, 374, 375, 361, 376, 380, 382).

Purnell Act approved February 24, 1925 (43 Stat. 970; 7 U.S.C. 370, 371, 373, 374, 375, 376, 366, 361, 380, 382).

The Acts extending the benefits of the foregoing Acts to the Territory of Hawaii, the Territory of Alaska, and Puerto Rico; Hawaii, Act of May 16, 1928 (45 Stat. 571; 7 U.S.C. 386, 386a, 386b); Alaska Act of June 20, 1936 (49 Stat. 1553), as amended by Public Law 739, approved August 29, 1950 (7 U.S.C. 369a); Alaska, Act of February 23, 1929 (45 Stat. 1256; 7 U.S.C. 386c); Puerto Rico, Act of March 4, 1931 (46 Stat. 1520; 7 U.S.C. 386d, e, f).

Such portion of the Department of Agriculture Appropriation Act of 1890, approved March 2, 1889, as related to examination of soils by experimental stations (25 Stat. 841; 7 U.S.C. 364).

That part of the Act of October 1, 1918, relating to the Georgia Agricultural Experiment Station (40 Stat. 998; 7 U.S.C. 383).

Approved August 11, 1955 (69 Stat. 671).

Public Law 87-788 of 1962 Assisting States in Forestry Research

[McIntire-Stennis Forestry Research Act]

To authorize the Secretary of Agriculture to encourage and assist the several States in carrying on a program of forestry research, and for other purposes.

Be it enacted by the Senate and House of Representatives of the United States of America in Congress assembled, That it is hereby recognized that research in forestry is the driving force behind progress in developing and utilizing the resources of the Nation's forest and related rangelands. The production, protection, and utilization of the forest resources depend on strong technological advances and continuing development of the knowledge necessary to increase the efficiency of forestry practices and to extend the benefits that flow from forest and related rangelands. It is recognized that the total forestry research efforts of the several State colleges and universities and of the Federal Government are more fully effective if there is close coordination between such programs, and it is further recognized that forestry schools are especially vital in the training of research workers in forestry.

Sec. 2. In order to promote research in forestry, the Secretary of Agriculture is hereby authorized to cooperate with the several States for the purpose of encouraging and assisting them in carrying out programs of forestry research.

Such assistance shall be in accordance with plans to be agreed upon in advance by the Secretary and (a) land-grant colleges or agricultural experiment stations established under the Morrill Act of July 2, 1862 (12 Stat. 503), as amended, and the Hatch Act of March 2, 1887 (24 Stat. 440), as amended, and (b) other State-supported colleges and universities offering graduate training in the sciences basic to forestry and having a forestry school; however, an appropriate State representative designated by the State's Governor shall, in any agreement drawn up with the Secretary of Agriculture for the purposes of this Act, certify those eligible institutions of the State which will qualify for assistance and shall determine the proportionate amounts of assistance to be extended these certified institutions.

Sec. 3. To enable the Secretary to carry out the provisions of this Act there are hereby authorized to be appropriated such sums as the Congress may from time to time determine to be necessary but not exceeding in any one fiscal year one-half the amount appropriated for Federal forestry research conducted directly by the Department of Agriculture for the fiscal year preceding the year in which the budget is presented for such appropriation. Funds appropriated and made available to the States under this Act shall be in addition to allotments or grants that may be made under other authorizations.

Sec. 4. The amount paid by the Federal Government to any State-certified institutions eligible for assistance under this Act shall not exceed during any fiscal year the amount available to and budgeted for expenditure by such college or university during the same fiscal year for forestry research from non-Federal sources. The Secretary is authorized to make such expenditures on the certificate of the appropriate official of the college or university having charge of the forestry research for which the expenditures as herein provided are to be made. If any or all of the colleges or universities certified for receipt of funds under this Act fails to make available and budget for expenditure for forestry research in any fiscal year sums at least as much as the amount for which it would be eligible for such year under this Act, the difference between the Federal funds available and the funds made available and budgeted for expenditure by the college or university shall be reapportioned by the Secretary to other eligible colleges or universities of the same State if there be any which qualify therefor and, if there be none, the Secretary shall reapportion such differences to the qualifying colleges and universities of other States participating in the forestry research program.

Sec. 5. Apportionments among participating States and administrative expenses in connection with the program shall be determined by the Secretary after consultation with a national advisory board of not less than seven officials of the forestry schools of the State-certified eligible colleges and universities chosen by a majority of such schools. In making such apportionments consideration shall be given to pertinent factors including, but not limited to, areas of non-Federal commercial forest land and volume of timber cut annually from growing stock.

Sec. 6. The Secretary is authorized and directed to prescribe such rules and regulations as may be necessary to carry out the provisions of this Act and to furnish such advice and assistance through a cooperative State forestry research unit in the Department of Agriculture as will best promote the purposes of this Act. The Secretary is further authorized and directed to appoint an advisory committee which shall be constituted to give equal representation to Federal-State agencies concerned with developing and utilizing the Nation's forest resources and to the forest industries. The Secretary and the national advisory board shall seek at least once each year the counsel and advice of the advisory committee to accomplish effectively the purposes of this Act.

Sec. 7. The term "forestry research" as used in this Act shall include investigations relating to: (1) Reforestation and management of land for the production of crops of timber and other related products of the forest; (2) management of forest and related watershed lands to improve conditions of waterflow and to protect resources against floods and erosion; (3) management of forest and related rangeland for production of forage for domestic livestock and game and improvement of food and habitat for wildlife; (4) management of forest lands for outdoor recreation; (5) protection of forest land and resources against fire, insects, diseases, or other destructive agents; (6) utilization of wood and other forest products; (7) development of sound policies for the management of forest lands and the harvesting and marketing of forest products; and (8) such other studies as may be necessary to obtain the fullest and most effective use of forest resources.

Sec. 8. The term "State" as used in this Act shall include Puerto Rico.
Approved October 10, 1962 (76 Stat. 806).

Public Law 89-106 of 1965 Facilitating the Work of the Department of Agriculture

[Specific Grants Law]

AN ACT To facilitate the work of the Department of Agriculture, and for other purposes.

Sec. 2. The Secretary of Agriculture is authorized to make grants, for periods not to exceed five years' duration, to State agricultural experiment stations, colleges, universities, and other research institutions and organizations and to Federal and private organizations and individuals for research to further the programs of the Department of Agriculture. Each recipient of assistance under this section shall keep such records as the Secretary shall prescribe, including records which fully disclose the amount and disposition by such recipient of the proceeds of such grants, the total cost of the project or undertaking in connection with which such funds are given or used, and the amount of that portion of the costs of the project or undertaking supplied by other sources, and such other records as will facilitate an effective audit. The Secretary of Agriculture and the Comptroller General of the United States or any of their duly authorized representatives shall have access for the purpose of audit and examination to any books, documents, papers, and records of the recipients that are pertinent to the grants received under this section.

Approved August 4, 1965 (79 Stat. 431).

Act of 1972 Improving the Economy and Living Conditions in Rural America

[Rural Development Act]

AN ACT To provide for improving the economy and living conditions in rural America

Title V—Rural Development and Small Farm Research and Education

Sec. 501. Purposes.—The purpose of this title is to encourage and foster a balanced national development that provides opportunities for increased numbers of Americans to work and enjoy a high quality of life dispersed throughout our Nation by providing the essential knowledge necessary for successful programs of rural development. It is further the purpose of this title—

(a) to provide multistate regional agencies, States, counties, cities, multicounty planning and development of districts, businesses, industries, organizations, Indian tribes on Federal and State reservations or other federally recognized Indian tribal groups, and others involved with public services and investments in rural areas or that provide or may provide employment in these areas the best available scientific, technical, economic, organizational, environmental, and management information, and knowledge useful to them, and to assist and encourage them in the interpretation and application of this information to practical problems and needs in rural development;

(b) to provide research and investigations in all fields that have as their purpose the development of useful knowledge and information to assist those planning, carrying out, managing, or investing in facilities, services, businesses, or other enterprises, public and private, that may contribute to rural development;

(c) to enhance the capabilities of colleges and universities to perform the vital public service roles of research, transfer, and practical application of knowledge in support of rural development;

(d) to expand research on innovative approaches to small farm management and technology and extend training and technical assistance to small farmers so that they may fully utilize the best available knowledge on sound economic approaches to small farm operations.

Sec. 502. Programs Authorized.—The Secretary of Agriculture (hereafter referred to as the "Secretary") is directed and authorized to conduct in cooperation and in coordination with colleges and universities the following programs to carry out the purposes of this title.

(a) Rural Development Extension Programs.—Rural development extension programs shall consist of the collection, interpretation, and dissemination of useful information and knowledge from research and other sources to units of multistate regional agencies, State, county, municipal, and other units of government, multicounty planning and development districts, organizations of citizens contributing to rural development, business, Indian tribes on Federal or State reservations or other federally recognized Indian tribal groups, or industries that employ or may employ people in rural areas. These programs also shall include technical services and educational activity, including instruction for persons not enrolled as students in colleges or universities, to facilitate and encourage the use and practical application of this information. These programs also may include feasibility studies and planning assistance.

(b) Rural Development Research.—Rural development research shall consist of research, investigations, and basic feasibility studies in any field or discipline which may develop principles, facts, scientific and technical knowledge, new technology, and other information that may be useful to agencies of Federal, State, and local government, industries in rural areas, Indian tribes on Federal and State reservations or other federally recognized Indian tribal groups, and other organizations involved in rural development programs and activities in planning and carrying out such programs and activities or otherwise be practical and useful in achieving increased rural development.

(c) Small Farm Extension, Research, and Development Programs.—Small farm extension and research and development programs shall consist of extension and research programs with respect to new approaches for small farms in management, agricultural production techniques, farm machinery technology, new products, cooperative agricultural marketing, and distribution suitable to the economic development of family size farm operations.

Sec. 503. Appropriation and Allocation of Funds.—(a) There is hereby authorized to be appropriated to carry out the purposes of this title not to exceed $10,000,000 for the fiscal year ending June 30, 1974, not to exceed $15,000,000 for the fiscal year ending June 30, 1975, and not to exceed $20,000,000 for the fiscal year ending June 30, 1976.

(b) Such sums as the Congress shall appropriate to carry out the purposes of this title pursuant to subsection (a) shall be distributed by the Secretary as follows:

(1) 4 per centum to be used by the Secretary for Federal administration, national coordination, and program assistance to the States;

(2) 10 per centum to be allocated by the Secretary to States to finance work serving two or more States in which universities in two or more States cooperate or which is conducted by one university to serve two or more States;

(3) 20 per centum shall be allocated equally among the States;

(4) 66 per centum shall be allocated to each State, as follows: One-half in an amount which bears the same ratio to the total amount to be allotted as the rural population of the States bears to the total rural population of all the States as determined by the last preceding decennial census current at the time each such additional sum is first appropriated; and one-half in an amount which bears the same ratio to the total amount to be allotted as the farm population of the State bears to the total farm population of all the States as determined by the last preceding decennial census current at the time such additional sum is first appropriated.

(c) Funds appropriated under this title may be used to pay salaries, and other expenses of personnel employed to carry out the functions authorized by this title, to obtain necessary supplies, equipment, services, and rent, repair, and maintenance of other facilities needed, but may not be used to purchase or construct buildings.

(d) Payment of funds to any State for programs authorized under section 502(a), (b), and (c) shall be contingent upon the Secretary's approval of an annual plan and budget for programs conducted under each part and compliance with such regulations as the Secretary may issue under this title. Funds shall be available for use by the State in the fiscal year for which appropriated and the next fiscal year following the year for which appropriated. Funds shall be budgeted and accounted for on such forms and at such times as the Secretary shall prescribe.

(e) Funds provided to each State under this title may be used to finance programs through or at private and publicly supported colleges and universities other than the university responsible for administering the programs authorized by this title.

Sec. 504. Cooperating Colleges and Universities.—(a) Each of the programs authorized by this title shall be organized and conducted by one or more colleges or universities in each State so as to provide a coordinated program in each State.

(b) To assure national coordination with programs under the Smith-Lever Act of 1914 and the Hatch Act (as amended, August 11, 1955), administration of each State program shall be a responsibility of the institution or university accepting the benefits of the Morrill Act of 1862 (12 Stat. 503) as amended. Such administration shall be in association with the programs conducted under the Smith-Lever Act and the Hatch Act. The Secretary shall pay funds available to each State to said institution or university.

(c) All private and publicly supported colleges and universities in a State including the land-grant colleges of 1890 (26 Stat. 417) shall be eligible to conduct or participate in conducting programs authorized under this title. Officials at universities or colleges other than those responsible for administering programs authorized by this title who wish to participate in these programs shall submit program proposals to the university officials responsible for administering these programs and they shall be responsible for approval of said proposals.

(d) The university in each State responsible for administering the program authorized by this title shall designate an official who shall be responsible for programs authorized by each part of section 502 and an official who shall be responsible for the overall coordination of said programs.

(e) The chief administrative officer of the university in each State responsible for administering the program authorized by this title shall appoint a State Rural Development Advisory Council, consisting of not more than fifteen members. The administrative head of agriculture of that university shall serve as chairman. The administrative head of a principal school of engineering in the State shall be a member. There shall be at least ten additional members who shall include persons representing farmers, business, labor, banking, local government, multicounty planning and development districts, public and private colleges and Federal and State agencies involved in rural development.

It shall be the function of the Council to review and approve annual program plans conducted under this title and to advise the chief administrative officer of the university on matters pertaining to the program authorized.

Sec. 505. Agreements and Plans.—(a) Programs authorized under this title shall be conducted as mutually agreed upon by the Secretary and the university responsible for administering said programs in a memorandum of understanding which shall provide for the coordination of the programs authorized under this title, coordination of these programs with other rural development programs of Federal, State, and local government, and such other matters as the Secretary shall determine.

(b) Annually said university shall submit to the Secretary an annual program plan for programs authorized under this title which shall include plans for the programs to be conducted by each cooperating and participating university or college and such other information as the Secretary shall prescribe. Each State program must include research and extension activities directed toward identification of programs which are likely to have the greatest impact upon accomplishing the objectives of rural development in both the short and longer term and the use of these studies to support the State's comprehensive program to be supported under this title.

Sec. 506. Withholding Funds.—When the Secretary determines that a

State is not eligible to receive part or all of the funds to which it is otherwise entitled because of a failure to satisfy conditions specified in this title, or because of a failure to comply with regulations issued by the Secretary under this title, the facts and reasons therefor shall be reported to the President, and the amount involved shall be kept separate in the Treasury until the expiration of the Congress next succeeding a session of the legislature of the State from which funds have been withheld in order that the State may, if it should so desire, appeal to Congress from the determination of the Secretary. If the next Congress shall not direct such sum to be paid, it shall be covered into the Treasury. If any portion of the moneys received by the designated officers of any State for the support and maintenance of programs authorized by this title shall by any action or contingency be diminished or lost, or be mis-applied, it shall be replaced by said State.

Sec. 507. Definitions.—For the purposes of this title—

(a) "Rural development" means the planning, financing, and development of facilities and services in rural areas that contribute to making these areas desirable places in which to live and make private and business investments; the planning, development, and expansion of business and industry in rural areas to provide increased employment and income; the planning, development, conservation, and use of land, water, and other natural resources of rural areas to maintain or enhance the quality of the environment for people and business in rural areas; and processes and procedures that have said objectives as their major purposes.

(b) The word "State" means the several States and the Commonwealth of Puerto Rico.

Sec. 508. Regulations.—The Secretary is authorized to issue such regulations as may be necessary to carry out the provisions of this title.

Approved August 30, 1972 (86 Stat. 671).

National Agricultural Research, Extension and Teaching Policy Act of 1977[1] with Amendments of 1981 and 1985

Subtitle A—Findings, Purposes, and Definitions

---

[1] The National Agricultural Research, Extension, and Teaching Policy Act of 1977 is set forth in Title XIV of the Food and Agriculture Act of 1977, Public Law 95-113, 91 Stat. 981, 7 U.S.C. 3101 et seq. Title XIV was amended by the Energy Security Act, Public Law 96-294, 94 Stat. 705, and further was extensively amended by the National Agricultural Research, Extension, and Teaching Policy Act Amendments of 1981, which were title XIV of the Agriculture and Food Act of 1981, Public Law 97-98, 95 Stat. 1294 et seq. and was further amended by the Amendments of 1985, which were title XIV of the Food Security Act of 1985. Public Law 99-198, 99 Stat. 1542 et. seq., signed December 23, 1985. This compilation was prepared by the Legislative Staff Agricultural Research Service in January 1986.

Findings

Sec. 1402. Congress finds that—

(1) the Federal Government of the United States has provided funding support for agricultural research and extension for many years in order to promote and protect the general health and welfare of the people of the United States, and this support has significantly contributed to the development of the Nation's agricultural system;

(2) the agencies conducting such federally supported research were established at different times in response to different and specific needs and their work is not fully coordinated;

(3) these agencies have only been partially successful in responding to the needs of all persons affected by their research, and useful information produced through such federally supported research is not being efficiently transferred to the people of the United States;

(4) expanded agricultural research and extension are needed to meet the rising demand for food and fiber caused by increases in worldwide population and food shortages due to short-term localized, and adverse climatic conditions;

(5) increased research is necessary to alleviate inadequacies of the marketing system (including storage, transportation, and distribution of agricultural and forest products) which have impaired United States agricultural production and utilization;

(6) advances in food and agricultural sciences and technology have become increasingly limited by the concentration upon the thorough development and exploitation of currently known scientific principles and technological approaches at the expense of more fundamental research, and a strong research effort in the basic sciences is necessary to achieve breakthroughs in knowledge that can support new and innovative food and agricultural technologies;

(7) Federal funding levels for agricultural research and extension in recent years have not been commensurate with needs stemming from changes in United States agricultural practices and the world food and agricultural situation;

(8) new Federal initiatives are needed in the areas of—

(A) research to find alternatives to technologies based on fossil fuels;

(B) research and extension on human nutrition and food consumption patterns in order to improve the health and vitality of the people of the United States;

(C) research to find solutions to environmental problems caused by technological changes in food and agricultural production;

(D) aquacultural research and extension;

(E) research and extension directed toward improving the management and use of the Nation's natural and renewable resources, in order to meet the increased demand for forest products, conserve water resources (through irrigation management, tail water reuse, desalination, crop conversion, and other water conservation techniques), conserve soil resources, and properly manage rangelands;

(F) improving and expanding the research and extension programs in home economics;

(G) extension programs in energy conservation;

(H) extension programs in forestry and natural resources, with special emphasis to be given to improving the productivity of small private woodlands, modernizing wood harvesting and utilization, developing and disseminating reliable multiple-use resource management information to all landowners and consumers, and the general public, wildlife, watershed, and recreational management, and cultural practices (including reforestation, protection, and related matters);

(I) research on climate, drought, and weather modification as factors in food and agricultural production;

(J) more intensive agricultural research and extension programs oriented to the needs of small farmers and their families and the family farm system, which is a vital component of the agricultural production capacity of this country;

(K) research to expand export markets for agricultural commodities;

(L) development and implementation, through research, of more efficient, less wasteful, and environmentally sound methods of producing, processing, marketing, and utilizing food, fiber, waste products, other nonfood agricultural products, and forest and rangeland products;

(M) expanded programs of animal disease and health care research and extension;

(N) research to develop new crops, in order to expand our use of varied soils and increase the choice of nutritional and economically viable crops available for cultivation;

(O) investigation and analysis of the practicability, desirability, and feasibility of using organic waste materials to improve soil tilth and fertility, and extension programs to disseminate practical information resulting from such investigations and analyses; and

(P) research on new or improved food processing (such as food irradiation) or value-added food technologies;

(9) the existing agricultural research system consisting of the Federal Government, the land-grant colleges and universities, other colleges and universities engaged in agricultural research, the agricultural experiment stations, and the private sector constitute an essential national resource which must serve as the foundation for any further strengthening of agricultural research in the United States;

(10) it is and has been the policy of the United States to support food and agricultural research, extension, and teaching in the broadest sense of these terms. The partnership between the Federal Government and the States, as consummated in legislation and cooperative agreements, and

the cooperative nature of efforts to implement this policy in cooperation with the food and agricultural industry has been eminently successful. Cooperative research, extension, and teaching programs have provided the United States with the most productive and efficient food and agricultural system in the world. This system is the basis of our national affluence and it provides vast amounts of food and fiber to other people around the world. However, the food and agricultural system is dynamic and constantly changing. The research, extension, and teaching programs must be maintained and constantly adjusted to meet ever changing challenges. National support of cooperative research, extension, and teaching efforts must be reaffirmed and strengthened to meet major needs and challenges in the following areas:

(A) Food and agricultural system productivity.—Increases in agricultural productivity have been outstanding, however, productivity growth in the past decade has slowed. It is imperative that improved technologies and management systems be developed to maintain and enhance agricultural productivity in order for agricultural production in the United States to meet the demand of a rising world population, rising costs of production, and limitations on energy consumption. Improved productivity in food and agricultural processing and marketing sectors is a critical need in the national effort to achieve a strong economy.

(B) Agricultural policy.—The effects of technological, economic, sociological, and environmental developments on the agricultural structure of the United States are strong and continuous. It is critical that emerging agricultural-related technologies, economic changes, and sociological and environmental developments, both national and international, be analyzed on a continuing basis in an interdisciplinary fashion to determine the effect of those forces on the structure of agriculture and to improve agricultural policy decisionmaking.

(C) Development of new food, fiber, and energy sources.—Programs to identify and develop new crop and animal sources of food, fiber, and energy must be undertaken to meet future needs.

(D) Agricultural energy use and production.—Much of the current agricultural technology is relatively energy intensive. It is critical that alternative technologies be developed to increase agricultural energy efficiency and to reduce dependence on petroleum based products. Furthermore, agriculture provides the United States with alternative potential sources of energy that must be assessed and developed.

(E) Coordination of biotechnology responsibilities of Federal Government.—Biotechnology guidelines and regulations must be made consistent throughout the Federal Government so they may promote scientific development and protect the public. The biotechnology risk assessment processes used by various Federal agencies must be standardized.

(F) Natural resources.—Improved management of soil, water, forest, and range resources is vital to maintain the resource base for food, fiber, and wood production. An expanded research program in the areas of soil and water conservation and forest and range production practices is needed to develop more economical and effective management systems. Key objectives of this research are—

(i) incorporating water and soil-saving technologies into current and evolving production practices;

(ii) developing more cost-effective and practical conservation technologies;

(iii) managing water in stressed environments;

(iv) protecting the quality of the surface water and groundwater resources of the United States;

(v) establishing integrated multidisciplinary organic farming research projects, including research on alternative farming systems, that will identify options from which individual farmers may select the production components that are most appropriate for their individual situations;

(vi) developing better targeted pest management systems; and

(vii) improving forest and range management technologies that meet demands more efficiently, better protect multiresource options, and enhance quality of output.

(G) Promotion of the health and welfare of people.—The basic objectives of food and agricultural research, extension, and teaching programs are to make the maximum contribution to the health and welfare of people and the economy of the United States through the enhancement of family farms, to improve community services and institutions, to increase the quality of life in rural America, and to improve the well-being of consumers. The rapid rate of social change, economic instability, and current energy problems increase the need for expanded programs of research and extension in family financial management, housing and home energy consumption, food preparation and consumption, human development (including youth programs), and development of community services and institutions.

(H) Human nutrition.—The challenge to meet the food needs of the world continues, but there is an increasing need to address nutrition research and educational issues associated with diet resulting from changing life styles and with respect to special groups such as the elderly, teenagers, infants, and pregnant women.

(I) International food and agriculture.—United States agricultural production has proven its ability to produce abundant quantities of food for an expanding world population. Despite rising expectation for improved diets in the world today, there are instances of drought, civil unrest, economic crisis, or other conditions that preclude the local production or distribution of food. There are instances where localized problems impede the ability of farmers to produce needed food products. It is also recognized that many nations have progressive and effective agricultural research programs that produce results of interest and applicability to United States agriculture. The exchange of knowledge and information between nations is essential to the well-being of all nations. A dedicated effort involving the Federal Government, the State cooperative institutions, and other colleges and universities is needed to expand international food and agricultural research, extension, and teaching programs. Improved cooperation and communication by the Department of Agriculture and the cooperators with international agricultural research centers, counterpart agencies, and universities in other nations are necessary to improve food and agricultural progress throughout the world.

(11) long-range planning for research, extension, and teaching is a key element in meeting the objectives of this title; accordingly, all of the elements in the food and agricultural science and education system are encouraged to expand their planning and coordination efforts; and

(12) the agricultural system of the United States—

(A) is increasingly dependent on science and technology to maintain and improve productivity levels, manage the resource base, provide high quality products, and protect the environment; and

(B) requires a constant source of food and agricultural scientific expertise to maintain this dynamic system.

Purposes

Sec. 1103. The purposes of this title are to—

(1) establish firmly the Department of Agriculture as the lead agency in the Federal Government for the food and agricultural sciences, and to emphasize that agricultural research, extension, and teaching are distinct missions of the Department of Agriculture;

(2) undertake the special measures set forth in this title to improve the coordination and planning of agricultural research, extension, and teaching programs, identify needs and establish priorities for these programs, assure that national agricultural research, extension, and teaching objectives are fully achieved, and assure that the results of agricultural research are effectively communicated and demonstrated to farmers, processors, handlers, consumers, and all other users who can benefit therefrom;

(3) increase cooperation and coordination in the performance of agricultural research by Federal departments and agencies, the States, State agricultural experiment stations, colleges and universities, and user groups;

(4) enable the Federal Government, the States, colleges and universities, and others to implement needed agricultural research, extension, and teaching programs through the establishment of new programs and the improvement of existing programs, as provided for in this title;

(5) establish a new program of grants for high-priority agricultural research to be awarded on the basis of competition among research workers and all colleges and universities;

(6) establish a new program of grants for facilities and instrumentation used in agricultural research; and

(7) establish a new program of education grants and fellowships to strengthen research, extension, and teaching programs in the food and agricultural sciences, to be awarded on the basis of competition.

Definitions

Sec. 1404. When used in this title—

(1) the term "Advisory Board" means the National Agricultural Research and Extension Users Advisory Board;

(2) the term "agricultural research" means research in the food and agricultural sciences;

(3) the term "aquaculture" means the propagation and rearing of aquacultural species, including, but not limited to, any species of finfish, mollusk, or crustacean (or other aquatic invertebrate), amphibian, reptile, or aquatic plant, in controlled or selected environments;

(4) the terms "college" and "university" mean an educational institution in any State which (A) admits as regular students only persons having a certificate of graduation from a school providing secondary education, or the recognized equivalent of such a certificate, (B) is legally authorized within such State to provide a program of education beyond secondary education, (C) provides an educational program for which a bachelor's degree or any other higher degree is awarded, (D) is a public or other nonprofit institution, and (E) is accredited by a nationally recognized accrediting agency or association;

(5) the term "cooperative extension services" means the organizations established at the land-grant colleges and universities under the Smith-Lever Act of May 8, 1914 (38 Stat. 372-374, as amended; 7 U.S.C. 341-349), and section 209(b) of the Act of October 26, 1974 (88 Stat. 1428, as amended; D.C. Code, sec. 31-1719(b));

(6) the term "Department of Agriculture" means the United States Department of Agriculture;

(7) the term "extension" means the informal education programs conducted in the States in cooperation with the Department of Agriculture;

(8) the term "food and agricultural sciences" means basic, applied, and developmental research, extension, and teaching activities in the food, agricultural, renewable natural resources, forestry, and physical and social sciences, in the broadest sense of these terms, including but not limited to, activities relating to:

(A) agriculture, including soil and water conservation and use, the use of organic waste materials to improve soil tilth and fertility, plant and animal production and protection, and plant and animal health;

(B) the processing, distributing, marketing, and utilization of food and agricultural products;

(C) forestry, including range management, production of forest and range products, multiple use of forest and rangelands, and urban forestry;

(D) aquaculture;

(E) home economics, including consumer affairs, food and nutrition, clothing and textiles, housing, and family well-being and financial management;

(F) rural community welfare and development;

(G) youth development, including 4-H clubs;

(H) domestic and export market expansion for United States agricultural products;

(I) production inputs, such as energy, to improve productivity; and

(J) international food and agricultural issues, such as agricultural development, development of institutions, germ plasm collection and preservation, information exchange and storage, and scientific exchanges;

(9) the term "Joint Council" means the Joint Council on Food and Agricultural Sciences;

(10) the term "land-grant colleges and universities" means those institutions eligible to receive funds under the Act of July 2, 1862 (12 Stat. 503-505, as amended; 7 U.S.C. 301-305, 307 and 308), or the Act of August 30, 1890 (26 Stat. 417-419, as amended; 7 U.S.C. 321-326 and 328), including the Tuskegee Institute;

(11) the term "Secretary" means the Secretary of Agriculture of the United States;

(12) the term "State" means any one of the fifty States, the Commonwealth of Puerto Rico, Guam, American Samoa, the Commonwealth of the Northern Marianas, the Trust Territory of the Pacific Islands, the Virgin Islands of the United States, and the District of Columbia;

(13) the term "State agricultural experiment stations" means those institutions eligible to receive funds under the Act of March 2, 1887 (24 Stat. 440-442, as amended; 7 U.S.C. 361a-361i);

(14) the term "teaching" means formal classroom instruction, laboratory instruction, and practicum experience in the food and agricultural sciences and matters relating thereto (such as faculty development, student recruitment and services, curriculum development, instructional materials and equipment, and innovative teaching methodologies) conducted by colleges and universities offering baccalaureate or higher degrees;

(15) the term "cooperating forestry schools" means those institutions eligible to receive funds under the Act of October 10, 1962 (16 U.S.C. 582a et seq.), commonly known as the McIntire-Stennis Act of 1962; and

(16) the term "State cooperative institutions" or "State cooperative agents" means institutions or agents designated by—

(A) the Act of July 2, 1862 (7 U.S.C. 301 et seq.), commonly known as the First Morrill Act;

(B) the Act of August 30, 1890 (7 U.S.C. 321 et seq.), commonly known as the Second Morrill Act, including the Tuskegee Institute;

(C) the Act of March 2, 1887 (7 U.S.C. 361a et seq.), commonly known as the Hatch Act of 1887;

(D) the Act of May 8, 1914 (7 U.S.C. 341 et seq.), commonly known as the Smith-Lever Act;

(E) the Act of October 10, 1962 (16 U.S.C. 582a et seq.), commonly known as the McIntire-Stennis Act of 1962; and

(F) subtitles E, L, and M of this title;

Subtitle B—Coordination and Planning of Agricultural Research, Extension, and Teaching

Responsibilities of the Secretary and Department of Agriculture

Sec. 1405. The Department of Agriculture is designated as the lead agency of the Federal Government for agricultural research (except with respect to the biomedical aspects of human nutrition concerned with diagnosis or treatment of disease), extension, and teaching in the food and agricultural sciences, and the Secretary, in carrying out the Secretary's responsibilities, shall—

(1) establish jointly with the Secretary of Health and Human Services procedures for coordination with respect to nutrition research in areas of mutual interest;

(2) keep informed of developments in, and the Nation's need for, research, extension, teaching, and manpower development in the food and agricultural sciences and represent such need in deliberations within the Department of Agriculture, elsewhere within the executive branch of the United States Government, and with the several States and their designated land-grant colleges and universities, other colleges and universities, agricultural and related industries, and other interested institutions and groups;

(3) coordinate all agricultural research, extension, and teaching activity conducted or financed by the Department of Agriculture and, to the maximum extent practicable, by other agencies of the executive branch of the United States Government;

(4) take the initiative in establishing coordination of State-Federal cooperative agricultural research, extension, and teaching programs, funded in whole or in part by the Department of Agriculture in each State, through the administrative heads of land-grant colleges and universities and the State directors of agricultural experiment stations and cooperative extension services, and other appropriate program administrators;

(5) consult the Joint Council, Advisory Board, and appropriate advisory committees of the Department of Agriculture in the formulation of

basic policies, goals, strategies, and priorities for programs of agricultural research, extension, and teaching;

(6) report (as a part of the Department of Agriculture's annual budget submissions) to the House Committee on Agriculture, the House Committee on Appropriations, the Senate Committee on Agriculture, Nutrition, and Forestry, and the Senate Committee on Appropriations actions taken or proposed to support the recommendations of the Advisory Board;

(7) establish appropriate review procedures to assure that agricultural research projects are timely and properly reported and published and that there is no unnecessary duplication of effort or overlapping between agricultural research units;

(8) establish Federal or cooperative multidisciplinary research teams on major agricultural research problems with clearly defined leadership, budget responsibility, and research programs;

(9) in order to promote the coordination of agricultural research of the Department of Agriculture, conduct a continuing inventory of ongoing and completed research projects being conducted within or funded by the Department;

(10) coordinate all agricultural research, extension, and teaching activities conducted or financed by the Department of Agriculture with the periodic renewable resource assessment and program provided for in sections 3 and 4 of the Forest and Rangeland Renewable Resources Planning Act of 1974 and the appraisal and program provided for in sections 5 and 6 of the Soil and Water Resources Conservation Act of 1977;

(11) coordinate the efforts of States, State cooperative institutions, State extension services, the Joint Council, the Advisory Board, and other appropriate institutions in assessing the current status of, and developing a plan for, the effective transfer of new technologies, including biotechnology, to the farming community, with particular emphasis on addressing the unique problems of small- and medium-sized farms in gaining information about those technologies; and

(12) establish appropriate controls with respect to the development and use of the application of biotechnology to agriculture.

Subcommittee on Food, Agricultural, and Forestry Research

Sec. 1406. Section 401(h) of the National Science and Technology Policy, Organization, and Priorities Act of 1976 (90 Stat. 471; 42 U.S.C. 6651(h)) is amended by adding at the end thereof the following: "Among such standing subcommittees and panels of the Council shall be the Subcommittee on Food, Agricultural, and Forestry Research. This subcommittee shall review Federal research and development programs relevant to domestic and world food and fiber production and distribution, promote planning and coordination of this research in the Federal Government, and recommend policies and other measures concerning the food and agricultural sciences for the consideration of the Council. The subcommittee shall include, but not be limited to, representatives of each of the following departments or agencies; the Department of Agriculture, the Department of State, the Department of Defense, the Department of the Interior, the Department of Health and Human Services, the National Oceanic and Atmospheric Administration, the Department of Energy, the National Science Foundation, the Environmental Protection Agency, and the Tennessee Valley Authority. The principal representatives of the Department of Agriculture shall serve as the chairman of the subcommittee."

Joint Council on Food and Agricultural Sciences

Sec. 1407. (a) The Secretary shall establish within the Department of Agriculture a committee to be known as the Joint Council on Food and Agricultural Sciences which shall have a term that expires September 30, 1990.

(b) The Joint Council shall be composed of not fewer than twenty-five representatives of organizations or agencies which conduct or assist in conducting programs of research, extension, or teaching in the food and agricultural sciences, including State cooperative institutions; other colleges and universities having a demonstrable capacity to carry out food and agricultural research, extension, or teaching; agencies within the Department of Agriculture which have significant research, extension, or teaching responsibilities; the Office of Science and Technology Policy; other Federal agencies determined by the Secretary to be appropriate, and other public and private institutions, producers, and representatives of the public who are interested in and have a potential to contribute, as determined by the Secretary, to the formulation of national policy in the food and agricultural sciences. Members shall be appointed for a term of up to three years by the Secretary from nominations made by the organizations and agencies described in the preceding sentence. The terms of members shall be staggered. To ensure that regional differences are properly considered, at least one-half of the members of the Joint Council shall be appointed by the Secretary from among distinguished persons engaged in agricultural research, extension, or teaching programs at land-grant colleges and universities and State agricultural experiment stations. To ensure that other agricultural institutional views are considered by the Joint Council, two of the members of the Joint Council shall be appointed by the Secretary from among persons who are distinguished representatives of other colleges and universities having a demonstrable capacity to carry out food and agricultural research, extension, or teaching. To ensure that the views of food technologists are considered by the Joint Council, one of the members of the Joint Council shall, as determined to be appropriate by the Secretary, be appointed by the Secretary from among distinguished persons who are food technologists from accredited or certified departments of food technology, as determined by the Secretary. The Joint Council shall be jointly chaired by the Assistant Secretary of Agriculture for research, extension, and teaching, and a person to be elected from among the non-Federal membership of the Joint Council.

(c) The Joint Council shall meet at least once during each three-month period. At least one meeting each year shall be a combined meeting with the Advisory Board.

(d)(1) The primary responsibility of the Joint Council is to bring about more effective research, extension, and teaching in the food and agricultural sciences in the United States by improving planning and coordination of publicly and privately supported food and agricultural science activities and by relating Federal budget development and program management to these processes.

(2) The Joint Council's responsibilities shall also be to—

(A) provide a forum for the interchange of information among the organizations represented by the members of the Joint Council that will assure improved awareness among these organizations concerning the agricultural research, extension, and teaching programs, results, and directions of each organization;

(B) analyze and evaluate the economic, environmental, and social impacts of agricultural research, extension, and teaching programs conducted in the United States and determine high priority agricultural research areas, and submit annual reports identifying such high priority research areas to the Secretary;

(C) develop and review the effectiveness of a system, for use by the Secretary, of compiling, maintaining, and disseminating information about each federally supported agricultural research or extension project and, to the maximum extent possible, information about private agricultural research and extension projects conducted by colleges and universities, foundations, contract research groups, businesses, and others. Information about private agricultural research and extension projects shall not be included in this system unless they are partially or entirely funded by the Federal Government or the organizations sponsoring the projects agree to the inclusion of information about such projects;

(D) assist the parties in developing, reviewing, and evaluating memoranda of understanding or other documents that detail the terms and conditions between the Secretary and the participants in agricultural research, extension, and teaching programs under this Act and other Acts;

(E) assist the Secretary in carrying out the responsibilities assigned to the Secretary under this title through planning and coordination in the food and agricultural sciences, by using, wherever possible, the existing regional research, extension, and teaching organizations of State cooperative institutions to provide regional planning and coordination, and by the development of recommendations and reports describing current and long-range needs, priorities, and goals in the food and agricultural sciences and means to achieve these goals;

(F) develop, and review the effectiveness of, guidelines for use by the Secretary in making competitive grants under section 2(b) of the Act of August 4, 1965 (79 Stat. 431; 7 U.S.C. 450i), as amended by section 1414 of this title;

(G) submit a report—

(i) not later than June 30 of each year, specifying the Joint Council's recommendations on priorities for food and agricultural research, extension, and teaching programs; delineating suggested areas of responsibility among Federal, State, and private organizations in carrying out such programs; and specifying the levels of financial and other support needed to carry out such programs;

(ii) not later than November 30 of each year, specifying ongoing research, extension, and teaching programs; accomplishments of such programs, and future expectations of these programs; and

(iii) not later than June 30, 1983, outlining a five-year plan for food and agricultural sciences that reflects the coordinated views of the research, extension, and teaching community; and updating this plan every two years thereafter.

Each such report shall be submitted to the Secretary of Agriculture. Minority views, if timely submitted, shall be included in such report; and

(H) coordinate with the Secretary in assessing the current status of, and developing a plan for, the effective transfer of new technologies to the farming community.

(e) The meetings of the Joint Council shall be publicly announced in advance and shall be open to the public. Appropriate records of the activities of the Joint Council shall be kept and made available to the public on request.

(f) The Federal Advisory Committee Act (5 U.S.C. App.) and title XVIII of the Food and Agriculture Act of 1977 shall not apply to the Joint Council.

National Agricultural Research and Extension Users Advisory Board

Sec. 1408. (a) The Secretary shall establish within the Department of Agriculture a board to be known as the National Agricultural Research and Extension Users Advisory Board which shall have a term that expires September 30, 1990.

(b) The Advisory Board shall be composed of the following twenty-five members to be appointed by the Secretary to serve staggered terms—

(1) eight members representing producers of agricultural, forestry, and aquacultural products, from the various geographical regions,

(2) four members representing consumer interests,

(3) two members representing farm suppliers and food and fiber processors,

(4) two members representing food marketing interests,

(5) two members representing environmental interests,

(6) one member engaged in rural development work,

(7) two members engaged in human nutrition work,

(8) one member representing animal health interests,

(9) one member engaged in transportation of food and agricultural products to domestic or foreign markets,

(10) one member representing labor organizations primarily concerned with the production, processing, distribution, or transportation of food and agricultural products, and

(11) one member representing private sector organizations involved in development programs and issues in developing countries.

(c) The Advisory Board shall select a chairman and vice-chairman from its membership, at its first meeting each year, who shall serve in those positions for a term of one year.

(d) The Advisory Board shall meet at least once during each four-month period. At least one meeting each year shall be a combined meeting with the Joint Council.

(e) The Advisory Board is authorized to establish such panels as it deems appropriate to develop information, reports, advice, and recommendations for the use of the Advisory Board in meeting its responsibilities. Members of such panels may include members of the Advisory Board, Advisory Board staff members, individuals from the Department of Agriculture and other departments and agencies of the Federal Government, and individuals from the private sector who have expertise in the subject to be examined by the panel.

(f) (1) The Advisory Board shall have general responsibility for preparing independent advisory opinions on the food and agricultural sciences.

(2) The Advisory Board shall have the specific responsibilities for—

(A) reviewing the policies, plans, and goals of programs within the Department of Agriculture involving the food and agricultural sciences, and related programs in other Federal and State departments and agencies and in the colleges and universities developed by the Secretary under this title;

(B) reviewing and assessing the extent of agricultural research and extension being conducted by private foundations and businesses, and the relationships of such research and extension to federally supported agricultural research and extension;

(C) reviewing and providing consultation to the Secretary on national policies, priorities, and strategies for agricultural research and extension for both the short and long term;

(D) assessing the overall adequacy of, and making recommendations to the Secretary with regard to, the distribution of resources and the allocation of funds authorized by this title;

(E) preparing and submitting to the Secretary, not later than July 1 of each year, a statement of recommendations as to allocations of responsibilities and levels of funding among federally supported agricultural research and extension programs, which shall include a review and an assessment of the allocation of funds for agricultural research and extension made for the preceding fiscal year by the organizations represented on the Joint Council. Minority views, if timely submitted, shall be included in the submission. The Secretary shall submit copies of the statement to the Subcommittee on Food and Renewable Resources of the Federal Coordinating Council for Science, Engineering, and Technology, and the Joint Council;

(F) not later than February 20 of each year submitting a report on its appraisal of the President's proposed budget for the food and agricultural sciences for the fiscal year beginning in such year and the recommendations of the Secretary contained in the annual report submitted by the Secretary pursuant to the provisions of section 1410 of this title. Such report shall be submitted to the President, the House Committee on Agriculture, the House Committee on Appropriations, the Senate Committee on Agriculture, Nutrition, and Forestry, and the Senate Committee on Appropriations. The report may include the separate views of members of the Advisory Board. The first report shall be due not later than March 1, 1979; and

(G) coordinating with the Secretary in assessing the current status of, and developing a plan for, the effective transfer of new technologies to the farming community.

Existing Research Programs

Sec. 1409. It is the intent of Congress in enacting this title to augment, coordinate, and supplement the planning, initiation, and conduct of agricultural research programs existing prior to the enactment of this title, except that it is not the intent of Congress in enacting this title to limit the authority of the Secretary of Health and Human Services under any Act which the Secretary of Health and Human Services administers.

Federal-State Partnership and Coordination

Sec. 1409A. (a) A unique partnership arrangement exists in food and agricultural research, extension, and teaching between the Federal Government and the governments of the several States whereby the States have accepted and have supported, through legislation and appropriations—

(1) research programs under—

(A) the Act of March 2, 1887 (7 U.S.C. 361a et seq.), commonly known as the Hatch Act of 1887;

(B) the Act of October 10, 1962 (16 U.S.C. 582a et seq.), commonly known as the McIntire-Stennis Act of 1962;

(C) subtitle E of this title; and

(D) subtitle G of this title;

(2) extension programs under subtitle G of this title and the Act of May 8, 1914 (7 U.S.C. 341 et seq.), commonly known as the Smith-Lever Act;

(3) teaching programs under—

    (A) the Act of July 2, 1862 (7 U.S.C. 301 et seq.), commonly known as the First Morrill Act;

    (B) the Act of August 30, 1890 (7 U.S.C. 321 et seq.), commonly known as the Second Morrill Act; and

    (C) the Act of June 29, 1935 (7 U.S.C. 329), commonly known as the Bankhead-Jones Act; and

    (4) international agricultural programs under title XII of the Foreign Assistance Act of 1961 (22 U.S.C. 2220a et seq.).

This partnership in publicly supported agricultural research, extension, and teaching involving the programs of Federal agencies and the programs of the States has played a major role in the outstanding successes achieved in meeting the varied, dispersed, and in many cases, site-specific needs of American agriculture. This partnership must be preserved and enhanced.

    (b) In order to promote research and education in food and human nutrition, the Secretary may establish cooperative human nutrition centers to focus resources, facilities, and scientific expertise on particular high priority nutrition problems identified by the Department. Such centers shall be established at State cooperative institutions; and at other colleges and universities, having a demonstrable capacity to carry out human nutrition research and education.

    (c) In order to meet the increasing needs of consumers and to promote the health and welfare of people, the Secretary shall ensure that the cooperative research, extension, and teaching programs of the various States adequately address the challenges described in paragraph (10) of section 1402 of this title. The Secretary may implement new cooperative initiatives in home economics and related disciplines to address such challenges.

    (d)(1) To promote research for purposes of developing agricultural policy alternatives, the Secretary is encouraged—

    (A) to designate at least one State cooperative institution to conduct research in an interdisciplinary fashion; and

    (B) to report on a regular basis with respect to the effect of emerging technological, economic, sociological, and environmental developments on the structure of agriculture.

    (2) Support for this effort should include grants to examine the role of various food production, processing, and distribution systems that may primarily benefit small- and medium-sized family farms, such as diversified farm plans, energy, water, and soil conservation technologies, direct and cooperative marketing, production and processing cooperatives, and rural community resource management.

    (e) To address more effectively the critical need for reducing farm input costs, improving soil, water, and energy conservation on farms and in rural areas, using sustainable agricultural methods, adopting alternative processing and marketing systems, and encouraging rural resources management, the Secretary is encouraged to designate at least one State agricultural experiment station and one Agricultural Research Service facility to examine these issues in an integrated and comprehensive manner, while conducting ongoing pilot projects contributing additional research through the Federal-State partnership.

Secretary's Report

Sec. 1410. The Secretary shall submit to the President and Congress by January 1 of each year a report on the Nation's agricultural research, extension, and teaching activities, and such report shall include—

(1) a review covering the following three categories of activities of the Department of Agriculture with respect to agricultural research, extension, and teaching activities and the relationship of these activities to similar activities of other departments and agencies of the Federal Government, the States, colleges and universities, and the private sector—

(A) a current inventory of such activities organized by statutory authorization and budget outlay;

(B) a current inventory of such activities organized by field of basic and applied science; and

(C) a current inventory of such activities organized by commodity and product category;

(2) the statements of recommendations of the Joint Council developed pursuant to the provisions of section 1407(d)(2)(G) of this title and the statement of recommendations of the Advisory Board developed pursuant to the provisions of section 1408(f)(2)(E) of this title; and

(3) in the second and succeeding years, a five-year projection of national priorities with respect to agricultural research, extension, and teaching, taking into account both domestic and international needs.

Support for the Joint Council and Advisory Board

Sec. 1412. (a) To assist the Joint Council and the Advisory Board in the performance of their duties, the Secretary may appoint, after consultation with the cochairpersons of the Joint Council and the chairperson of the Advisory Board—

(1) a full-time executive director who shall perform such duties as the cochairpersons of the Joint Council and the chairperson of the Advisory Board may direct and who shall receive compensation at a rate not to exceed the rate payable for GS-18 of the General Schedule established in section 5332 of title 5, United States Code; and

(2) a professional staff of not more than five full-time employees qualified in the food and agricultural sciences, of which one shall serve as the executive secretary to the Joint Council and one shall serve as the executive secretary to the Advisory Board.

(b) The Secretary shall provide such additional clerical assistance and staff personnel as may be required to assist the Joint Council and Advisory Board in carrying out their duties.

(c) In formulating their recommendations to the Secretary, the Joint

Council and Advisory Board may obtain the assistance of Department of Agriculture employees, and, to the maximum extent practicable, the assistance of employees of other Federal departments and agencies conducting related programs of agricultural research, extension, and teaching and of appropriate representatives of colleges and universities, including State agricultural experiment stations, cooperative extension services, and other non-Federal organizations conducting significant programs in the food and agricultural sciences.

General Provisions

Sec. 1413. (a) Any vacancy in the Joint Council or the Advisory Board shall not affect their powers under this title and shall be filled in the same manner as the original position.

(b) Members of the Joint Council and Advisory Board shall serve without compensation, if not otherwise officers or employees of the United States, except that they shall, while away from their homes or regular places of business in the performance of services under this title, be allowed travel expenses, including per diem in lieu of subsistence, in the same manner as persons employed intermittently in the Government service are allowed expenses under sections 5701 through 5707 of title 5 of the United States Code.

(c) There are authorized to be appropriated annually such sums as Congress may determine necessary to carry out the provisions of section 1412 of this title and subsection (b) of this section.

(d) The Subcommittee on Food, Agricultural, and Forestry Research, the Joint Council, and the Advisory Board shall improve communication and interaction among themselves and with others in the agricultural sciences and education system through such mechanisms as the exchange of reports, joint meetings, and the use of liaison representatives.

(e) The President shall appoint, by and with the advice and consent of the Senate; an Assistant Secretary of Agriculture who shall perform such duties as are necessary to carry out this title and who shall receive compensation at the rate now or hereafter prescribed by law for Assistant Secretaries of Agriculture.

Biomass Energy Educational and Technical Assistance Programs

Sec. 1413A. (a) The Secretary, in cooperation with State directors of cooperative extension, administrators of extension for land-grant colleges and universities, State foresters or equivalent State officials and the heads of other Federal departments and agencies, shall provide educational programs for producers of agricultural commodities, wood, and wood products to—

(1) inform such producers of the feasibility of using biomass for energy;

(2) disseminate to such producers information regarding the results of

research regarding the use of biomass for energy;

(3) inform such producers of the best available technology for the use of biomass for energy;

(4) provide technical assistance to such producers to improve their ability to efficiently use biomass for energy; and

(5) disseminate to such producers the results of research on energy conservation techniques and encourage such producers to adopt such techniques.

(b) All appropriate educational methods, including meetings, short courses, workshops, tours, demonstrations, publications, news releases, and radio and television programs may be used to carry out subsection (a).

(c) The State director of cooperative extension in each State shall develop a single, comprehensive, and coordinated plan which includes every biomass energy educational and technical assistance program in effect or proposed in such State, except that in those States which contain more than one land-grant college or university, such plan shall be jointly developed by the administrative heads of extension of such institutions. Such plan shall be developed with the full participation of the State forester or the equivalent State officials of such State. Each State's plan shall be submitted to the Secretary annually for approval. The Advisory Board shall review and make recommendations to the Secretary pertaining to programs conducted under this section. Each State shall submit an annual progress report on the operation of its plan to the Secretary before January 1 following the fiscal year for which such report is made.

(d) Funds made available under this section shall be provided to the State director of cooperative extension and the administrators of extension for land-grant colleges and universities in each State in a manner consistent with the effective implementation of this section.

(e) For purposes of this section—

(1) the term "biomass" means any organic matter which is available on a renewable basis, including agricultural crops and agricultural wastes and residues, wood and wood wastes and residues, and animal wastes, except that such term does not include aquatic plants and municipal wastes;

(2) the term "biomass energy" means any gaseous, liquid, or solid fuel produced by conversion of biomass, and energy or steam derived from the direct combustion of biomass for the generation of electricity, mechanical power, or industrial process heat; and

(3) the term "municipal wastes" means any organic matter, including sewage, sewage sludge, and industrial or commercial waste, and mixtures of such matter and inorganic refuse—

(i) from any publicly or privately operated municipal waste collection or similar disposal system; or

(ii) from similar waste flows (other than such flows which constitute agricultural or wood wastes or residues from wood harvesting activities or production of forest products).

(f) there is authorized to be appropriated to carry out this section $10,000,000 for each of the fiscal years 1981, 1982, 1983, and 1984.

Subtitle C—Agricultural Research and Education Grants and Fellowships

Program of Competitive, Special, and Facilities Grants for Agricultural Research

Sec. 1414. Section 2 of the Act of August 4, 1965 (79 Stat. 431; 7 U.S.C. 450i), is amended to read as follows:

Sec. 2. (a) In order to promote research in food, agriculture, and related areas, a research grants program is hereby established in the Department of Agriculture.

(b) The Secretary of Agriculture is authorized to make competitive grants, for periods not to exceed five years, to State agricultural experiment stations, all colleges and universities, other research institutions and organizations, Federal agencies, private organizations or corporations, and individuals, for research to further the programs of the Department of Agriculture. To the greatest extent possible the Secretary shall allocate these grants to high priority research taking into consideration, when available, the determinations made by the Joint Council on Food and Agricultural Sciences and the National Agricultural Research and Extension Users Advisory Board identifying high priority research areas. For purposes of the preceding sentence, high priority research shall include—

(1) basic research aimed at the discovery of new scientific principles and techniques that may be applicable in agriculture and forestry;

(2) research, with emphasis on biotechnology, aimed at the development of new and innovative products, methods, and technologies relating to biological nitrogen fixation, photosynthesis, and other processes which will improve and increase the production of agricultural and forestry resources;

(3) basic and applied research in the fields of animal productivity and health;

(4) basic and applied research in the fields of soil and water;

(5) basic and applied research in the field of human nutrition;

(6) research to develop new strains of crops and new promising crops, including guayule, jojoba, and others;

(7) research to reduce farm input costs through the collection of national and international data and the transfer of appropriate technology relating to sustainable agricultural systems, soil, energy, and water conservation technologies, rural and farm resource management, and the diversification of farm product processing and marketing systems; and

(8) research to develop new and alternative industrial uses for agricultural crops.

In seeking research proposals and in performing peer review evaluation of such proposals under this subsection, the Secretary shall seek the widest participation of qualified scientists in the Federal Government, all colleges and universities, State agricultural experiment stations, and the private sector. No grant may be made under this subsection for any purpose for which a grant may be made under subsection (d) or for the planning, repair, rehabilitation, acquisition, or construction of a building or a facility. The research grants shall be made without regard to matching funds by the recipient or recipients of such grants. There are authorized to be appropriated, for the purpose of carrying out this subsection, $70,000,000 for each of the fiscal years ending September 30, 1986, through September 30, 1990. Four percent of the amount appropriated for each of such fiscal years to carry out this subsection may be retained by the Secretary to pay administrative costs incurred by the Secretary to carry out this subsection.

(c) The Secretary of Agriculture is authorized to make grants, for periods not to exceed five years in duration—

(1) to land-grant colleges and universities, research foundations established by land-grant colleges and universities, State agricultural experiment stations, and to all colleges and universities having a demonstrable capacity in food and agricultural research, as determined by the Secretary to carry out research to facilitate or expand promising breakthroughs in areas of the food and agricultural sciences of importance to the Nation; and

(2) to State agricultural experiment stations, land-grant colleges and universities, research foundations established by land-grant colleges and universities, colleges and universities receiving funds under the Act of October 10, 1962 (16 U.S.C. 582a et seq.) and accredited schools or colleges of veterinary medicine, to facilitate or expand ongoing State-Federal food and agricultural research programs that (A) promote excellence in research, (B) promote the development of regional research centers, (C) promote the research partnership between the Department of Agriculture and such colleges and universities, such research foundations or State agricultural experiment stations, or (D) facilitate coordination and cooperation of research among States.

No grant may be made under this subsection for any purpose for which a grant may be made under subsection (d) or for the planning, repair, rehabilitation, acquisition, or construction of a building or facility. These grants shall be made without regard to matching funds. Four percent of the amount appropriated for any fiscal year to carry out this subsection may be retained by the Secretary to pay administrative costs incurred by the Secretary to carry out this subsection.

(d) The Secretary of Agriculture shall make annual grants to support the renovation and refurbishment (including energy retrofitting) of research spaces in buildings or spaces to be used for research, and the purchase and installation of fixed equipment in such spaces. Such grants may be used for new construction only for auxiliary facilities and fixed equipment used for research in such facilities, such as greenhouses, insectaries, and research farm structures and installations. Such grants shall be made to—

(1) each State agricultural experiment station in an amount of $100,000 or an amount which is equal to 10 per centum of the funds received by such station under the Act of March 2, 1887 (24 Stat. 440-442, as amended; 7 U.S.C. 361a-361i), and the Act of October 10, 1962 (76 Stat. 806-807, as amended; 16 U.S.C. 582a, 582a-1—582a-7), whichever is greater: *Provided,* That of any amount in excess of $50,000 made available under this paragraph during any year for allotment to a State agricultural experiment station, no payment thereof shall be made in excess of the amount which the station makes available during that year for the purposes for which grants under this paragraph are made available;

(2) each accredited college of veterinary medicine and State agricultural experiment station which receives funds from the Federal Government for animal health research, in an amount which is equal to 10 per centum of the animal health research funds received by such college or experiment station from the Federal Government during the previous fiscal year;

(3) each forestry school not described in paragraph (1) of this subsection, which is eligible to receive funds under the Act of October 10, 1962 (16 U.S.C. 582a et seq.), in an amount which is equal to 10 per centum of the funds received by such school under that Act; and

(4) each college eligible to receive funds under the Act of August 30, 1890 (7 U.S.C. 321 et seq.), including Tuskegee Institute, in an amount which is equal to 10 per centum of the funds received by such college under section 1445 of the National Agricultural Research, Extension, and Teaching Policy Act of 1977.

Any college or State agricultural experiment station eligible for annual grants under this subsection may elect to defer the receipt of an annual grant for any fiscal year for up to five years: *Provided,* That the total amounts deferred may not exceed $1,000,000. Application may be made for receipt of deferred grants at any time during the five years, subject to the matching funds requirement of this subsection and the availability of appropriations under this subsection.

(e) Each recipient of assistance under this section shall keep such records as the Secretary of Agriculture shall, by regulation, prescribe, including records which fully disclose the amounts and disposition by such recipient of the proceeds of such grants, the total cost of the project or undertaking in connection with which such funds are given or used, and the amount of that portion of the costs of the project or undertaking in connection with which such funds are given or used, and the amount of that portion of the costs of the project or undertaking supplied by other sources, and such other records as will facilitate an effective audit. The Secretary of Agriculture and the Comptroller General of the United States or any of their duly authorized representatives shall have access for the purpose of audit and examination to any books, documents, papers, and records of the recipients that are pertinent to the grants received under this section.

(f) The Secretary of Agriculture shall limit allowable overhead costs, with respect to grants awarded under this section, to those necessary to carry out the purposes of the grants.

(g) Except as otherwise provided in subsection (b) of this section, there are hereby authorized to be appropriated such sums as are necessary to carry out the provisions of this section.

(h) The Secretary of Agriculture is authorized to issue such rules and regulations as the Secretary deems necessary to carry out the provisions of this section.

Sec. 1416. Extends and amends the Research Facilities Act of 1963.

Grants for Research on the Production and Marketing of Alcohols and Industrial Hydrocarbons from Agricultural Commodities and Forest Products, and Agricultural Chemicals and Other Products from Coal Derivatives

Sec. 1419. (a) The Secretary shall make grants under this subsection to colleges, universities, Government corporations, and Federal laboratories for the purpose of conducting research related to the production and marketing of (1) coal tar, producer gas, and other coal derivatives for the manufacture of agricultural chemicals, methanol, methyl fuel, and alcohol-blended motor fuel (such agricultural chemicals to include, but not be limited to, fertilizers, herbicides, insecticides, and pesticides), (2) alcohol and other forms of biomass energy as substitutes for petroleum or natural gas, and (3) other industrial hydrocarbons made from agricultural commodities and forest products. The authority to conduct research under paragraph (2) does not include authority to conduct research with respect to technology demonstrations of integrated systems for commercialization of technologies for applications other than agricultural or uniquely rural applications. The Secretary may make grants under this subsection to such colleges, universities, Government corporations, and Federal laboratories for the purpose of conducting research relating to the development of the most economical and commercially feasible means of collecting and transporting wastes, residues, and by-products for use as feedstocks for the production of alcohol and other forms of biomass energy. At least 25 per centum of the amount appropriated in any fiscal year for research under paragraph (2) shall be made available for grants under this subsection for research, relating to the production of alcohol, to identify and develop agricultural commodities, including alfalfa, sweet sorghum, black locust, and cheese whey, which may be suitable for such production. At least 25 per centum of the amount appropriated in any fiscal year for research under paragraph (2) shall be made available for grants under this subsection for research relating to the development of technologies for increasing the energy efficiency and commercial feasibility of alcohol production, including processes of cellulose conversion and cell membrane technology. There are hereby authorized to be appropriated for the purposes of carrying out the provision of this subsection, $3,000,000 for the fiscal year ending September 30, 1978, and such sums as may be necessary for the subsequent fiscal years ending September 30, 1979, September 30, 1980, September 30, 1981, September 30, 1982, September 30, 1983, September 30, 1984, and September 30, 1985: *Provided*, That the total amount of such appropriations shall not exceed $40,000,000 during the eight-year period beginning October 1, 1977, and shall not exceed such sums as may be authorized by law for any fiscal year subsequent to such period: *Provided further*, That not more than a total of $5,000,000 may be awarded to the colleges and universities of any one State. In addition to the authorization of appropriations provided in the preceding sentence, there is authorized to be appropriated for grants to conduct research described in paragraph (2) and in the third sentence of this subsection $12,000,000 for each of the fiscal years ending September 30, 1981; September 30, 1982; September 30, 1983; and September 30, 1984.

(b) For purposes of subsection (a)—

(1) the term "biomass" means any organic matter which is available on a renewable basis, including agricultural crops and agricultural wastes and residues, wood and wood wastes and residues, and animal wastes, except that such term does not include aquatic plants and municipal wastes;

(2) the term "biomass energy" means any gaseous, liquid, or solid fuel produced by conversion of biomass, and energy or steam derived from the direct combustion of biomass for the generation of electricity, mechanical power, or industrial process heat; and

(3) the term "municipal wastes" means any organic matter, including sewage, sewage sludge, and industrial or commercial waste, and mixtures of such matter and inorganic refuse—

(i) from any publicly or privately operated municipal waste collection or similar disposal system; or

(ii) from similar waste flows (other than such flows which constitute agricultural wastes or residues, or wood wastes or residues from wood harvesting activities or production of forest products).

Subtitle D—National Food and Human Nutrition Research and Extension Program

Findings and Declarations

Sec. 1421. (a) Congress hereby finds that there is increasing evidence of a relationship between diet and many of the leading causes of death in the United States: that improved nutrition is an integral component of preventive health care; that there is a serious need for research on the chronic effects of diet on degenerative diseases and related disorders; that nutrition and health considerations are important to United States agricultural policy; that there is insufficient knowledge concerning precise human nutritional requirements, the interaction of the various nutritional constituents of food, and differences in nutritional requirements among different population groups such as infants, children, adolescents, elderly men and women, and pregnant women; and that there is a critical need for objective data concerning food safety, the potential of food enrichment, and means to encourage better nutritional practices.

(b) It is hereby declared to be the policy of the United States that the Department of Agriculture conduct research in the fields of human nutrition and the nutritive value of foods and conduct human nutrition and education activities, as provided in this subtitle.

Definitions

Sec. 1430. When used in this subtitle—

(1) the term "eligible institution" means an accredited school or college of veterinary medicine or a State agricultural experiment station that conducts animal health and disease research;

(2) the term "dean" means the dean of an accredited school or college of veterinary medicine;

(3) the term "director" means the director of a State agricultural experiment station which qualifies as an eligible institution;

(4) the term "Board" means the Animal Health Science Research Advisory Board; and

(5) the term "animal health research capacity" means the capacity of an eligible institution to conduct animal health and disease research, as determined by the Secretary.

Authorization to the Secretary of Agriculture

Sec. 1431. In order to carry out the purpose of this subtitle, the Secretary is hereby authorized to cooperate with, encourage, and assist the States in carrying out programs of animal health and disease research at eligible institutions in the manner hereinafter described in this subtitle.

Animal Health Science Research Advisory Board

Sec. 1432. (a) the Secretary shall establish a board to be known as the Animal Health Science Research Advisory Board which shall have a term that expires September 30, *1990*, and which shall be composed of the following eleven members—

(1) a representative of the Agricultural Research Service of the Department of Agriculture,

(2) a representative of the Cooperative State Research Service of the Department of Agriculture,

(3) a representative of the Animal and Plant Health Inspection Service of the Department of Agriculture,

(4) a representative of the Bureau of Veterinary Medicine of the Food and Drug Administration of the Department of Health, Education, and Welfare, and

(5) seven members appointed by the Secretary—

(A) two persons representing accredited colleges of veterinary medicine,

(B) two persons representing State agricultural experiment stations, and

(C) three persons representing national livestock and poultry organizations.

The members shall serve without compensation, if not otherwise officers or employees of the United States, except that they shall, while away from their homes or regular places of business in the performance of services for the Board, be allowed travel expenses, including per diem in lieu of subsistence, in the same manner as persons employed intermittently in the Government service are allowed expenses under sections 5701 through 5707 of title 5 of the United States Code.

(b) The Board shall meet at the call of the Secretary, but at least once annually, to consult with and advise the Secretary with respect to the implementation of this subtitle and to recommend immediate priorities for the conduct of research programs authorized under this subtitle, under such rules and procedures for conducting business as the Secretary shall, in the Secretary's discretion, prescribe.

Duties of the Secretary of Agriculture

Sec. 1422. In order to carry out the policy of this subtitle, the Secretary shall develop and implement a national food and human nutrition research and extension program that shall include, but not be limited to—

(1) research on human nutritional requirements;

(2) research on the nutrient composition of foods and the effects of agricultural practices, handling, food processing, and cooking on the nutrients they contain;

(3) surveillance of the nutritional benefits provided to participants in the food programs administered by the Department of Agriculture;

(4) research on the factors affecting food preference and habits; and

(5) the development of techniques and equipment to assist consumers in the home or in institutions in selecting food that supplies a nutritionally adequate diet.

Research by the Department of Agriculture

Sec. 1423. (a) The Secretary shall establish research into food and human nutrition as a separate and distinct mission of the Department of Agriculture, and the Secretary shall increase support for such research to a level that provides resources adequate to meet the policy of this subtitle.

(b) The Secretary, in administering the food and human nutrition research program, shall periodically consult with the administrators of the other Federal departments and agencies that have responsibility for programs dealing with human food and nutrition, as to the specific research needs of those departments and agencies.

Subtitle E—Animal Health and Disease Research

Purpose

Sec. 1429. It is the purpose of this subtitle to promote the general welfare through the improved health and productivity of domestic livestock, poultry, aquatic animals, and other income-producing animals which are essential to the Nation's food supply and the welfare of producers and consumers of animal products; to improve the health of horses; to facilitate the effective treatment of, and, where possible, prevent animal and poultry diseases in both domesticated and wild animals which, if not controlled, would be disastrous to the United States livestock and poultry industries and endanger the Nation's food supply; to minimize livestock and poultry losses due to transportation and handling; to protect human health through control of animal diseases transmissible to humans; to improve methods of controlling the births of predators and other animals; and otherwise to promote the general welfare through expanded programs of research and extension to improve animal health. It is recognized that the total animal health and disease research and extension efforts of the several State colleges and universities and of the Federal Government would be more effective if there were close coordination between such programs, and it is further recognized that colleges and universities having accredited schools or colleges of veterinary medicine and State agricultural experiment stations that conduct animal health and disease research are especially vital in training research workers in animal health.

Appropriations for Continuing Animal Health and Disease Research Programs

Sec. 1433. (a) There are authorized to be appropriated such funds as Congress may determine necessary to support continuing animal health and disease research programs at eligible institutions, but not to exceed $25,000,000 annually for the period beginning Octber 1, 1981, and ending September 30, 1990, and not in excess of such sums as may after the date of enactment of this title be authorized by law for any subsequent fiscal year. Funds appropriated under this section shall be used: (1) to meet expenses of conducting animal health and disease research, publishing and disseminating the results of such research, and contributing to the retirement of employees subject to the provisions of the Act of March 4, 1940 (54 Stat.

39-40, as amended; 7 U.S.C. 331); (2) for administrative planning and direction; and (3) to purchase equipment and supplies necessary for conducting such research.

(b) Funds appropriated under subsection (a) of this section for any fiscal year shall be apportioned as follows:

(1) Four per centum shall be retained by the Department of Agriculture for administration, program assistance to the eligible institutions and program coordination.

(2) Forty-eight per centum shall be distributed among the several States in the proportion that the value of an income to producers from domestic livestock and poultry in each State bears to the total value of and income to producers from domestic livestock and poultry in all the States. The Secretary shall determine the total value of and income from domestic livestock and poultry in all the States and the proportionate value of and income from domestic livestock and poultry for each State, based on the most current inventory of all cattle, sheep, swine, horses, and poultry published by the Department of Agriculture.

(3) Forty-eight per centum shall be distributed among the several States in the proportion that the animal health research capacity of the eligible institutions in each State bears to the total animal health research capacity in all the States. The Secretary shall determine the animal health research capacity of the eligible institutions with the advice, when available, of the Board.

(c) In each State with one or more accredited colleges of veterinary medicine, the deans of the accredited college or colleges and the director of the State agricultural experiment station shall develop a comprehensive animal health and disease research program for the State based on the animal health research capacity of each eligible institution in the State, which shall be submitted to the Secretary for approval and shall be used for the allocation of funds available to the State under this section.

(d) When the amount available under this section for allotment to any State on the basis of domestic livestock and poultry values and income exceeds the amount for which the eligible institution or institutions in the State are eligible on the basis of animal health research capacity, the excess may be used, at the discretion of the Secretary, for remodeling of facilities, construction of new facilities, or increase in staffing, proportionate to the need for added research capacity.

(e) Whenever a new college of veterinary medicine is established in a State and is accredited, the Secretary, after consultation with the dean of such college and the director of the State agricultural experiment station and, where applicable, deans of other accredited colleges in the State, shall provide for the reallocation of funds available in the State, shall provide for the reallocation of funds available to the State pursuant to subsection (b) of this section between the new college and other eligible institutions in the State, based on the animal health research capacity of each eligible institution.

(f) Whenever two or more States jointly establish an accredited regional college of veterinary medicine or jointly support an accredited college of veterinary medicine serving the States involved the Secretary is authorized to make funds which are available to such States pursuant to subsection (b)(2) of this section available for such college in such amount that reflects the combined relative value of and income from domestic livestock and poultry in the cooperating States, such amount to be adjusted, as necessary, pursuant to the provisions of subsections (c) and (e) of this section.

Appropriations for Research on National or Regional Problems

Sec. 1434. (a) There are authorized to be appropriated such funds as Congress may determine necessary to support research on specific national or regional animal health or disease problems, but not to exceed $35,000,000 annually for the period beginning October 1, 1981, and ending September 30, 1990, and not in excess of such sums as may after the date of enactment of this title be authorized by law for any subsequent fiscal year.

(b) Notwithstanding the provisions of section 1435 of this title, funds appropriated under this section shall be awarded in the form of grants, for periods not to exceed five years, to eligible institutions.

(c) In order to establish a rational allocation of funds appropriated under this section, the Secretary shall establish annually priority lists of animal health and disease problems of national or regional significance. Such lists shall be prepared after consultation with the Joint Council, the Advisory Board, and the Board. Any recommendations made in connection with such consultation shall not be controlling on the Secretary's determination of priorities. In establishing such priorities, the Secretary, the Joint Council, the Advisory Board, and the Board shall consider the following factors;

(1) any health or disease problem which causes or may cause significant economic losses to any part of the livestock production industry;

(2) whether current scientific knowledge necessary to prevent, cure, or abate such a health or disease problem is adequate; and

(3) whether the status of scientific research is such that accomplishments may be anticipated through the application of scientific effort to such health or disease problem.

(d) Without regard to any consultation under subsection (c), the Secretary shall, to the extent feasible, award grants to eligible institutions on the basis of the priorities assigned through a peer review system. Grantees shall be selected on a competitive basis in accordance with such procedures as the Secretary may establish.

(e) In the case of multiyear grants, the Secretary shall distribute funds to grant recipients on a schedule which is reasonably related to the timetable required for the orderly conduct of the research project involved.

Availability of Appropriated Funds

Sec. 1435. Funds available for allocation under the terms of this subtitle shall be paid to each State or eligible institution at such times and in such amounts as shall be determined by the Secretary. Funds shall remain available for payment of unliquidated obligations for one additional fiscal year following the year of appropriation.

Withholding of Appropriated Funds

Sec. 1436. If the Secretary determines that a State is not entitled to receive its allocation of the annual appropriation under section 1433 of this title because of its failure to satisfy requirements of this subtitle or regulations issued under it, the Secretary shall withhold such amount. The facts and reasons concerning the determination and withholding shall be reported to the President; and the amount involved shall be kept separate in the Treasury until the close of the next Congress. If the next Congress does not direct such sum to be paid; it shall be carried to surplus.

Requirements for Use of Funds

Sec. 1437. With respect to research projects on problems of animal health and disease to be performed at eligible institutions and supported with funds allocated to the States under section 1433 of this title, the dean or director of each eligible institution shall cause to be prepared and shall review proposals for such research projects, which contain data showing compliance with the purpose in section 1429 of this title and the provisions for use of funds specified in section 1433(a) of this title, and with general guidelines for project eligibility to be provided by the Secretary with the advice, when available, of the Board. Such research proposals that are approved by the dean or director shall be submitted to the Secretary prior to assignment of funds thereto with a brief summary showing compliance with the provisions of this subtitle and the Secretary's general guidelines.

Matching Funds

Sec. 1438. No funds in excess of $100,000, exclusive of the funds provided for research on specific national or regional animal health and disease problems under the provisions of section 1434 of this title, shall be paid by the Federal Government to any State under this subtitle during any fiscal year in excess of the amount from non-Federal sources made available to and budgeted for expenditure by eligible institutions in the State during the same fiscal year by animal health and disease research. The Secretary is authorized to make such payments in excess of $100,000 on the certificate of the appropriate official of the eligible institution having charge of the animal health and disease research for which such payments are to be made. If any eligible institution certified for receipt of matching funds fails to make available and budget for expenditure for animal health and disease research in any fiscal year sums at least equal to the amount for which it is certified, the difference between the Federal matching funds available and the funds made available to and budgeted for expenditure by the eligible institution shall be reapportioned by the Secretary among other eligible institutions of the same State, if there are any which qualify therefor, and, if there are none, the Secretary shall reapportion such difference among the other States.

Allocations Under This Subtitle Not Substitutions

Sec. 1439. The sums appropriated and allocated to States and eligible institutions under this subtitle shall be in addition to, and not in substitution for, sums appropriated or otherwise made available to such States and institutions pursuant to other provisions of law.

Subtitle G—1890 Land-Grant College Funding

Agricultural Research at 1890 Land-Grant Colleges, Including Tuskegee Institute

Sec. 1445. (a) There are hereby authorized to be appropriated annually such sums as Congress may determine necessary to support continuing agricultural research at colleges eligible to receive funds under the Act of August 30, 1890 (26 Stat. 417-419, as amended; 7 U.S.C. 321-326, and 328), including Tuskegee Institute (hereinafter referred to in this section as "eligible institutions"). Beginning with the fiscal year ending September 30, 1979, there shall be appropriated under this section for each fiscal year an amount not less than 15 per centum of the total appropriations for such year under section 3 of the Act of March 2, 1887 (24 Stat. 441, as amended; 7 U.S.C. 361c): *Provided,* That the amount appropriated for the fiscal year ending September 30, 1979, shall not be less than the amount made available in the fiscal year ending September 30, 1978, to such eligible institutions under the Act of August 4, 1965 (79 Stat. 431, 7 U.S.C. 450i). Funds appropriated under this section shall be used for expenses of conducting agricultural research, printing, disseminating the results of such research, contributing to the retirement of employees subject to the provisions of the Act of March 4, 1940 (54 Stat. 39-40, as amended; 7 U.S.C. 331), administrative planning and direction, and purchase and rental of land and the construction, acquisition, alteration, or repair of buildings necessary for conducting agricultural research. The eligible institutions are authorized to plan and conduct agricultural research in cooperation with each other and such agencies, institutions, and individuals as may contribute to the solution of agricultural problems, and moneys appropriated pursuant to this section shall be available for paying the necessary expenses of planning, coordinating, and conducting such cooperative research. No more than 5 percent of the funds received by an institution in any fiscal year, under this section, may be carried forward to the succeeding fiscal year.

(b) Beginning with the fiscal year ending September 30, 1979, the funds appropriated in each fiscal year under this section shall be distributed as follows:

(1) Three per centum shall be available to the Secretary for administration of this section. These administrative funds may be used for transportation of scientists who are not officers or employees of the United States to research meetings convened for the purpose of assessing research opportunities or research planning.

(2) The remainder shall be allocated among the eligible institutions as follows:

(A) Funds up to the total amount made available to all eligible institutions in the fiscal year ending September 30, 1978, under section 2 of the Act of August 4, 1965 (79 Stat. 431; 7 U.S.C. 450i) shall be allocated among the eligible institutions in the same proportion as funds made available under section 2 of the Act of August 4, 1965, for the fiscal year ending September 30, 1978, are allocated among the eligible institutions.

(B) Of funds in excess of the amount allocated under subparagraph (A) of this paragraph, 20 per centum shall be allotted among eligible institutions in equal proportions; 40 per centum shall be allotted among the eligible institutions in the proportion that the rural population of the State in which each eligible institution is located bears to the total rural population of all the States in whch eligible institutions are located, as determined by the last preceding decennial census current at the time each such additional sum is first appropriated; and the balance shall be allotted among the eligible institutions in the proportion that the farm population of the State in which each eligible institution is located bears to the total farm population of all the States in which the eligible institutions are located, as determined by the last preceding decennial census current at the time each such additional sum is first appropriated. In computing the distribution of funds allocated under this subparagraph, the allotments to Tuskegee Institute and Alabama Agricultural and Mechanical University shall be determined as if each institution were in a separate State.

(c) The director of the State agricultural experiment station in each State where an eligible institution is located and the research director specified in subsection (d) of this section in each of the eligible institutions in such State shall jointly develop, by mutual agreement, a comprehensive program of agricultural research in such State, to be submitted for approval by the Secretary within one year after the date of enactment of this title.

(d) Sums available for allotment to the eligible institutions under the terms of this section shall be paid to such institutions in equal quarterly payments beginning on or about the first day of October of each year upon vouchers approved by the Secretary. The President of each eligible institution shall appoint a research director who shall be responsible for administration of the program authorized herein. Each eligible institution shall designate a treasurer or other officer who shall receive and account for all funds allotted to such institution under the provisions of this section and shall report, with the approval of the research director to the Secretary on or before the first day of December of each year a detailed statement of the amount received under the provisions of this section during the preceding fiscal year and its disbursement on schedules prescribed by the Secretary. If any portion of the allotted moneys received by any eligible institution shall be any action or contingency be diminished, lost, or misapplied, it shall be replaced by such institution and until so replaced no subsequent appropriation shall be allotted or paid to such institution. Funds made available to eligible institutions shall not be used for payment of negotiated overhead or indirect cost rates.

(e) Bulletins, reports, periodicals, reprints or articles, and other publications necessary for the dissemination of results of the research and experiments funded under this section, including lists of publications available for distribution by the eligible institutions, shall be transmitted in the mails of the United States under penalty indicia: *Provided,* That each publication shall bear such indicia as are prescribed by the Postmaster General and shall be mailed under such regulations as the Postmaster General may from time to time prescribe. Such publications may be mailed from the principal place of business of each eligible institution or from an established subunit of such institution.

(f) The Secretary shall be responsible for the proper administration of this section, and is authorized and directed to prescribe such rules and regulations as may be necessary to carry out its provisions. It shall be the duty of the Secretary to furnish such advice and assistance as will best promote the purposes of this section, including participation in coordination of research initiated under this section by the eligible institutions, from time to time to indicate such lines of inquiry as to the Secretary seem most important, and to encourage and assist in the establishment and maintenance of cooperation by and between the several eligible institutions, the State agricultural experiment stations, and between them and the Department of Agriculture.

(g)(1) On or before the first day of October in each year after the enactment of this title, the Secretary shall ascertain whether each eligible institution is entitled to receive its share of the annual appropriations under this section and the amount which thereupon each is entitled, respectively, to receive.

(2) If it appears to the Secretary from the annual statement of receipts and expenditures of funds by any eligible institution that an amount in excess of 5 percent of the preceding annual appropriation allotted to that institution under this section remains unexpended, such amount in excess of 5 percent of the preceding annual appropriation allotted to that institution shall be deducted from the next succeeding annual allotment to the institution.

(3) If the Secretary withholds from any eligible institution any portion of the appropriations available for allotment, the facts and reasons therefor shall be reported to the President and the amount involved shall be kept separate in the Treasury until the close of the next Congress. If the

next Congress does not direct such sum to be paid, it shall be carried to surplus.

(4) The Secretary shall make an annual report to Congress during the first regular session of each year of the receipts and expenditures and work of the eligible institutions under the provisions of this section and also whether any portion of the appropriation available for allotment to any institution has been withheld and if so the reasons therefor.

(h) Nothing in this section shall be construed to impair or modify the legal relationship existing between any of the eligible institutions and the government of the States in which they are respectively located.

Dairy Goat Research Program

[Section 1432(b)(1) of the Agriculture and Food Act of 1981, Public Law 97-98, signed December 22, 1981, mandated this program. Section 1432 of the Food Security Act of 1985, Public Law 99-198, signed December 23, 1985, extended the authorization for appropriations through September 30, 1990.]

The Secretary of Agriculture shall make a grant of funds appropriated under paragraph (5) of this subsection to the one college of all the colleges eligible to receive funds under the Act of August 30, 1890 (7 U.S.C. 321 et seq.), including Tuskegee Institute, which on the date of the enactment of this title—

(A) has initiated a dairy goat research program; and

(B) has the best demonstrable capacity to carry out dairy goat research.

(2) Any grant received under paragraph (1) by such college may be expended to—

(A) pay expenses incurred in conducting dairy goat research;

(B) print and disseminate the results of such research;

(C) contribute to the retirement of employees engaged in such research;

(D) plan, administer, and direct such research; and

(E) construct, acquire, alter, and repair buildings necessary to conduct such research.

(3)(A) Under the terms of such grant, funds appropriated under paragraph (5) of this subsection for a fiscal year shall be paid to such college in equal quarterly installments beginning on or about the first day of October of such year upon vouchers approved by the Secretary of Agriculture.

(B) Not later than sixty days after the end of each fiscal year for which funds are paid under this subsection to such college, the research director of such college shall submit to the Secretary a detailed statement of the disbursements in such fiscal year of funds received by such college under this subsection.

(C) If any of the funds so received by such college are by any action or contingency misapplied, lost, or diminished, then—

(i) such college shall replace such funds; and

(ii) the Secretary shall not distribute to such college any other funds under this subsection until such replacement is made.

(4) For purposes of section 1445(e) of the National Agricultural Research, Extension, and Teaching Policy Act of 1977 (7 U.S.C. 3222(e)), research and experiments funded under this subsection shall be deemed to be research and experiments funded under section 1445 of such Act.

(5) There is authorized to be appropriated to the Secretary to carry out this subsection, for each of the fiscal years ending September 30, 1986, through September 30, 1990, an amount equal to one per centum of the aggregate amount of funds appropriated under section 1445 of the National Agricultural Research, Extension, and Teaching Policy Act of 1977 (7 U.S.C. 3222) in the fiscal year preceding the fiscal year for which funds are authorized to be appropriated under this paragraph.

Authority to Award Grants to Upgrade 1890 Land-Grant College Research Facilities

[Section 1433 of the Agriculture and Food Act of 1981, Public Law 97-98, signed December 22, 1981, mandated this authority. Section 1433 of the Food Security Act of 1985, Public Law 99-198, signed December 23, 1985, added "libraries" to the facilities and equipment and extended the authorization for appropriations through September 30, 1987.]

(a) It is hereby declared to be the intent of Congress to assist the institutions eligible to receive funds under the Act of August 30, 1890 (7 U.S.C. 321 et seq.), including Tuskegee Institute (hereinafter referred to in this section as "eligible institutions"), in the acquisition and improvement of research facilities and equipment, including agricultural libraries, so that eligible institutions may participate with the State agricultural experiment stations in a balanced attack on the research needs of the people of their States.

(b) There are authorized to be appropriated to the Secretary of Agriculture for the purpose of carrying out the provisions of this section $10,000,000 for each of the fiscal years ending September 30, 1982, September 30, 1983, September 30, 1984, September 30, 1985, September 30, 1986, and September 30, 1987, such sums to remain available until expended.

(c) Four per centum of the sums appropriated pursuant to this section shall be available to the Secretary for administration of this grants program. The remaining funds shall be available for grants to the eligible institutions for the purpose of assisting them in the purchase of equipment and land, and the planning, construction, alteration, or renovation of buildings to strengthen their capacity to conduct research in the food and agricultural sciences.

(d) Grants awarded pursuant to this section shall be made in such amounts and under such terms and conditions as the Secretary shall determine necessary for carrying out the purposes of this section.

(e) Federal funds provided under this section may not be utilized for the payment of any overhead costs of the eligible institutions.

(f) The Secretary may promulgate such rules and regulations as the Secretary may deem necessary to carry out the provisions of this section.

Subtitle H—Solar Energy Research and Development

Part 1—Existing Programs

Agricultural Research

Sec. 1446. [Amendments to section 1 of the Bankhead-Jones Act of 1935 (49 Stat. 436, as amended; 7 U.S.C. 427), which was further amended on June 30, 1980, by Public Law 96-294, section 253 (94 Stat. 707).]

Part 2—Competitive Grants Program

Sec. 1449. The Secretary shall carry out a program of competitive grants to persons and organizations, subject to the requirements and conditions provided for in sections 2(e), 2(f), and 2(h) of the Act of August 4, 1965 (79 Stat. 431; 7 U.S.C. 450i), as amended by section 1414 of this title, for carrying out research and development relating to—

(1) uses of solar energy with respect to farm buildings, farm homes, and farm machinery (including, but not limited to, equipment used to dry or cure farm crops or forest products, or to provide irrigation); and

(2) uses of biomass derived from solar energy, including farm and forest products, byproducts, and residues, as substitutes for nonrenewable fuels and petrochemicals.

Part 3—Information System and Advisory Committee

Solar Energy Research Information System

Sec. 1450. The Secretary shall, through the Cooperative State Research Service and other agencies within the Department of Agriculture which the Secretary considers appropriate, in consultation with the Energy Research and Development Administration, other appropriate United States Government agencies, the National Academy of Sciences, and private nonprofit institutions involved in solar energy research projects, by June 1, 1978, and by June 1 in each year thereafter, make a compilation of solar energy research projects related to agriculture which are being carried out during such year by Federal, State, private, and nonprofit institutions and, where available, the results of such projects. Such compilations may include, but are not limited to, projects dealing with heating and cooling methods for farm structures and dwellings (such as greenhouses, curing barns, and livestock shelters), storage of power, operation of farm equipment (including irrigation pumps, crop dryers and curers, and electric vehicles), and the development of new technologies to be used on farms which are powered by other than fossil fuels or derivatives thereof.

Advisory Committee

Sec. 1451. In order to assist the Secretary in carrying out functions assigned to the Secretary under part 4 of this subtitle, the Secretary is authorized to establish an advisory committee within the Department of Agriculture or utilize an existing advisory committee, if a suitable one exists, for such purposes.

Subtitle I—International Agricultural Research and Extension

Sec. 1458. (a) The Secretary, subject to such coordination with other Federal officials, departments, and agencies as the President may direct, is authorized to—

(1) expand the operational coordination of the Department of Agriculture with institutions and other persons throughout the world performing agricultural and related research and extension activities by exchanging research materials and results with such institutions or persons and by conducting with such institutions or persons joint or coordinated research and extension on problems of significance to food and agriculture in the United States;

(2) assist the Agency for International Development with food, agricultural, research and extension programs in developing countries;

(3) work with developed and transitional countries on food, agricultural and related research and extension, including providing technical assistance, training, and advice to persons from such countries engaged in such activities and the stationing of scientists at national and international institutions in such countries;

(4) assist United States colleges and universities in strengthening their capabilities for food, agricultural, and related research and extension relevant to agricultural development activities in other countries through the development of highly qualified scientists with specialization in international development; and

(5) further develop within the Department of Agriculture highly qualified and experienced scientists who specialize in international programs, to be available for the activities described in this section.

(b) The Secretary shall draw upon and enhance the resources of the land-grant colleges and universities, and other colleges and universities, for developing linkages among these institutions, the Federal Government, international research centers, and counterpart agencies and institutions in both the developed and less-developed countries to serve the purposes of agriculture and the economy of the United States and to make a substantial contribution to the cause of improved food and agricultural progress throughout the world.

(c) The Secretary may provide specialized or technical services, on an advance of funds or a reimbursable basis, to United States colleges and universities carrying out international food, agricultural, and related research, extension, and teaching development projects and activities. All funds received in payment for furnishing such specialized or technical services shall be deposited to the credit of the appropriation from which the cost of providing such services has been paid or is to be charged.

Grants to States for International Trade Development Centers

Sec. 1458A. (a) The Secretary shall establish and carry out a program to make grants to States for the establishment and operation of international trade development centers, or the expansion of existing international trade development centers, in the United States to enhance the exportation of agricultural products and related products. Such grants shall be based on a matching formula of 50 per centum Federal and 50 per centum State funding (including funds received by the State from private sources and from units of local government).

(b) In making grants under subsection (a), the Secretary shall give preference to States that intend to use, as sites for international trade development centers, land-grant colleges and universities (as defined in section 1404(10) of this Act) that—

(1) operate agricultural programs;

(2) have existing international trade programs that use an interdisciplinary approach and are operated jointly with State and Federal agencies to address international trade problems; and

(3) have an effective and progressive communications system that might be linked on an international basis to conduct conferences or trade negotiations.

(c) Such centers may—

(1) through research, establish a permanent data base to address the problems faced by potential exporters, including language barriers, interaction with representatives of foreign governments, transportation of goods and products, insurance and financing within foreign countries, and collecting international marketing data;

(2) be used to house permanent or temporary exhibits that will stimulate and educate trade delegations from foreign nations with respect to agricultural products and related products produced in the United States and be made available for use by State and regional entities for exhibits, trade seminars, and negotiations involving such products; and

(3) carry out such other activities relating to the exportation of agricultural products and related products as the Secretary may approve.

(d) There are hereby authorized to be appropriated such sums as are necessary to carry out the provisions of this section.

Subtitle K—Funding and Miscellaneous Provisions

Authorization for Appropriations for Existing and Certain New Agricultural Research Programs

Sec. 1463. (a) Notwithstanding any authorization for appropriations for agricultural research in any Act enacted prior to the date of enactment of this title, there are hereby authorized to be appropriated for the purposes of carrying out the provisions of this title, except subtitle H and sections 1416, 1417, 1419, 1420, and the competitive grants program provided for in section 1414, and except that the authorization for moneys provided under the Act of March 2, 1887 (24 Stat. 440-442, as amended: 7 U.S.C. 361a-361i), is excluded and is provided for in subsection (b) of this section, $600,000,000 for the fiscal year ending September 30, 1986, $610,000,000 for the fiscal year ending September 30, 1987, $620,000,000 for the fiscal year ending September 30, 1988, $630,000,000 for the fiscal year ending September 30, 1989, and $640,000,000 for the fiscal year ending September 30, 1990.

(b) Notwithstanding any authorization for appropriations for agricultural research at State agricultural experiment stations in any Act enacted prior to the date of enactment of this title, there are hereby authorized to be appropriated for the purpose of conducting agricultural research at State agricultural experiment stations pursuant to the Act of March 2, 1887 (24 Stat. 440-442, as amended; 7 U.S.C. 361a-361i), $270,000,000 for the fiscal year ending September 30, 1986, $280,000,000 for the fiscal year ending September 30, 1987, $290,000,000 for the fiscal year ending September 30, 1988, $300,000,000 for the fiscal year ending September 30, 1989, and $310,000,000 for the fiscal year ending September 30, 1990.

(c) Notwithstanding any other provision of law effective beginning October 1, 1983, not less than 25 per centum of the total funds appropriated to the Secretary in any fiscal year for the conduct of the cooperative research program provided for under the Act of March 2, 1887, commonly known as the Hatch Act (7 U.S.C. 361a et seq.); the cooperative forestry research program provided for under the Act of October 10, 1962, commonly known as the McIntire-Stennis Act (16 U.S.C. 582a et seq.); the special and competitive grants programs provided for in sections 2(b) and 2(c) of the Act of August 4, 1965 (7 U.S.C. 450i); the animal health research program provided for under sections 1433 and 1434 of this title; the native latex research program provided for in the Native Latex Commercialization and Economic Development Act of 1978 (7 U.S.C. 178 et seq.); and the research provided for under various statutes for which funds are appropriated under the Agricultural Research heading or a successor heading, shall be appropriated for research at State agricultural experiment stations pursuant to the provision of the Act of March 2, 1887.

Payment of Funds

Sec. 1467. Except as provided elsewhere in this Act or any other Act of Congress, funds available for allotment under this title shall be paid to each eligible institution or State at such time and in such amounts as shall be determined by the Secretary.

Withholding of Funds

Sec. 1468. Except as provided elsewhere in this Act or any other Act of Congress, if the Secretary determines that an institution or State is not entitled to receive its allotment of an annual appropriation under any provision of this title because of a failure to satisfy requirements of this title or regulations issued under it, the Secretary shall withhold such amounts, the facts and reasons concerning the determination and withholding shall be reported to the President, and the amount involved shall be deposited in the miscellaneous receipts of the Treasury.

Auditing, Reporting, Bookkeeping, and Administrative Requirements

Sec. 1469. Except as provided elsewhere in this Act or any other Act of Congress—

(1) assistance provided under this title shall be subject to the provisions of sections 2(e), 2(f), and 2(h) of the Act of August 4, 1965 (79 Stat. 431; 7 U.S.C. 450i), as amended by section 1414 of this title;

(2) the Secretary shall provide that each recipient of assistance under this title shall submit an annual report, at such times and on such forms as the Secretary shall prescribe, stating the accomplishments of projects (on a project-by-project basis) for which such assistance was used and accounting for the use of all such assistance. If the Secretary determines that any portion of funds made available under this title has been lost or applied in a manner inconsistent with the provisions of this title or regulations issued thereunder the recipient of such funds shall reimburse the Federal Government for the funds lost or so applied, and the Secretary shall not make available to such recipient any additional funds under this Act until the recipient has so reimbursed the Federal Government;

(3) three per centum of the appropriations shall be retained by the Secretary for the administration of the programs authorized under this title; and

(4) the Secretary shall establish appropriate criteria for grant and assistance approval and necessary regulations pertaining thereto.

Rules and Regulations

Sec. 1470. The Secretary is authorized to issue such rules and regulations as the Secretary deems necessary to carry out the provisions of this title.

Program Evaluation Studies

Sec. 1471. (a) The Secretary shall regularly conduct program evaluations to meet the purposes of this title and the responsibilities assigned to the Secretary and the Department of Agriculture in this title. Such evaluations shall be designed to provide information that may be used to improve the administration and effectiveness of agricultural research, extension, and teaching programs in achieving their stated objectives.

(b) The Secretary is authorized to encourage and foster the regular evaluation of agricultural research, extension, and teaching programs within the State agricultural experiment stations, cooperative extension services, and colleges and universities, through the development and support of cooperative evaluation programs and program evaluation centers and institutes.

General Authority to Enter Into Contracts, Grants, and Cooperative Agreements

Sec. 1472. (a) The purpose of this section is to confer upon the Secretary, general authority to enter into contracts, grants, and cooperative agreements to further the research, extension, or teaching programs in the food and agricultural sciences of the Department of Agriculture. This authority supplements all other laws relating to the Department of Agriculture and is not to be construed as limiting or repealing any existing authorities.

(b)(1) Notwithstanding chapter 63 of title 31, United States Code, the Secretary may use a cooperative agreement as the legal instrument reflecting a relationship between the Secretary and a State cooperative institution, State department of agriculture, college, university, other research or educational institution or organization, Federal or private agency or organization, individual, or any other party, if the Secretary determines that—

(A) the objectives of the agreement will serve a mutual interest of the parties to the agreement in agricultural research, extension, and teaching activities, including statistical reporting; and

(B) all parties will contribute resources to the accomplishment of those objectives.

(2) Notwithstanding any other provision of law, any Federal agency may participate in any such cooperative agreement by contributing funds through the appropriate agency of the Department of Agriculture or otherwise if it is mutually agreed that the objectives of the agreement will further the authorized programs of the contributing agency.

(c) The Secretary may enter into contracts, grants, or cooperative agreements, for periods not to exceed five years, with State agricultural experiment stations, State cooperative extension services, all colleges and universities, other research or education institutions and organizations, Federal and private agencies and organizations, individuals, and any other contractor or recipient, either foreign or domestic, to further research, extension, or teaching programs in the food and agricultural sciences of the Department of Agriculture.

(d) The Secretary may vest title to expendable and nonexpendable equipment and supplies and other tangible personal property in the contractor or recipient when the contractor or recipient purchases such equipment, supplies, and property with contract, grant, or cooperative agreement funds and the Secretary deems such vesting of title a furtherance of the agricultural research, extension, or teaching objectives of the Department of Agriculture.

(e) Unless otherwise provided in this title, the Secretary may enter into contracts, grants, or cooperative agreements, as authorized by this section, without regard to any requirements for competition, the provisions of section 3709 of the Revised Statutes (41 U.S.C. 5), and the provisions of section 3648 of the Revised Statutes (31 U.S.C. 529).

Restriction on Treatment of Indirect Costs and Tuition Remission

Sec. 1473. Funds made available by the Secretary under established Federal-State partnership arrangements to State cooperative institutions under the Acts referred to in section 1404(16) of this title and funds made available under subsection (c)(2) and subsection (d) of section 2 of the Act of August 4, 1965 (7 U.S.C. 450i) shall not be subject to reduction for indirect costs or for tuition remission. No indirect costs or tuition remission shall be charged against funds in connection with cooperative agreements between the Department of Agriculture and State cooperative institutions if the cooperative program or project involved is of mutual interest to all the parties and if all the parties contribute to the cooperative agreement involved. The prohibition on the use of such funds for the reimbursement of indirect costs shall not apply to funds for international agricultural programs conducted by the Secretary or to funds provided by a Federal agency for such cooperative program or project through a fund transfer, advance, or reimbursement. The Secretary shall limit the amount of such reimbursement to an amount necessary to carry out such program or agreement.

Cost-Reimbursable Agreements

Sec. 1473A. Notwithstanding any other provision of law, the Secretary of Agriculture may enter into cost-reimbursable agreements with State cooperative institutions without regard to any requirement for competition, for the acquisition of goods or services, including personal services, to carry out agricultural research, extension, or teaching activities of mutual interest. Reimbursable costs under such agreements shall include the actual direct costs of performance, as mutually agreed on by the parties, and the indirect costs of performance, not exceeding 10 percent of the direct cost.

Technology Development for Small- and Medium-Sized Farming Operations

Sec. 1473B. It is the sense of Congress that the agricultural research, extension, and teaching activities conducted by the Secretary of Agriculture relating to the development, application, transfer, or delivery of agricultural technology, and, to the greatest extent practicable, any funding that is received by the Secretary of Agriculture for such activities, should be directed to technology that can be used effectively by small- and medium-sized farming operations.

Special Technology Development Research Program

Sec. 1473C. (a) Notwithstanding chapter 63 of title 31, United States Code, the Secretary may enter into a cooperative agreement with a private agency, organization, or individual to share the cost of a research project, or to allow the use of a Federal facility or service on a cost-sharing or cost reimbursable basis, to develop new agricultural technology to further a research program of the Secretary.

(b) For each of the fiscal years ending September 30, 1986, through September 30, 1990, not more than $3,000,000 of the funds appropriated to the Agricultural Research Service for such fiscal year may be used to carry out this section.

(c)(1) To be eligible to receive a contribution under this section, matching funds in an amount equal to at least 50 percent of such contribution shall be provided from non-Federal sources by the recipient or recipients of such contribution.

(2) Funds received by the Secretary under this section shall be deposited in a separate account or accounts, to be available until expended. Such funds may be used to pay directly the costs of such research projects and to repay or make advances to appropriations or funds that do or will initially bear all or part of such costs.

(3) The amount of funds or in kind assistance that may be made available under this section by the Secretary for a particular research project may not exceed—

    (A) an amount of $50,000 in any fiscal year; or

    (B) a total amount of $150,000.

Supplemental and Alternative Crops

Sec. 1473D. (a) Notwithstanding any other provision of law, during the period beginning October 1, 1986, and ending September 30, 1990, the Secretary shall develop and implement a research and pilot project program for the development of supplemental and alternative crops, using such funds as are appropriated to the Secretary each fiscal year under this title.

(b) The development of supplemental and alternative crops is of critical importance to producers of agricultural commodities whose livelihood is threatened by the decline in demand experienced with respect to certain of their crops due to changes in consumption patterns or other related causes.

(c)(1) The Secretary shall use such research funding, special or competitive grants, or other means, as the Secretary determines, to further the purposes of this section in the implementation of a comprehensive and integrated program.

(2) The program developed and implemented by the Secretary shall include—

(A) an examination of the adaptation of supplemental and alternative crops;

(B) the establishment and extension of various methods of planting, cultivating, harvesting, and processing supplemental and alternative crops at pilot sites in areas adversely affected by declining demand for crops grown in the area;

(C) the transfer of such applied research from pilot sites to on-farm practice as soon as practicable;

(D) the establishment through grants, cooperative agreements, or other means of such processing, storage, and transportation facilities near such pilot sites for supplemental and alternative crops as the Secretary determines will facilitate the achievement of a successful pilot program; and

(E) the application of such other resources and expertise as the Secretary considers appropriate to support the program.

(3) The pilot program may include, but shall not be limited to, agreements, grants, and other arrangements—

(A) to conduct comprehensive resource and infrastructure assessments;

(B) to develop and introduce supplemental and alternative income-producing crops;

(C) to develop and expand domestic and export markets for such crops; and

(D) to provide technical assistance to farm owners and operators, marketing cooperatives, and others.

(d) The Secretary shall use the expertise and resources of the Agricultural Research Service, the Cooperative State Research Service, the Extension Service, and the land-grant colleges and universities for the purpose of carrying out this section.

Subtitle L—Aquaculture

Purpose

Sec. 1474. It is the purpose of this subtitle to promote research and extension activities of the institutions hereinafter referred to in section

1475(b), and to coordinate their efforts as an integral part in the implementation of the National Aquaculture Act of 1980 (16 U.S.C. 2801 et seq.) by encouraging landowners, individuals, and commercial institutions to develop aquaculture production and facilities and sound aquacultural practices that will, through research and technology transfer programs, provide for the increased production and marketing of aquacultural food products.

Aquaculture Assistance Programs

Sec. 1475. (a) The Secretary may develop and implement a cooperative research and extension program to encourage the development, management, and production of important aquatic food species within the several States and territories of the United States, in accordance with the national aquaculture development plan, and revisions thereto, developed under the National Aquaculture Act of 1980.

(b) The Secretary may make grants to—

(1) land-grant colleges and universities;

(2) State agricultural experiment stations;

(3) colleges, universities, and Federal laboratories having a demonstrable capacity to conduct aquacultural research, as determined by the Secretary; and

(4) nonprofit private research institutions; for research and extension to facilitate or expand promising advances in the production and marketing of aquacultural food species and products. Except in the case of Federal laboratories, no grant may be made under this subsection unless the State in which the grant recipient is located makes a matching grant (of which amount an in-kind contribution may not exceed 50 percent) to such recipient equal to the amount of the grant to be made under this subsection, and unless the grant is in implementation of the national aquaculture development plan, and revisions thereto, developed under the National Aquaculture Act of 1980.

(c) The Secretary may assist States to formulate aquaculture development plans for the enhancement of the production and marketing of aquacultural species and products from such States and may make grants to States on a matching basis, as determined by the Secretary. The aggregate amount of the grants made to any one State under this subsection may not exceed $50,000. The plans shall be consistent with the national aquaculture development plan, and revisions thereto, developed under the National Aquaculture Act of 1980.

(d) To provide for aquacultural research, development, and demonstration projects having a national or regional application, the Secretary may establish in existing Federal facilities or in cooperation with any of the non-Federal entities specified in subsection (b) up to four aquacultural research, development, and demonstration centers in the United States for the performance of aquacultural research, extension work, and demonstration projects. Funds made available for the operation of such regional centers may be used for the rehabilitation of existing buildings or facilities to house such centers, but may not be used for the construction or acquisition of new buildings or facilities. To the extent practicable, the aquaculture research, development, and demonstration centers established under this subsection shall be geographically located so that they are representative of the regional aquaculture opportunities in the United States.

(e) Not later than one year after the effective date of this subtitle and not later than March 1 of each subsequent year, the Secretary shall submit a report to the President, the House Committee on Agriculture, the House Committee on Merchant Marine and Fisheries, the House Committee on Appropriations, the Senate Committee on Agriculture, Nutrition, and Forestry, and the Senate Committee on Appropriations, containing a summary outlining the progress of the Department of Agriculture in meeting the purposes of the programs established under this subtitle.

Aquaculture Advisory Board

Sec. 1476. REPEALED. (Food Security Act of 1985, P. L. 99-198, December 23, 1985.)

Authorization for Appropriations

Sec. 1477. There is authorized to be appropriated $7,500,000 for each fiscal year beginning after the effective date of this subtitle, and ending with the fiscal year ending September 30, 1990.

Subtitle M—Rangeland Research

Purpose

Sec. 1478. It is the purpose of this subtitle to promote the general welfare through improved productivity of the Nation's rangelands, which comprise 60 per centum of the land area of the United States. Most of these rangelands are unsuited for cultivation, but produce a great volume of forage that is inedible by humans but readily converted, through an energy efficient process, to high quality food protein by grazing animals. These native grazing lands are located throughout the United States and are important resources for major segments of the Nation's livestock industry. In addition to the many livestock producers directly dependent on rangelands, other segments of agriculture are indirectly dependent on range-fed livestock and on range-produced forage that can be substituted for grain in times of grain scarcity. Recent resource assessments indicate that forage production of rangeland can be increased at least 100 per centum through development and application of improved range management practices while simultaneously enhancing wildlife, watershed, recreational, and aesthetic values and reducing hazards of erosion and flooding.

Rangeland Research Program

Sec. 1479. The Secretary may develop and implement a cooperative rangeland research program in coordination with the program carried out under the Renewable Resources Extension Act of 1978 to improve the production and quality of desirable native forages or introduces forages which are managed in a similar manner to native forages for livestock and wildlife. The program shall include studies of: (1) management of rangelands and agricultural land as integrated systems for more efficient utilization of crops and waste products in the production of food and fiber; (2) methods of managing rangeland watersheds to maximize efficient use of water and improve water yield, water quality, and water conservation, to protect against onsite and offsite damage of rangeland resources from fllods, erosion, and other detrimental influences, and to remedy unsatisfactory and unstable rangeland conditions; (3) revegetation and rehabilitation of rangelands including the control of undesirable species of plants; and (4) such other matters as the Secretary considers appropriate.

Rangeland Research Grants

Sec. 1480. The Secretary may make grants to land-grant colleges and universities, State agricultural experiment stations, and to colleges, universities, and Federal Laboratories having a demonstrable capacity in rangeland research, as determined by the Secretary, to carry out rangeland research. Except in the case of Federal laboratories, this grant program shall be based on a matching formula of 50 per centum Federal and 50 per centum non-Federal funding.

Reports

Sec. 1481. Not later than one year after enactment of this subtitle, and not later than March 1 of each successive year, the Secretary shall submit a report to the President, the House Committee on Agriculture, the House Committee on Appropriations, the Senate Committee on Agriculture, Nutrition, and Forestry, and the Senate Committee on Appropriations, outlining the progress of the Department of Agriculture in meeting the program requirements set forth in section 1479 of this subtitle.

Rangeland Research Advisory Board

Sec. 1482. (a) The Secretary shall establish a board to be known as the Rangeland Research Advisory Board which shall have a term that expires

September 30, 1990, and which shall be composed of the following twelve members appointed by the Secretary:

(1) four representative of agencies of the Department of Agriculture which have significant research, extension, or teaching responsibilities;

(2) four representatives of the State agricultural experiment stations; and

(3) four representatives of national rangeland and range livestock organizations.

The members shall serve without compensation, if not otherwise officers or employees of the United States, except that they shall, while away from their homes or regular places of business in the performance of services for the Board, be allowed travel expenses, including per diem in lieu of subsistence, in the same manner as persons employed intermittently in the Government service are allowed expenses under sections 5701 through 5707 of title 5, United States Code.

(b) The Board shall meet at the call of the Secretary, but at least once annually, to consult with and advise the Secretary with respect to the implementation of this subtitle and to recommend priorities for the conduct of programs authorized under this subtitle, under such rules and procedures for conducting business as the Secretary shall prescribe.

Appropriations

Sec. 1483. (a) There are authorized to be appropriated, to implement the provisions of this subtitle, such sums not to exceed $10,000,000 annually for the period beginning October 1, 1981, and ending September 30, 1990.

(b) Funds appropriated under this section shall be allocated by the Secretary to eligible institutions for work to be done as mutually agreed upon between the Secretary and the eligible institution or institutions. The Secretary shall, whenever possible, consult with the Board in developing plans for the use of these funds.

[The Food Security Act of 1985, Public Law 99-198, approved December 23, 1985, added the following two new subtitles to the National Agricultural Research, Extension, and Teaching Policy Act (Title XIV).]

Subtitle B—Human Nutrition Research

Findings

Sec. 1451. Congress finds that—

(1) nutrition and health considerations are important to United States agricultural policy;

(2) section 1405 of the National Agricultural Research, Extension, and Teaching Policy Act of 1977 (7 U.S.C. 3121) designates the Department of Agriculture as the lead agency of the Federal Government for human

nutrition research (except with respect to the biomedical aspects of human nutrition concerned with diagnosis or treatment of disease);

(3) section 1423 of such Act (7 U.S.C. 3173) requires the Secretary of Agriculture to establish research into food and human nutrition as a separate and distinct mission of the Department of Agriculture;

(4) the Secretary has established a nutrition education program; and

(5) nutrition research continues to be of great importance to those involved in agricultural production.

Human Nutrition Research

Sec. 1452. (a) Not later than 1 year after the date of enactment of this Act, the Secretary of Agriculture (hereafter in this subtitle referred to as the "Secretary") shall submit to the appropriate committees of Congress a comprehensive plan for implementing a national food and human nutrition research program, including recommendations relating to research directions, educational activities, and funding levels necessary to carry out such plan.

(b) Not later than 1 year after the date of the submission of the plan required under subsection (a), and each year thereafter, the Secretary shall submit to such committees an annual report on the human nutrition research activities conducted by the Secretary.

Dietary Assessment and Studies

Sec. 1453. (a) The Secretary of Agriculture and the Secretary of Health and Human Services shall jointly conduct an assessment of existing scientific literature and research relating to—

(1) the relationship between dietary cholesterol and blood cholesterol and human health and nutrition; and

(2) dietary calcium and its importance in human health and nutrition. In conducting the assessments under this subsection, the Secretaries shall consult with agencies of the Federal Government involved in related research. On completion of such assessments, the Secretaries shall each recommend such further studies as the Secretaries consider useful.

(b) Not later than 1 year after the date of enactment of this Act, the Secretary of Agriculture and the Secretary of Health and Human Services shall each submit to the House Committees on Agriculture and Energy and Commerce and the Senate Committees on Agriculture, Nutrition, and Forestry and Labor and Human Resources a report that shall include the results of the assessments conducted under subsection (a) and recommendations made under such subsection, for more complete studies of the issues examined under such subsection, including a protocol, feasibility assessment, budget estimates and a timetable for such research as each Secretary shall consider appropriate.

Subtitle C—Agricultural Productivity Research

Definitions

Sec. 1461. For purposes of this subtitle:

(1) The term "extension" shall have the same meaning given to such term by section 1404(7) of the National Agricultural Research, Extension, and Teaching Policy Act of 1977 (7 U.S.C. 3103(7).

(2) The term "Secretary" means the Secretary of Agriculture.

(3) The term "State" means each of the 50 States, the District of Columbia, the Commonwealth of Puerto Rico, Guam, the Virgin Islands of the United States, American Samoa, the Commonwealth of the Northern Mariana Islands, or the Trust Territory of the Pacific Islands.

(4) The term "State agricultural experiment stations" shall have the meaning given to such term by section 1404(13) of the National Agricultural Research, Extension, and Teaching Policy Act of 1977 (7 U.S.C. 3101(13)).

Findings

Sec. 1462. Congress finds that—

(1) highly productive and efficient agricultural systems and sound conservation practices are essential to ensure the long-term agricultural viability and profitability of farms and ranches in the United States;

(2) agricultural research and technology transfer activities of the Secretary (including activities of the Extension Service, the Agricultural Research Service, and the Cooperative State Research Service), State cooperative extension services, land-grant and other colleges and universities, and State agricultural experiment stations—

(A) have contributed greatly to innovation in agriculture; and

(B) have a continuing role to play in improving agricultural productivity;

(3) the annual irretrievable loss of billions of tons of precious topsoil through wind and water erosion reduces agricultural productivity;

(4) many farmers and ranchers are highly dependent on machines and energy resources for agricultural production;

(5) public funding of a properly planned and balanced agricultural research program is essential to improving efficiency in agricultural production and conservation practices; and

(6) expanded agricultural research and extension efforts are needed to assist farmers and ranchers to—

(A) improve agricultural productivity; and

(B) implement soil, water, and energy conservation practices.

Purposes

Sec. 1463. It is the purpose of this subtitle to—

(1) facilitate and promote scientific investigation in order to—

(A) enhance agricultural productivity;

(B) maintain the productivity of land;

(C) reduce soil erosion and loss of water and plant nutrients; and

(D) conserve energy and natural resources; and

(2) facilitate the conduct of research projects in order to study agricultural production systems that—

(A) are located, to the extent practicable, in areas that possess various soil, climatic, and physical characteristics;

(B) have been, and will continue to be, managed using farm production practices that rely on—

(i) items purchased for the production of an agricultural commodity; and

(ii) a variety of conservation practices; and

(C) are subjected to a change from the practices described in subparagraph (B)(i) to the practices described in subparagraph (B)(ii).

Information Study

Sec. 1464. (a) Subject to section 1468, the Secretary shall inventory and classify by subject matter all studies, reports, and other materials developed by any person or governmental agency with the participation or financial assistance of the Secretary, that could be used to promote the purposes of this subtitle.

(b) In carrying out subsection (a), the Secretary shall—

(1) identify, assess, and classify existing information and research reports that will further the purposes of this subtitle, including information and research relating to legume-crop rotation, the use of green manure, animal manures, and municipal wastes in agricultural production, soil acidity, liming in relation to nutrient release, intercropping, the role of organic matter in soil productivity and erosion control, the effect of topsoil loss on soil productivity, and biological methods of weed, disease, and insect control;

(2) identify which of such reports provide useful information and make such useful reports available to farmers and ranchers; and

(3) identify gaps in such information and carry out a research program to fill such gaps.

Research Projects

Sec. 1465. (a) Subject to section 1468, in cooperation with Federal and State research agencies and agricultural producers, the Secretary shall conduct such research projects as are needed to obtain data, draw conclusions, and demonstrate technologies necessary to promote the purposes of this subtitle.

(b) In carrying out subsection (a), the Secretary shall conduct projects and studies in areas that are broadly representative of United States agricultural production, including production on small farms.

(c) In carrying out subsection (a), the Secretary may conduct research projects involving crops, soils, production methods, and weed, insect, and disease pests on individual fields or other areas of land.

(d) In the case of a research project conducted under this section that involves the planting of a sequence of crops, the Secretary shall conduct such project for a term of—

(1) at least 5 years; and

(2) to the extent practicable, 12 to 15 years.

(e)(1) In coordination with the Extension Service and State cooperative extension services, the Secretary shall take such steps as are necessary to ensure that farmers and ranchers are aware of projects conducted under this section.

(2) The Secretary shall ensure that such projects are open for public observation at specified times.

(f)(1) Subject to paragraph (2), the Secretary may indemnify an operator of a project conducted under this section for damage incurred or undue losses sustained as a result of a rigid requirement of research or demonstration under such project that is not experienced in normal farming operations.

(2) An indemnity payment under paragraph (1) shall be subject to any agreement between a project grantee and operator entered into prior to the initiation of such project.

Coordination

Sec. 1466. The Secretary shall—

(1) establish a panel of experts consisting of representatives of the Agricultural Research Service, Cooperative State Research Service, Soil Conservation Service, Extension Service, State cooperative extension services, State agricultural experiment stations, and other specialists in agricultural research and technology transfer; and

(2) ensure that a research project under this subtitle is designed after taking into consideration the views of such panel.

Reports

Sec. 1467. The Secretary shall submit to the Committee on Agriculture of the House of Representatives and the Committee on Agriculture, Nutrition, and Forestry of the Senate—

(1) not later than 180 days after the effective date of this subtitle, a report describing the design of research projects established in accordance with sections 1465 and 1466;

(2) not later than 15 months after the effective date of this subtitle, a report describing the results of the program carried out under section 1464; and

(3) not later than April 1, 1987, and each April 1 thereafter, a report describing the progress of projects conducted under this subtitle, including—
(A) a summary and analysis of data collected under such projects; and
(B) recommendations based on such data for new basic or applied research.

Agreements

Sec. 1468. The Secretary may carry out sections 1464 and 1465 through agreements with land-grant colleges or universities, other universities, State agricultural experiment stations, nonprofit organizations, or Federal or State governmental entities, that have demonstrated appropriate expertise in agricultural research and technology transfer.

Dissemination of Data

Sec. 1469. The Secretary shall—
(1) make available through the Extension Service and State cooperative extension services—
(A) the information and research reports identified under section 1464; and
(B) the information and conclusions resulting from any research project conducted under section 1465; and
(2) otherwise take such steps as are necessary to ensure that such material is made available to the public.

Authorization for Appropriations

Sec. 1470. There are authorized to be appropriated such sums as may be necessary to carry out this subtitle, to remain available until expended.

Effective Date

Sec. 1471. This subtitle shall become effective on October 1, 1985.

Selected Bibliography

Manuscript and Unpublished Sources

American Agricultural Economics Association Committee. "A Report by the AAEA Committee on the Current Research Information System." Paper submitted to the AAEA Board of Directors, July 1983.

Beacher, Bruce F. "Committee of Nine—A Reference History of RRF Policy and Procedures, 1947-1973." Washington, 1973.

Brown, George E., Jr. "Agricultural Policy, Agricultural Research, and the Future." Address to the Organization of Professional Employees of the Department of Agriculture, Beltsville, Maryland, April 15, 1983.

Danbom, David B. "Publicly-Sponsored Agricultural Research in the United States From an Historical Perspective." [1985].

Gilmore, Francis Richard. "A Historical Study of the Oklahoma Agricultural Experiment Station." Ed.D. dissertation, Oklahoma State University, 1967.

Halpin, James E. Correspondence with the author, December 16, 1985.

Huffman, Wallace E. "Institutional Development of the Public Agricultural Experiment Station System: Scientists and Departments." May 1985.

Huston, Keith A. Correspondence with the author, January 26, 1986.

Inter-Regional Research Projects Files. Cooperative State Research Service, Washington.

Law, Ernest M. "The Agricultural Experiment Station Movement in Connecticut, 1840-1900: A Case Study of Tax-Supported Scientific Discovery." Ph.D. dissertation, Yale University, 1951.

"Minutes of the Committee on Experiment Station Organization and Policy." 1941-1986.

Records of the Office of Experiment Stations. Record Group 164. National Archives, Washington.

Ronningen, Thomas S. Correspondence with the author, December 12, 1985.

Special Panel. "Meeting the Expanding Need for Agricultural Research: Review of the Cooperative State Research Service, February 8-12, 1982 by Special Panel."

Spielman, A.A. "Some Biased Observations on the Administration of the Regional Research Fund." Paper presented to the Annual Meeting of the New England Agricultural Economics Council, Amherst, Massachusetts, June 15, 1959.

Stansbury, Dale L. "Context and Implications of the National Agricultural Research, Extension, and Teaching Act of 1977." [1985].

United States Department of Agriculture, Cooperative State Research Service. "Cooperative State Research Service Appropriation History." Summary chart prepared by Cooperative State Research Service Program Development and Budget Office, Washington, 1984.

————————— . "Selected Short Abstracts of Cooperative State Research Policy Including Rulings and Opinions on Federal-Grant Fund Research." CSRS-Office Document-1125 revised, January 1, 1966.

_____ . "A Situation Statement on the Southern Corn Leaf Blight." Report by Joint State-Federal Task Force on the Southern Corn Leaf Blight, Washington, February 1971.

_____ . "CSRS-Office Memoranda."

_____ . "CSRS-Station Letters."

_____ . "Strategic Plan of the Cooperative State Research Service of the United States Department of Agriculture." 3 pts. CSRS Internal Working Paper, May 1986.

United States Department of Agriculture, Office of the Secretary. "Secretary's Memoranda."

Personal Interviews

Barton, Donald W. Director Emeritus, New York State Agricultural Experiment Station (Geneva). Interview, Ithaca, New York, June 18, 1986.

Bateman, Durward F. Director, North Carolina Agricultural Research Service. Interview, Raleigh, North Carolina, April 22, 1986.

Baumgardt, Billy R. Director, Indiana Agricultural Experiment Station. Interview, West Lafayette, Indiana, July 22, 1986.

Bentley, Orville G. Assistant Secretary of Science and Education, USDA. Interview, Washington, D.C., May 23, 1986.

Byerly, Theodore C. Administrator, Cooperative State Research Service, USDA, retired. Interview, Beltsville, Maryland, April 10, 1986.

Jordan, John Patrick. Administrator, Cooperative State Research Service, USDA. Interview, Washington, D.C., May 28, 1986.

Kennedy, W. Keith. Provost Emeritus, Cornell University. Interview, Ithaca, New York, June 18, 1986.

Lovvorn, Roy L. Administrator, Cooperative State Research Service, USDA, retired. Interview, Raleigh, North Carolina, April 22, 1986.

Mayberry, Benny D. Research Director Emeritus, Tuskegee Institute. Interview, Tuskegee, Alabama, April 15, 1986.

Neufville, Mortimer H. Dean, School of Agricultural Science, University of Maryland-Eastern Shore. Interview, Princess Anne, Maryland, June 13, 1986.

Ronningen, Thomas S. Director-At-Large, Northeastern Region, retired. Interviews, Washington, D.C., February 28, 1985 and Beltsville, Maryland, February 10, 1986.

Rouse, R. Dennis. Dean and Director Emeritus, Alabama Agricultural Experiment Station. Interview, Auburn, Alabama, April 16, 1986.

Tolbert, Margaret E.M. Director, Carver Agricultural Research Foundation, Tuskegee Institute. Interview, Tuskegee, Alabama, April 15, 1986.

Volk, Norman J. Director Emeritus, Indiana Agricultural Experiment Station. Interview, West Lafayette, Indiana, July 23, 1986.

Published Sources

Agricultural Research Policy Advisory Committee. *Research to Meet U.S. and World Food Needs, Report of a Working Conference.* 2 vols. Kansas City, Missouri, July 9-11, 1975.

Agricultural Research Policy Advisory Committee, CRIS Subcommittee. *The Current Research Information System: Report of a Study*. [Washington]: USDA and NASULGC, January 1975.

Arndt, Thomas M.; Dalyrmple, Dana G.; and Ruttan, Vernon W., eds. *Resource Allocation and Productivity in National and International Agricultural Research*. Minneapolis: University of Minnesota Press, 1977.

Arnon, Itzhak. *Organisation and Administration of Agricultural Research*. Amsterdam: Elsevier Publishing Co., 1968.

Association of Administrators of Home Economics. *National Goals and Guidelines for Research in Home Economics: A Study*. East Lansing, Michigan: AAHE, October 1970.

Association of American Agricultural Colleges and Experiment Stations [and successors]. *Proceedings of the Annual Conventions: 1889-1937*. Washington: 1890-1938.

Association of Research Directors and Cooperative State Research Service, USDA. *Progress and Productivity Through Research and Service: Agricultural Research at the 1890 Institutions*. N.p.: n.p., 1986.

Atwater, Wilbur O. *First Annual Report of the Connecticut Agricultural Experiment Station: 1876*. Middletown: Wesleyan University, 1877.

Aull, G.H. "South Carolina Agricultural Experiment Station: A Brief History, 1887-1930." South Carolina Station *Circular 44* (December 1930).

Babb, Emerson M. *Report to Cooperative State Research Service, U.S. Department of Agriculture on Impacts of Federal Funding Requirements on Marketing Research at State Agricultural Experiment Stations*. Washington: USDA, CSRS, January 1977.

Bailey, John W. *The Mississippi Agricultural Experiment Stations: An Historical Sketch*. A&M College: Mississippi A.E.S. Bulletin 216, March 1923.

Baker, Gladys L. *The County Agent*. Chicago: University of Chicago Press, 1939.

——————. "The Face of the Bureaucrat: A Profile of USDA Leadership." In *Farmers, Bureaucrats, and Middlemen: Historical Perspectives on American Agriculture*, pp. 65-79. Edited by Trudy Huskamp Peterson. Washington: Howard University Press, 1980.

Baker, Gladys L.; Rasmussen, Wayne D.; Wiser, Vivian; and Porter, Jane M. *Century of Service: The First 100 Years of the United States Department of Agriculture*. Washington: USDA, 1963.

Barnes, William D. "Farmers Versus Scientists: The Grange, the Farmers' Alliance, and the West Virginia Agricultural Experiment Station." *Proceedings of the West Virginia Academy of Science* 37 (1965): 197-206.

Battelle Columbus Laboratories. *Science, Technology, and Innovation: Prepared for the National Science Foundation*. Columbus, Ohio: Battelle Columbus Laboratories, 1973.

Bonnen, James T. "Some Observations on the Organizational Nature of a Great Technological Payoff." *Journal of Farm Economics* 44 (1962): 1279-1294.

Bowers, Douglas E. "The Research and Marketing Act of 1946 and Its Effects on Agricultural Marketing Research." *Agricultural History* 56 (January 1982): 249-263.

Bredahl, Maury E.; Bryant, W. Keith; and Ruttan, Vernon W. "Behavior Implications of Institutional and Project Funding of Research." *American Journal of Agricultural Economics* 62 (August 1980): 371-383.

Brunner, Henry S. *Land-Grant Colleges and Universities: 1862-1962*. Washington: U.S. Department of Health, Education, and Welfare, 1962.

Bryan, Enoch Albert. *Historical Sketch of the State College of Washington: 1890-1925*. Pullman: State College of Washington, 1928.

Bunker, Nancy J. and Dupree, Tom. *100 Years: A Century of Growth Through Agricultural Research*. Athens: University of Georgia College of Agricultural Experiment Stations, 1975.

Busch, Lawrence and Lacy, William B. *Science, Agriculture, and the Politics of Research*. Boulder, Colorado: Westview Press, 1983.

Buttel, Frederick H. "The Land-Grant System: A Sociological Perspective on Value Conflicts and Ethical Issues." *Agriculture and Human Values* 2 (Spring 1985): 78-95.

Buttel, Frederick H.; Kloppenburg, Jack, Jr.; Kenney, Martin; and Cowan, J. Tadlock. "Genetic Engineering and the Restructuring of Agricultural Research." *Rural Sociologist* 3 (May 1983): 132-144.

Buttel, Frederick; Kenney, Martin; Kloppenburg, Jack, Jr.; and Cowan, J. Tadlock. "Problems and Prospects in Agricultural Research: The Winrock Report." *Rural Sociologist* 3 (March 1983): 67-75.

Callcott, George H. *A History of the University of Maryland*. Baltimore: Maryland Historical Society, 1966.

Cary, Harold Whiting. *The University of Massachusetts: A History of One Hundred Years*. Amherst: University of Massachusetts, 1962.

Cartenson, Vernon. "The Genesis of an Agricultural Experiment Station." *Agricultural History* 34 (January 1960): 13-20.

Castle, Emery N. "Agricultural Education and Research: Academic Crown Jewels Or Country Cousin?" Kellogg Foundation Lecture, National Association of State Universities and Land-Grant Colleges, November 18, 1980.

Coleman, Gould P. "Pioneering in Agricultural Education: Cornell University, 1867-1890." *Agricultural History* 36 (October 1962): 200-206.

Congressional Quarterly. *Farm Policy: The Politics of Soil, Surpluses, and Subsidies*. Washington: Congressional Quarterly Inc., 1984.

Conover, Milton. *The Office of Experiment Stations: Its History, Activities, and Organization*. Baltimore: Johns Hopkins Press, 1924.

Cope, Alexis. *History of The Ohio State University: Volume I, 1870-1910*. Columbus: Ohio State University Press, 1920.

Dallavalle, Rita S. *Agricultural Research in the United States—The Federal Role: Origins, Evolution, and Current Status*. Washington: Congressional Research Service, Library of Congress, 1981.

Doten, Samuel B. *The Nevada Agricultural Experiment Station, 1888-1943: An Administrative History, With Comment Upon It*. Reno: University of Nevada A.E.S. Bulletin 163, March 1943.

Dupree, A. Hunter. *Science in the Federal Government: A History of Policies and Activities to 1940*. New York: Belknap Press, 1957; reprint ed., New York: Harper and Row, 1964.

Eddy, Edward D. *Colleges for Our Land and Time: The Land-Grant Idea in American Education*. New York: Harper, 1957.

Edmond, Joseph B. *The Magnificent Charter: The Origin and Role of the Morrill Land-Grant Colleges and Universities*. Hicksville, New York: Exposition Press, 1978.

Eschenbacher, Herman F. *The University of Rhode Island: A History of Land-Grant Education in Rhode Island*. New York: Appleton-Century-Crofts, 1967.

Evenson, Robert E.; Waggoner, Paul E.; and Ruttan, Vernon W. "Economic Benefits from Research: An Example from Agriculture." *Science* 205 (September 14, 1979): 1101-1107.

Experiment Station Committee on Organization and Policy. *Research and the Family Farm*. Ithaca, New York: Cornell University, 1981.

Experiment Station Committee on Organization and Policy and Cooperative State Research Service. *Research Initiatives: A Research Agenda for the State Agricultural Experiment Stations.* College Station: Texas A.E.S., 1986.

Experiment Station Committee on Organization and Policy and Cooperative State Research Service. *Research 1984: The State Agricultural Experiment Stations.* [N.p.: n.p., 1984].

Experiment Station Committee on Organization and Policy and Cooperative State Research Service. *Research Perspectives: Proceedings of the Symposium on the Research Agenda for the State Agricultural Experiment Stations.* College Station: Texas A.E.S., 1985.

Fitzharris, Joseph C. "Science for the Farmer: The Development of the Minnesota Agricultural Experiment Station, 1868-1910." *Agricultural History* 48 (January 1974): 202-214.

Gaus, John M. and Wolcott, Leon O. *Public Administration and the United States Department of Agriculture.* Chicago: Public Administration Service, 1940.

Glaser, Lewrene K. *Provisions of the Food Security Act of 1985.* Washington: USDA, Economic Research Service Agriculture Information Bulletin Number 498, 1986.

Hadwiger, Don F. *The Politics of Agricultural Research.* Lincoln: University of Nebraska Press, 1982.

Hardin, Charles. *Freedom in Agricultural Education.* Chicago: University of Chicago Press, 1955.

Harris, Marshall and Hildreth, R J. "Reflections on the Organization of Regional and Research Activities." *American Journal of Agricultural Economics* 50 (November 1968) 815-826.

Hedrick, Ulysses Prentiss. *A History of Agriculture in the State of New York.* New York: 1933; reprint ed., New York: Hill and Wang, 1966.

Hightower, Jim. *Hard Tomatoes, Hard Times.* Washington: Agribusiness Accountability Project, 1972.

Hills, J.L. *Five and Fifty Years: 1888-1942.* Burlington: Vermont A.E.S. Bulletin 515, September 1944.

Huffman, Wallace E. "The Production of Scientists for U.S. Agriculture by Land Grant Universities: 1920-1980." Iowa State University Department of Economics Staff Paper No. 138, March 1984.

Huffman, Wallace E. and Miranowski, J.A. "An Economic Analysis of Expenditures on Agricultural Experiment Station Research." *American Journal of Agricultural Economics* 63 (February 1981): 104-118.

Hungerford, C.W. *An Historical Review of the Idaho Agricultural Experiment Station.* N.p.: Idaho Agricultural Research Progress Report 36, 1960.

Hunter, William C. *Beacon Across the Prairie: North Dakota's Land-Grant College.* Fargo: North Dakota Institute for Regional Studies, 1961.

Johnson, Glenn L. and Wittwer, Sylvan H. *Agricultural Technology Until 2030: Prospects, Priorities, and Policies.* East Lansing: Michigan State University A.E.S. Special Report 12, July 1984.

Joint Council on Food and Agricultural Sciences. *1985 Accomplishments for Research, Extension, and Higher Education: A Report to the Secretary of Agriculture.* Washington: n.p., 1985.

Kerr, Norwood Allen. *A History of the Alabama Agricultural Experiment Station: 1883-1983.* Auburn: Alabama A.E.S., 1985.

Knoblauch, H.C.; Law, E.M.; Meyer, W.P.; Beacher, B.F.; Nestler, R.B.; and White, B.S., Jr., *State Agricultural Experiment Stations: A History of Research Policy and Procedure.* Washington: USDA Miscellaneous Publication 904, May 1962.

Krauss, R.E. "About the Experiment Station—A Centennial Celebration." New York State A.E.S., Geneva, *Special Report* 48 (May 1983): 3-7.

Krauss, William E. "History: 1882-1982." *Ohio Report on Research and Development in Agriculture, Home Economics, and Natural Resources* 67 (May-June 1982): 35-39.

Krogmann, David W. and Key, Joe. "The Agriculture Grants Program." *Science* 213 (July 10, 1981): 178-182.

Lavallard, Marie L., ed. "Arkansas Agricultural Experiment Station." In *Agricultural Progress in Arkansas.* [Fayetteville]: Arkansas A.E.S., May 1976.

LeDuc, Thomas. "State Disposal of the Agricultural College Land Scrip." *Agricultural History* 28 (July 1954): 99-107.

Marcus, Alan I. *Agricultural Science and the Quest for Legitimacy: Farmers, Agricultural Colleges, and Experiment Stations, 1870-1890.* Ames: Iowa State University Press, 1985.

Mayberry, B.D., ed. *Development of Research at Historically Black Land-Grant Institutions.* N.p.: Association of Research Coordinators, Land-Grant 1890 Colleges and Universities, [1976].

Mayer, Andre and Mayer, Jean. "Agriculture: The Island Empire." *Daedalus* (Summer 1974): 83-95.

Moore, Ernest G. *The Agricultural Research Service.* New York: Praeger, 1967.

Mumford, Frederick B. *History of the Missouri College of Agriculture.* Columbia: Missouri A.E.S. Bulletin 483, 1944.

National Academy of Sciences. *Report of the Committee on Research Advisory to the U.S. Department of Agriculture.* Washington: NAS, National Research Council, Division of Biology and Agriculture, 1972.

National Association of State Universities and Land-Grant Colleges. *The Leading Object. . . .* Washington: NASULGC, 1980.

National Association of State Universities and Land-Grant Colleges, Division of Agriculture Committee on Biotechnology. *Emerging Biotechnologies in Agriculture: Issues and Policies.* Washington: NASULGC, March 1985.

National Association of State Universities and Land-Grant Colleges and United States Department of Agriculture. *A National Program of Research for Agriculture.* [Washington: NASULGC and USDA], 1966.

National Association of State Universities and Land-Grant Colleges and United States Department of Agriculture. *Federal-State Experiment Station Relations in Agricultural Research: Report of a Task Force Sponsored Jointly by the National Association of State Universities and Land-Grant Colleges and the U.S. Department of Agriculture.* [Washington: USDA], October 1968.

National Rural Center and Pennsylvania State University. *Rural Development and the Land-Grant Universities: An Evaluation of Title V of the Rural Development Act of 1972.* University Park, Pennsylvania: NRC, 1977.

"National Science Foundation: A General Review of Its First Fifteen Years." In *The Politics of Science*, pp. 139-189. Edited by William R. Nelson. New York: Oxford University Press, 1968.

Nelson, Lowry. *Rural Sociology: Its Origin and Growth in the United States.* Minneapolis: University of Minnesota Press, 1969.

Nevins, Allan. *The State Universities and Democracy.* Urbana: University of Illinois Press, 1962.

North Carolina Agricultural Experiment Station. *A Century of Service*. Raleigh: North Carolina State University at Raleigh Agricultural Experiment Station Bulletin 459, February 1979.

Nye, Ronald L. "Federal vs. State Agricultural Research Policy: The Case of California's Tulare Experiment Station, 1888-1909." *Agricultural History* 54 (October 1983): 436-449.

Office of Science and Technology Policy, Executive Office of the President and the Rockefeller Foundation. *Science for Agriculture: Report of a Workshop on Critical Issues in American Agricultural Research, Winrock International Conference Center, June 14-15, 1982*. Winrock, Arkansas: OSTP, 1982.

Proctor, Samuel. "The Early Years of the Florida Experiment Station: 1888-1906." *Agricultural History* 36 (October 1962): 213-221.

Pursell, Carroll W., Jr. "The Administration of Science in the Department of Agriculture: 1933-1940." *Agricultural History* 42 (July 1968): 231-240.

Rand, Frank P. *Yesterdays at Massachusetts State College: 1863-1933*. Amherst: Massachusetts State College, 1933.

Rasmussen, Wayne D. "Lincoln and the Liberation of the Man on the Land." In *That We May Eat*, pp. 23-30. Washington: USDA *Yearbook of Agriculture*, 1975.

————— . "The Structure of Farming and American History." In *Farm Structure: A Historical Perspective on Changes in the Number and Size of Farms*, pp. 3-13. Edited by United States Senate Committee on Agriculture, Nutrition, and Forestry. 96th Cong., 2nd sess., April 1980.

Rasmussen, Wayne D. and Baker, Gladys L. *The Department of Agriculture*. New York: Praeger, 1972.

Robinson, Roland R. *Administration of Federal Agricultural Research Funds by the Science and Education Administration/Cooperative Research: A Report to the Deputy Director of the Science and Education Administration/Cooperative Research*. Washington: SEA/CR, September 1978.

Rosenberg, Charles E. "The Adams Act: Politics and the Cause of Scientific Research." *Agricultural History* 38 (January 1964): 3-12.

————— . "Science, Technology, and Economic Growth: The Case of the Agricultural Experiment Station Scientist, 1875-1914." *Agricultural History* 45 (January 1971): 1-20.

Ross, Earle D. *The Land-Grant Idea at Iowa State College: A Centennial Trial Balance, 1858-1958*. Ames: Iowa State College Press, 1958.

Rossiter, Margaret W. *The Emergence of Agricultural Science: Justis Liebig and the Americans, 1840-1880*. New Haven: Yale University Press, 1975.

————— . "Organization of Agricultural Improvement in the United States, 1785-1865." In *The Pursuit of Knowledge in the Early American Republic*, pp. 279-298. Edited by Alendra Oleson and Sanborn C. Brown. Baltimore: Johns Hopkins, 1976.

Ruttan, Vernon W. *Agricultural Research Policy*. Minneapolis: University of Minnesota Press, 1982.

Scott, Roy V. *The Reluctant Farmer: The Rise of Agricultural Extension to 1914*. Urbana: University of Illinois Press, 1970.

Shannon, Fred A. *The Farmers Last Frontier: Agriculture, 1860-1897*. New York: Harper and Row, 1945.

Shoemyen, Janos. "A History of the Florida Agricultural Experiment Stations." *Sunshine State Agricultural Research Report* 20 (Summer 1975): 13-18.

Smith, David C. *The Maine Agricultural Experiment Station: A Bountiful Alliance of Science and Husbandry*. Orono: Life Sciences and A.E.S., University of Maine at Orono, 1980.

Smith, C. Beaman and Atwood, K.H. *The Relation of Agricultural Extension to Farm Practices.* Washington: United States Bureau of Plant Industry Circular 117, 1913.

Steinel, A.T. and Working, D.W. *History of Agriculture in Colorado.* Fort Collins: Colorado State Agricultural College, 1926.

Thorne, Wynne. *Report of Study of Federal-State Relationships in Agricultural Research for the Cooperative State Research Service, United States Department of Agriculture.* [Logan]: Utah A.E.S., 1975.

Trelogan, Harry C. "Research and Marketing Advisory Committees." *Journal of Farm Economics* 38 (February 1956): 1-7.

True, Alfred C. *A History of Agricultural Experimentation and Research in the United States: 1607-1925.* Washington: USDA Miscellaneous Publication 251, 1937.

True, Alfred C. and Clark, V.A. *The Agricultural Experiment Stations in the United States.* Washington: USDA, Office of Experiment Stations Bulletin 80, 1900.

United States Congress. House. Committee on Agriculture. *Agriculture Act of 1977: Report.* 95th Cong., 1st sess., Report No. 95-348, May 1977.

——————————— . *Federal Agricultural Research: Hearings.* 81st Cong., 2nd sess., July 11-21, 1950.

——————————— . *Food and Agriculture Act of 1981: Report.* 97th Cong., 1st sess., Report No. 97-106, May 1981.

——————————— . *Miscellaneous Hearings: Additional Facilities for Research at State Agricultural Experiment Stations.* 87th Cong., 2nd sess., March 5, 1962.

——————————— . *National Agricultural Research Policy Act of 1976: Hearings.* 94th Cong., 2nd sess., Report No. 94-1172, May 1976.

United States Congress. House. Committee on Agriculture. Subcommittee on Forests, Family Farms, and Energy. *Organic Farming Act of 1982: Hearings.* 97th Cong., 2nd sess., June 1982.

United States Congress. House. Committee on Appropriations. Subcommittee on Agriculture-Environmental and Consumer Protection. *Agriculture-Environmental and Consumer Protection Appropriations for 1974: Hearings.* Pt. 3. 93rd Cong., 1st sess., March 1973.

United States Congress. House. Committee on Appropriations. Subcommittee on Agriculture, Rural Development, and Related Agencies. *Agriculture, Rural Development, and Related Agencies Appropriations for 1987: Hearings.* Pt. 4. 99th Cong., 2nd sess., March 1986.

——————————— . *Agriculture, Rural Development, and Related Agencies Appropriations for 1979: Hearings.* 95th Cong., 2nd sess., March 1978.

United States Congress. House. Committee on Appropriations. Surveys and Investigations Staff. "A Report on the Scientific Research Programs of the Department of Agriculture." In *Agriculture, Rural Development, and Related Agencies Appropriations for 1981: Hearings.* Pt. 4, pp. 786-906. Edited by U.S. Congress, House, Committee on Appropriations, Subcommittee on Agriculture, Rural Development, and Related Agencies. 96th Cong., 2nd sess., March 1980.

United States Congress. House. Committee on Science and Technology. Subcommittee on Science, Research, and Technology and Subcommittee on Domestic and International Scientific Planning and Analysis. *Agricultural Research and Development: Special Oversight Hearings.* 2 vols. 94th Cong., 1st sess., September and October 1975.

United States Congress. Office of Technology Assessment. *An Assessment of the United States Food and Agricultural Research System.* 2 vols. Washington: U.S. Congress, OTA, 1981 and 1982.

United States Congress. Senate. Committee on Agriculture, Nutrition, and Forestry. Subcommittee on Agricultural Research and General Legislation. *Rural Research in USDA: Hearings.* 95th Cong., 2nd sess., May 4-5, 1978.

United States Congress. Senate. Committee on Appropriations. *Agriculture, Rural Development, and Related Agencies Appropriation Bill, 1986.* 99th Cong., 1st sess., Report 99-137, September 1985.

_____ . *Report on the Proposed Elimination of Agricultural Research Stations and Lines of Research.* 89th Cong., 1st sess., Report 156, April 1965.

United States Congress. Senate. Select Committee on Small Business. *Agricultural Research Policy: Report.* 96th Cong., 2nd sess., April 1980.

United States Department of Agriculture. *A Time to Choose: Summary Report on the Structure of Agriculture.* Washington: USDA, 1981.

United States Department of Agriculture, Agricultural Research Service. *Reports on the Agricultural Experiment Stations: 1954-1960.* Washington: USDA, ARS, 1955-1961.

United States Department of Agriculture, Cooperative State Experiment Station Service. *Funds for Research at State Agricultural Experiment Stations: 1961 and 1962.* Washington: USDA, CSESS, 1961-1963.

United States Department of Agriculture, Cooperative State Research Service. *First Two Years of Operation of the Competitive Research Grants Office.* Washington: USDA, CSRS, 1982.

_____ . *Funds for Research at State Agricultural Experiment Stations and Other Cooperating Institutions: 1963-1974.* Washington. USDA, CSRS, 1964-1975.

_____ . *Inventories of Agricultural Research: FY 1966-1984.* Washington: USDA, CSRS, 1967-1985.

_____ . *The Mission of the Cooperative State Research Service.* [Washington: USDA, CSRS, 1982].

_____ . *Regional Research in Agriculture: State Agricultural Experiment Stations and USDA, Cooperative State Research Service.* [Washington: USDA, CSRS, 1984].

United States Department of Agriculture, Office of Experiment Stations. *Reports on the Agricultural Experiment Stations: 1890-1954.* Washington. U.S. Government Printing Office, 1891-1955.

United States Department of Agriculture, Science and Education. *The Paradox of Success: The Impact of Priority Setting in Agricultural Research and Extension.* Washington: USDA, SE, 1984.

United States Department of Agriculture, Science and Education Administration. *USDA's Science and Education Administration: What It Is—What It Does.* Washington: USDA, 1980.

United States Department of Agriculture, Science and Education Administration/Cooperative Research. *Administrative Manual for the Hatch (Experiment Station) Act as Amended.* Washington: USDA Agriculture Handbook 381, November 1980.

United States Department of Agriculture, Science and Education, Office of Grants and Program Systems. *Food and Agriculture Competitively Awarded Research and Education Grants: Fiscal Year 1984.* Washington: USDA, December 1984.

United States General Accounting Office. *Agricultural Research—Its Organization and Management.* Washington: GAO, 1976.

_____ . *Biotechnology: The U.S. Department of Agriculture's Biotechnology Research Efforts, Briefing Report.* Washington: GAO, 1985.

Wade, Nicholas. "Agriculture: NAS Panel Charges Inept Management, Poor Research." *Science* 179 (January 5, 1973): 45-47.

Waggoner, Paul E. "Research and Education in American Agriculture." *Agricultural History* 50 (January 1976): 230-247.

Washington State University College of Agriculture and Home Economics Research Center. *Report to the Legislature on Agricultural Research*. [Pullman: Washington State University]: January 1986.

Webber, H.J. "A Plan of Publication for Agricultural Experiment Station Investigations." *Science* 26 (October 18, 1907): 509-512.

Western Association of Agricultural Experiment Station Directors, ed. *Federal Funding Philosophies, Policies, and Procedures*. N.p.: n.p., July 1980.

Willard, Julius T. *History of the Kansas State College of Agriculture and Applied Science*. Manhattan: Kansas State College Press, 1940.

Wiser, Vivian and Bowers, Douglas E. *Marketing Research and Its Coordination in USDA: A Historical Approach*. Washington: USDA Agricultural Economic Report 475, August 1981.

Wood, William W., Jr. "Discussion: Assessing and Projecting the Effects of Agricultural Research, Extension, and Technology." *American Journal of Agricultural Economics* 60 (December 1978): 983-984.

Woodward, Carl R. and Waller, Ingrid N. *New Jersey's Agricultural Experiment Station: 1880-1930*. New Brunswick: New Jersey A.E.S., 1932.

Young, Harold N. *The Virginia Agricultural Experiment Station: 1886-1966*. Charlottesville: University Press of Virginia, 1975.

Youngblood, Bonney. "The Status of Rural Sociological Research in the State Agricultural Experiment Stations." *Rural Sociology* 14 (June 1949): 111-115.

Index

Italicized page numbers refer to the specific Acts listed in the Appendix. Italicized entries are publications.

A

N

O

P

R